Commissio Mental Health Services

Graham Thornicroft & Geraldine Strathdee

London: HMSO

ISBN 0 11 321974 0

The views expressed in this publication are those of the authors and not necessarily those of the Department of Health.

Pubished by HMSO and available from:

HMSO Publication Centre
(Mail, fax and telephone orders only)
PO Box 276, London, SW8 5DT
Telephone orders 0171 873 9090
General enquiries 0171 873 0011
(queuing system in operation for both numbers)
Fax orders 0171 873 8200

HMSO Bookshops
49 High Holborn, London WC1V 6HB
(counter service only)
0171 873 0011 Fax 0171 831 1326
68-69 Bull Street, Birmingham B4 6AD
0121 236 9696 Fax 0121 236 9699
33 Wine Street, Bristol BS1 2BQ
0117 9264306 Fax 0117 9294515
9-21 Princess Street, Manchester M60 8AS
0161 834 7201 Fax 0161 833 0634
16 Arthur Street, Belfast BT1 4GD
01232 238451 Fax 01232 235401
71 Lothian Road, Edinburgh EH3 9AZ
0131 479 3141 Fax 0131 479 3142
The HMSO Oriel Bookshop
The Friary, Cardiff CF1 4AA
01222 395548 Fax 01222 384347

HMSO's Accredited Agents
(see Yellow Pages)

and through good booksellers

Commissioning Mental Health Services

Announcement by the Secretary of State for Health 20 February 1996

The Secretary of State for Health, Mr. Stephen Dorrell, announced the following five publications, which are designed to assist purchasers and providers of mental health services;

1   **The Spectrum of Care, Local Services for People with Mental Health Problems. Department of Health, London.**

    This booklet supplements the guidance set out in the Health of the Nation Key Area Handbook on Mental Health, and provides further confirmation that a comprehensive services includes the adequate provision of hospital beds.

2   **24 hour nursed care for people with severe and enduring mental illness. NHS Executive, Leeds. (HSG(96)6/LASSL(96)16).**

    This report describes the importance of 24 hour nurse staffed accommodation as one vital component of comprehensive mental health services, and highlights the key obstacles to its provision, making recommendations on how the commissioning process could be improved.

3   **The Patient's Charter. Mental Health Services (draft consultation edition, Department of Health, London. (EL(96)2).**

    This booklet explains how the rights and standards in the Patient's Charter apply to people using NHS adult mental health services, and also explains some special standards for these services.

    (Copies available from Patient's Charter & You, Freepost, London SE99 7XU)

4   **An Audit Pack for Monitoring the Care Programme Approach. Monitoring Tool. NHS Executive, Leeds. (HSG(96)6/LASSL(96)16).**

    This document links with the wider development of clinical audit within the NHS and supplements 'Building Bridges' - a guide to Arrangements for Inter-Agency Working for the Care and Protection of Severely Mentally Ill People (Department of Health, 1995).

5   **Review of purchasing of mental health services by health authorities in England. NHS Executive, Leeds.**

    The purpose of this review was to assess whether Health Authorities had plans for 1996-7 which: were consistent with national policy on mental health, reflected local circumstances, and were practicable and deliverable. Where authorities had not developed adequate plans NHS Executive Regional Directors were asked to indicate what steps would be taken to support them in developing those plans.

    (Copies available from Department of Health, PO Box 410 Wetherby LS23 7LN.)

Copies of documents 1-4 are also available from the Health Literature Line, Tel. 0800 555 777.

Contents

In Respect of Providers

In Respect of Implementation

APPENDIX

List of Contributors

Jennifer Beecham
Lecturer in Mental Health Economics
Centre for the Economics of Mental Health,
Institute of Psychiatry
and
Research Fellow
Personal Social Services Research Unit
University of Kent at Canterbury

Marion Beeforth
User Consultant
Brighton Insight and Survivors Speak Out

Dr Kamaldeep Bhui
Senior Registrar, PACT Team
Maudsley Hospital, London SE5 8AF

Dr Andrew C Burnett
Director of Primary Care Development
and
Medical Adviser
Kent Family Health Services Authority

Yvonne Christie
Director and Independent Consultant
Aveleon Associates

Dr Mel Conway
Senior Registrar in Public Health
Suffolk Health Authority

Margaret Cudmore
Chairman
Independent Healthcare Association, Psychiatry
and Substance Abuse Committee

Dr Stuart Cumella
Senior Research Fellow
Centre for the Research and Information into Mental Disability
University of Birmingham

Dr Sara Davies
Senior Registrar
Hope Hospital, Salford

Mike Farrar
Principal Officer, Mental Health
NHS Executive
On Secondment from
North Yorkshire Health Authority

Sue Gallagher
Director of Borough Focus Commissioning
Merton Sutton and Wandsworth Health Authority

Dr Gyles Glover
Senior Medical Officer
Department of Health

Peter Gluckman
Director of Commissioning, Priority Services
Lambeth, Southwark and Lewisham Health Authority

Tony Goss
Contract Manager, Mental Health and Substance Misuse
Lambeth, Southwark and Lewisham Health Authority

Mary Hancock
Social Services Inspector
Department of Health

Dr Rachel Jenkins
Principal Medical Officer
Health Care (Medical), Mental Health, Elderly, Disability and
Ethics Policy Branch
Department of Health

Dr Sonia Johnson
Clinical Lecturer and MCC Project Co-ordinator
PRiSM (Psychiatric Research in Service Measurement)
Institute of Psychiatry

Edna Kamis-Gould
Research Fellow
Centre for Mental Health Policy and Services Research
University of Pennsylvania

Dr David Kingdon
Consultant Psychiatrist
Bassetlaw NHS Trust

Alan Langlands
Chief Executive
NHS Executive

Paul McCrone
Lecturer in Health Economics
PRiSM (Psychiatric Research in Service Measurement)
Institute of Psychiatry

Vanessa Malin
Assistant Director of Planning
East Riding Health Authority

Dr David Melzer
Consultant in Public Health Medicine
Cambridge and Huntingdon Health Commission

Richard W Moore
Independant Consultant
and formerly
District Review Co-ordinator for Mental Health Task Force

Edward Peck
Director
Centre for Mental Health Service Development
Kings College, London

Dr Christina Perring
Regional Director
Trent & Yorkshire Mind

Maurice Perry
Team Leader
PACT Team, Nunhead Sector
Maudsley Hospital

Dr Michael Phelan
Consultant Psychiatrist
Charing Cross and Westminster Hospital Medical School

Dr Robin Powell
Consultant Psychiatrist
Park Royal Centre for Mental Health
Central Middlesex Hospital

Cliff Prior
Director of Grants and Projects
Mental Health Foundation

Mr Bob Sang
Fellow
King's Fund, London

Professor Geoff Shepherd
Head of Research
The Sainsbury Centre for Mental Health

Mike Slade
Honorary Research Worker
PRiSM (Psychiatric Research in Service Measurement)
Institute of Psychiatry

Helen Smith
Senior Consultant
Centre for Mental Health Service Development
King's College London

Dr Geraldine Strathdee
Head of Service Development
The Sainsbury Centre for Mental Health and formerly
Consultant Psychiatrist, PACT Team,
Maudsley Hospital

Ms Kelly Thompson
Service Development Training Manager
Sainsbury Centre for Mental Health

Professor Graham Thornicroft
Director
Section of Community Psychiatry (PRiSM)
Institute of Psychiatry

Dr David Tod
FRCGP
Raynes Park Surgery
London SW20

Charles Waddicor
Director of Housing and Social Services
London Borough of Sutton

Dr Richard Williams
Director
NHS Health Advisory Service

Jenny Willmott
Policy Officer
National Association for Mental Health (MIND)

Fedelma Winkler
Former Chief Executive
Kent Family Health Services Authority

Helen Wood
Head Occupational Therapist
PACT Team, Maudsley Hospital

Judith Young
Director of Health Care Purchasing
West Yorkshire Health Authority

Acknowledgements

We are pleased to acknowledge the wholehearted support of Dr Rachel Jenkins of the Department of Health and Tony Goss and Peter Gluckman at Lambeth Southwark and Lewisham Health Authority, who jointly sponsored, with the PRiSM team (Psychiatric Research in Service Measurement) at the Maudsley Hospital/Institute of Psychiatry, the Conference upon which this book is based. Ruth Fermo, Carol Burnham and Derek Flannery have contributed superb administrative support to the production of the manuscript. This book is dedicated to those people suffering from mental illness, who are the intended beneficiaries of commissioned mental health services.

GRAHAM THORNICROFT
GERALDINE STRATHDEE

London
March 1996

Foreword

The development and provision of the spectrum of care for people with mental health problems is one of the greatest challenges facing the NHS. It requires collaboration between providers – in primary care and in specialist services, in health and social care.

It also needs effective partnerships among those who purchase mental health services – health authorities, local authorities and, increasingly, general practitioners and primary care teams.

This practical and authoritative book provides a useful resume of the issues which face those with responsibility for purchasing. It builds on a number of reports which have been published during the last few years – including the Mental Illness Key Area Handbook, the Audit Commission report "Finding a Place" and the publications from the Mental Health Task Force.

More recently, there has been a review of mental health service purchasing, which has provided a systematic assessment of the present state of the art. Progress to date has been variable. The task now is to bring services everywhere up to the level of the best, whilst enabling leaders in the field to continue to innovate and to achieve new goals. This timely book shows ways in which the NHS, working with partners agencies, can meet this challenge.

ALAN LANGLANDS
NHS Chief Executive

29 March 1996

Introduction

GRAHAM THORNICROFT AND GERALDINE STRATHDEE

This book aims to inform those concerned with the purchasing and commissioning of mental health services about good practice in the United Kingdom, current areas of debate about the development and implementation of mental health services, and the fundamental facts on population-based service planning. We aim to summarise here how these issues relate to national mental health policy and new implementation strategies being developed by the Department of Health and the NHS Executive.

The book was inspired by a conference on 'Purchasing Mental Health Services', organised jointly by PRiSM (Psychiatric Research in Service Measurement), Department of Health, and Lambeth, Southwark and Lewisham Health Commission. Indeed in recent years a number of landmark reports have appeared which inquire into the shape mental health services should assume for the remainder of this decade; especially the Ritchie Report, the House of Commons Health Select Committee Inquiry into Mental Health Services, the Mental Health Foundation Inquiry, the Audit Commission Report called Finding a Place and the Mental Health Task Force London Project report.

The issues emerging from these findings will be presented and synthesised within this book directly in relation to the purchasing process. It is clear that although there is now a widespread consensus on policies for the development of mental health services, which is supported by most managers and clinicians, the implementation of these policies is at best patchy and represents the major challenge facing mental health.

This book is published at a time when the NHS is more subject to market forces than at any other stage in its history. The creation of the division between purchasers and providers, in both the health and the social services by the 1990 NHS and Community Care Act, has produced intended and unintended consequences throughout mental health services. Opportunities for the rapid development of new services at the programme level have never been more favourable. At the same time, the proliferation of statutory, for-profit, and not-for-profit providers leaves open the possibility of hitherto unparalleled fragmentation. The previous culture of roll-over budgets and NHS decisions often heavily guided by precedent has been supplanted in less than a decade. A new impetus has been added to the NHS which can revitalise its original intent to plan and provide services specific to the local populations within Britain.

The book attempts to harness and clarify this impetus within four sections. The first details the national policy framework within which the commissioning of mental health services takes place, and includes a definition of severe mental illness, the category of need which is identified as the highest priority for mental health services. The second part of the book orientates the reader to the perspective of purchasers and commissioners of services, acknowledging that the needs of many people with mental illnesses span health, social and housing domains.

The third portion of the book describes the commissioning process from the viewpoint of providers, and identifies many ways in which integrated local service provision depends upon a collateral approach across traditional boundaries. The largest section of the book concerns implementation, and reflects our view that in recent years policy has often preceded practice. Indeed, we are convinced that the implementation of the basic elements of policy is now the highest priority for the improvement of mental health services. Included here are the views about implementation of specific groups of service users, and contributions on purchaser development and monitoring service quality standards.

A word on definitions. While buying mental health services has hitherto usually been a process of purchasing, that is contracting largely for services already running or in development by providers, we expect the emphasis to change. Increasingly health authorities will become more active in the contracting process, and undertake local needs assessment excercises, and tender for new services to fill gaps of underprovision. This more active role is the commissioning process, and the trend in this direction is reflected in the title of this book.

In short, 'Commissioning Mental Health Services' therefore aims to support those who are in a practical position to inform purchasing and implementation so that they may be better able to achieve the mental health targets set out in the Health of the Nation.

1 Adult Mental Health Policy

DAVID KINGDON & RACHEL JENKINS

Introduction

The aims of mental health policy are:

a   to promote mental health

b   to ensure early and effective intervention when mental health problems emerge

c   to reduce the disability, distress, and deaths associated with mental health problems.

For this to happen, local and continuing assessment of needs should lead to the development and continuing evolution of a comprehensive network of health and social services facilities in each district health authority. Services should be based on empirical assessment of needs and specialist services should be targeted on people who are most severely mentally ill. This can only be achieved if proper attention is paid to recognition and management of mental health in primary care and the workplace. The basis for this policy is now well founded in research (see for example [1,2]).

A locally based adult specialist psychiatric service needs to include mental health teams; short-term and long-term hospital provision including residential places for those requiring asylum or sanctuary; health and local authority residential and respite provision eg hostels, sheltered housing; day care services; co-ordinated arrangements between health and local authorities, voluntary agencies, the private sector and the criminal justice system.

Table 1: *Example of a range of services:*

	Acute/emergency care	Rehabilitation/ continuing care
Home-based	Intensive home support	Domiciliary services
	Emergency duty teams	Key workers
	Sector teams	Care management
	Court diversion schemes	
Day Care	Day Hospitals	Drop-in centres Support groups Employment schemes Day care
Residential support	Crisis accommodation	Ordinary housing
	Acute units	Unstaffed group homes
	Local secure units	Adult placement schemes Residential care homes Mental nursing homes 24 hour NHS accommodation Medium secure units High security units

The realignment of the resources tied up in the old hospitals into more appropriate district based services is needed urgently for clinical and financial reasons. This has recently been supported by the Audit Commission[3]. Patients moved from old style mental hospitals to community programmes usually do well on transfer; re-admissions are generally short-term and rarely happen frequently (but for which provision needs to be made) and the majority of patients and their relatives prefer community facilities. However approval is not given to the closure of any mental hospital unless it can be demonstrated that adequate alternatives have been developed.

Background

This policy was established by the Minister of Health in 1961, Enoch Powell, in the 'Watertowers Speech' at a MIND conference, was further developed in 1975 in 'Better Services for the Mentally Ill' and has been carried forward since. 'Care in Action' (1981) identified three main tasks for health authorities developing services for people with mental illness:

- to create a local, comprehensive mental illness service in each health district, reducing the catchment area of multi-district mental illness hospitals to their own districts

- to create a psychogeriatric service in each health district

- to arrange for the closure of those mental illness hospitals which are not well-placed to provide a service to their local district, and which are already near the end of their useful life.

'Care in the Community' (1983) reinforced this bringing together of a number of themes including joint working and cost-effectiveness. MIND's 'Common Concern' published in the same year has been influential by describing the views of a multi-disciplinary group on the philosophy and components of comprehensive services and drawing attention to the importance of user and carer participation in planning and providing services.

'Caring for People' (1989) and subsequently, the NHS and Community Care Act (1990) developed this further. The relevant general policy aims underlying the Act were to enable people to live as normal lives as possible in their own communities; to provide the type and quality of service that will support each individual to take the fullest possible part in social and community life; and to give more choice and influence to service users and carers. It gives a leading role to Local Authority Social Service Departments as purchasers of services for 'care in the community', making explicit the duty to assess the social needs of the individual for services and requiring community care plans to be formulated in consultation with other key agencies.

MIND's Eight Principles:
A local comprehensive service is one which:

1   Values the client as a full citizen with rights and responsibilities, entitled to be consulted and to have an active opportunity to shape and influence relevant services, no matter how severe his or her disability.

2   Aims to promote the greatest self-determination of the individual on the basis of informed and realistic choice.

3   Aims to provide and evaluate a programme of treatment, care and support based on the unique needs of the individual, regardless of age or severity of disability.

4   Aims to minimise the dependence of the client on professional resources, but which does not allow this as an excuse to withdraw appropriate services.

5   Aims to meet the special needs arising from disability through a locally accessible, fully co-ordinated multi-disciplinary service offered by appropriately trained staff.

6   Is easily accessible locally, and delivered, wherever possible, to the client's usual environment.

7   Plans actively for those in institutions to reintergrate into society if they so wish.

8   Aims to enhance the individual or collective capacity to cope with or alleviate distress.

However by the mid-1980's, serious problems were emerging in relation to the implementation of mental health policy. The Social Services Select Committee of the House of Commons (1985) expressed concern about community services and commented that 'any fool can close a mental hospital: it takes time and effort to do it properly and compassionately'. The Audit Commission reported similarly in 'Making a Reality of Community Care' (1986). The Report of the Committee of Inquiry into the Care and After-Care of Sharon Campbell (1988) investigated the circumstances in which a social worker, Isobel Schwarz, was killed by a severely mentally ill person. It concluded with a series of recommendations for action which especially highlighted the importance of interprofessional collaboration and systematic assessment and aftercare. Research evidence also began to demonstrate that significant numbers of people in prison and amongst the homeless had severe mental illness and also that mental health teams were frequently failing to identify and deliver services to them. A series of policy initiatives were established to address these concerns.

Mental Health Policy Developments 1957–1994

1957   Report of the Royal Commission on the Law relating to Mental Illness and Deficiency

1959   Mental Health Act

1962   Hospital Plan for England and Wales. Ministry of Health White Paper

1975   Better Services for the Mentally Ill. DHSS White Paper

1976   Joint Care Planning: Health and Local Authorities. DHSS Circular

1981   Care in Action. A Handbook of Policies and Priorities for the Health and Personal Social Services in England. DHSS

1983   Mental Health Act
Care in Community. DHSS Consultative Document

1985   House of Commons Social Services Committee Report on Community Care with special reference to adult mentally ill and mentally handicapped people

1986   Making a Reality of Community Care. Audit Commission

1988   Community Care: Agenda for Action. Sir Roy Griffiths
The Report of the Committee of Inquiry into the Care and After-Care of Sharon Campbell (1988)

1990   Caring for People. Community Care in the Next Decade and Beyond. White Paper.
NHS and Community Care Act.
House of Commons Social Services Committee Report on Community Care.
Community Care in the next Decade and Beyond: Policy Guidance DH [Care Programme Approach]
Mental Illness Specific Grant

continued

---

continued

1992   Mental Illness Key Area in 'Health of the Nation'.
DH White Paper Joint Department of Health/Home Office Review
of Services for Mentally Disordered Offenders

1993   Mental Illness Key Area Handbook
Review of Legal Powers on the Care of Mentally Ill People in the
Community
Secretary of State's 10 point plan

1994   Guidance on establishing supervision registers.
Guidance on discharge of mentally disordered people.
House of Commons Health Select Committee Report on Mental
Health Services
Ritchie Report on the care of Christopher Clunis
Mental Health Foundation Report
Mental Health Task Force—London Project
Audit Commission 'Finding a place'.

Targeting severe mental illness
The Care Programme Approach

From April 1991, all district health authorities were required to have introduced the care programme approach—**systematic arrangements for assessment and after-care** to try to ensure that people being treated in the community receive the health and social care they need[4,5]. This involves:

- discharge from hospital only if community care is available
- appointment of a key worker
- drawing up and regular review of care plans
- inter-professional collaboration.

The mental illness specific grant

This has been payable since April 1991, to local authorities to encourage them to increase the level of social care available to people with a severe mental illness. Local authorities have to make a 30% contribution. £21 million was initially made available in 1991/2 supporting total expenditure of £30 million, risen by 1993/4 to £36 million, 1994/5 supporting expenditure of £50.5 million. Supplementary Credit Approvals (permissions to borrow) of £10 million in 1991/92 and £10.9 million in 1994/5 were authorised to enable local authorities to finance the capital elements of new social care services.

The homeless mental illness initiative

The HMI initiative was announced in July 1990 to offer accommodation and psychiatric care for homeless people sleeping rough in central London. It is a £20 million programme includes up to 150 specialist short term hostel places:

5 hostels are open and further hostels are planned. Five community based multi-disciplinary psychiatric teams provide outreach work and support for the short term hostels as well as direct access hostels set up by the Department of the Environment under its 'Rough Sleepers Initiative' and resettlement work. 'Move on'—permanent—accommodation is now being provided through the Housing Corporation.

Mentally disordered offenders

A Joint Department of Health/Home Office Review of Services for Mentally Disordered Offenders and others requiring similar services was established in 1991. The Steering Committee met under the chairmanship of Dr John Reed. Its task was to determine whether changes were needed in the level, pattern or operation of services and to see if ways of promoting such changes can be identified. It was to give regard to The NHS and Community Care Act, the recommendations of the Efficiency Scrutiny on the Prison Medical Service (now Health Care Services for Prisons) and relevant recommendations from the Woolf Inquiry. Consultation papers were issued during the course of the review (January 1991–July 1992) which contained 270 recommendations. A final report was published in November 1992[6]. Ministers have reaffirmed the Government's policy that wherever possible mentally disordered offenders should receive care and treatment from health and social services rather than in custodial care. They have also endorsed five guiding principles which are that patients should be cared for:

- with regard to the quality of care and proper attention to the needs of individuals

- as far as possible, in the community, rather than in institutional settings

- under conditions of no greater security than is justified by the degree of danger they present to themselves or others

- in such a way as to maximise rehabilitation and their chances of sustaining an independent life

- as near as possible to their own homes or families, if they have them.

Confidential inquiry into homicides and suicides by mentally ill people

In 1992, the Department of Health established a Confidential Enquiry into Homicides and Suicides by Mentally Ill People with the purpose of eliciting avoidable causes of death and determine best practice by detailed examination of the circumstances surrounding such events. A multi-disciplinary Steering Committee, including management, nursing, psychiatric and social work representation, has been formed. The inquiry is being led by the Royal College of Psychiatrists supported by other relevant professional organisations. A preliminary report[7] on homicides in 1994 established that of a collection of cases over a period covering three years, 34 homicides were committed by people currently or recently in contact with services.

The Secretary of State's 10 point plan for developing safe and successful community care

In January 1993, following a series of highly publicised incidents involving people with severe mental illness, the Secretary of State for Health announced the establishment of a Department of Health Review of legal powers on the care of mentally ill people in the community[8] which reported in July 1993, the review concluded that the present Mental Health Act contains powers which provide for most relevant situations but they are not always used to greatest effect. A power of supervised discharge should therefore supplement them.

It should apply to patients who have been admitted to hospital and who '… the Responsible Medical Officer is satisfied in the light of their history after consultation with others that there would be a serious risk to the health or safety of the patient or the safety of other people … unless care was supervised.' A treatment plan should be negotiated and if the patient fails to comply, his or her key worker will call an immediate review at which consideration will be given as to whether the patient has deteriorated to the extent that the criteria for admission have been met and a decision about such admission can be taken. European Court of Human Rights rulings preclude compulsory readmission to hospital if the person is not currently showing clear signs of mental illness.

In announcing the review's conclusions, a 10 point plan was announced by the Secretary of State for Health[9]. This comprised:

1   Publication of the review of legal powers.

2   To seek legislation for:

    a   the new power of supervised discharge.

    b   extending leave under section 3 of the Mental Health Act to 1 year.

    Proposals for legislation are in the Queen's Speech for the 1994/5 session.

3   Publication of revised Code of Practice for Mental Health Act. This particularly emphasises the importance of considering the interests of a person's health, as well as risk to self or others, in considering the use of detention under section 2 & 3 of the Act.

4   A Review by the Clinical Standards Advisory Group (a professional group established as part of the NHS reforms) of standards of care for people with schizophrenia.

5   Measures to ensure that Health Authority and GP fund-holder plans cover the essential needs for mental health services: a focus in the NHS Executive Performance Management Division has been established to take this forward.

6   The London Implementation Group was instructed to take forward an action plan to improve mental health services in the capital.

7   Better training for keyworkers under the CPA was to occur; a conference held in March 1994 on 'Key Workers' and an edited report is to be distributed.

8   Guidance on discharge.

    o   'The discharge from hospital of mentally disordered people and their continuing care in the community[10] circulated in May 1994. This includes details of risk assessment. It says that whilst 'it is widely agreed that assessing the risk of a patient acting in an aggressive or violent way (to self or others) at some time in the future is at best an inexact science ... there are some ways in which uncertainty may be reduced'. For example, making sure relevant information is available, conducting a full assessment of risk and defining situations and circumstances known to be present increased risk.

9   Development of better information systems.

    o   'Introduction of supervision registers for mentally ill people from 1 April 1994' (HSG (94) 5) circulated February 1994. Their aim is to ensure that severely mentally ill people who are at greatest need receive the services they require. The mechanisms for patient inclusion on the supervision register are that consideration for inclusion and withdrawal should be a normal part of the discussion of the Care Programme before and after discharge but the decision about inclusion rests with the Responsible Medical Officer in consultation with the other members of the mental health team. The categories of inclusion are significant risk of suicide, or of serious violence to others or of severe self neglect.

10   An agreed work programme for the Mental Health Task Force which was completed in 1994.

Mental health task force

A Mental Health Task Force was established in 1992 to promote and assist the more concerted, comprehensive and speedy implementation of policies for mental health services, with particular regard to the replacement of the large long-stay institutions and the creation of more locally based and accessible services. It was led by David King (formerly District General Manager at Exeter) and has worked from January 1993 to December 1994. It produced a series of good practice videos, publications and conferences on user and black and minority ethnic issues. From March to July 1994, The 'London Project' brought together a group of clinicians and managers who visited all twelve Inner London DHAs, and their associated Social Service Departments and provider units; immediate feedback was provided to Districts and to Ministers, action plans drawn up and a report published[11]. A review of progress in each district was made in November and December 1994.

Health of The Nation—mental illness in key area

In 1992, mental illness was included as a key area in 'The Health of the Nation'. Three primary targets have been set:

- to improve significantly the health and social functioning of mentally ill people;

- to reduce the overall suicide rate (from 11.0/100 000) by at least 15% by the year 2000;

- to reduce the suicide rate of severely mentally ill people by at least 33% by the year 2000.

Strategies for achieving the targets have been described in detail elsewhere[1,12]. To refine the first target, improving information and understanding is essential. A National Psychiatric Morbidity Survey undertaken by OPCS for the Department of Health is now beginning to provide definitive results on the level of mental illness in the community and service contacts. In its first bulletin, it includes estimates (for private households):

- about 1 in 7 adults (16–64) were suffering from *neurotic disorder* in the week prior to OPCS interview:

  o mixed anxiety and depressive disorder—7.1%

  o generalised anxiety disorder—2.9%

- 0.4% were suffering from a *functional psychosis* (ie schizophrenia and severe affective disorder) in the previous year.

- rates of *alcoholic dependence* were 4.7% and *drug dependence* were 2.2% in the previous year.

'Health of the Nation Outcome Scales (HoNOS)' for mental health teams have been developed and circulated widely by the Research Unit of the Royal College of Psychiatrists. These set brief but reliable standards enabling outcome data to be gathered. They are intended to be used on entry, at intervals and on discharge from services.

A Public Information Strategy (Mental Illness) has been established with the objective of increasing the understanding of mental illness and reducing the stigma associated with it. It was launched in Spring 1993 with a £300 000 budget each year for 3 years. An omnibus survey assessing attitudes to mental illness (to provide baseline data in 1993) showed, eg: over 90% believed in greater tolerance towards people with mental illness, 77% in community based services for mentally ill people, less than half however agreed that people who have a history of mental illness should hold public office and only 39% thought that there should be less emphasis on protecting the public from people with mental illness. This survey was repeated in 1994 confirming the generally positive attitudes with the exception of increasing concern about the association of aggression with mental illness. A successful series of booklets about mental illness, eg 'Mental illness: what does it mean?' , 'Sometimes I think I can't go on any more', 'Mental illness: what can you do about it?' and versions for children and old people—have been produced by DH and widely distributed to libraries, advice centres, GP surgeries, etc.

Suicide reduction requires a multifaceted approach, including;

a improved management of depression in general practice: recognition by GPs of depression occurs in only about 50% of those who are depressed. Improvement in recognition and management leads to better symptomatic outcomes and there is evidence from Hungary and Sweden of improvements in suicide rates with improved GP management. The 'Defeat Depression' Campaign (run by the Royal Colleges of General Practitioners and Psychiatrists) has developed training packages for GPs and Management Guidelines, produced and distributed by DH, based on the Colleges' consensus statement on depression. DH is funding a Senior GP Fellow to work with Regional trainers.

b reducing availability of certain methods used in suicide may assist, eg by increased use of catalytic converters on vehicle exhausts reducing toxicity of fumes; adaptation of exhausts to prevent fitting tubes is being pursued. **Other public health—safety—measures,** for example, in relation to the availability of paracetamol, are also now being considered.

c targeting high risk groups: eg the prison service in developing suicide prevention policies through improving reception procedures, use of 'buddies' and the Samaritans and training of medical and other prison officers; the Samaritans are working with farmers organisations.

d developing mental health services in relation to the first general target can be expected to assist, particularly for those with severe mental illness, by producing local accessible services with effective supervision systems; by measures to improve the support and supervision of users of services in the community, especially, the care programme approach, care management and the development of supervision registers and other effective information systems. These assist in ensuring that when suicidal risk or other risk emerges, the person is in contact with a key worker who they know, can talk to, and who can ensure that the appropriate reassessment and management occurs. Clear, agreed observation policies for managing suicidal people in hospital and assessing and managing those who have deliberately self-harmed.

e audit can improve practice: multi-disciplinary audits have now been set up in many services; the Confidential Inquiry into Homicides and Suicides by Mentally Ill People will provide information in suicides in the near future.

The strategy is a developing one. The Mental Illness Key Area Handbook published in January 1993 was the first comprehensive guidance for both health and social services, providing practical advice to managers on developing local strategies to achieve the mental health targets and encouraging the development of joint commissioning and purchasing. Follow up to the White Paper has included the publication in November 1992 of "First Steps for the NHS", setting out a range of possible actions which the NHS might take in 1993–94. **A second edition** of the handbook was published by HMSO in 1994 substantially revised including practical details on the care programme approach, targeting of services and bed management.

Resources expended on mental illness

Considerable resources are expended on mental health services—approximately £2 billion per annum is spent directly. £1,764 million in 1990/91 on Hospital & Community Health Services (a 37% increase in real terms since 1979/80). A Capital Loans Fund offers bridging finance to Health Authorities and NHS Trusts to facilitate the closure of the old mental hospitals; £68 million has been allocated so far. £116.5 million in 1990/91 is estimated to have been spent on Local authority social services (an 86% increase of real terms from 1978/79). In addition, the Mental Illness Specific Grant is increasing spending (see above). The manner in which this resource is used has caused concern as the amount expended has not been demonstrated to correlate with the effectiveness of services[3] and, in particular, poor targeting of resources in relation to need. Until such problems are rectified, it is difficult for purchasers of services to determine whether sufficient resources are being made available.

In relation to NHS provision for people with mental illness, the number of community psychiatric nurses has risen by 290% from 1,100 in 1981 to 4,210 in 1992. The number of consultant psychiatrists working in mental illness specialities rose by 39.9% from 1,335 in 1979 to 1,867 in 1991. [However there remain many vacancies—an estimated 10–20% of posts are unfilled.]. The number of inpatients in mental illness hospitals has fallen from 143 500 (1954) to 76 400 (1979) to 39,500 (1993). Local authority personal social services provision for people with mental illness consists of Local Authority residential places for people with mental illness which have risen by 14% from 3,600 to 4,100 in 1993; voluntary and private residential provision for people with mental illness has risen by 405% from 2,000 places in 1979 to 10,100 places in 1992. Local authority day centre places specifically for people with mental illness increased by 70% from 4,600 in 1979 to 7,800 in 1991. The total number of day centre places for people with mental illness (including estimated places in LA day centres catering for mixed client groups) increased by 116% from 7,000 in 1979 to 15,100 in 1991. Total residential home places have risen from 179 500 (1978/9) to 289 900 (1990/1). These include an estimated third to two-thirds with dementia.

Conclusions

Mental health policy has moved on during the 1990s at a rapid rate with a series of developments aimed at improving the care given. In general terms, there has been agreement about the policy but there have been concerns about the pace of change (from eg the National Schizophrenia Fellowship and SANE) and the targeting of services on those most at need. The Ritchie Report on the care of Christopher Clunis highlighted the lack of coordination of care with tragic consequences. Providing local care in communities does not mean reducing the support and supervision available although there have been instances where this has happened. The aim of policy is to minimise the chances of these happening in the future.

References

[1] Department of Health. (1994) *Health of the Nation. Mental Illness Key Area Handbook*. 2nd Edition. London: HMSO.

[2] Freeman, H. Bennet, D. (1989) *Community Psychiatry*. Longmans: London.

[3] Audit Commission (1994) *Finding a Place*. London: HMSO.

[4] Kingdon, D.G. (1994) The care programme approach. *Psychiatric Bulletin*, **18(2)**, 68–70.

[5] Kingdon, D.G. (1994) The care programme approach. *Psychiatric Bulletin*, **18(2)**, 68–70.

[6] Department of Health/Home Office (1992) *Review of health and social services for mentally disordered offenders and others requiring similar services: Final Summary Report (Cm 2088)*. London: HMSO.

[7] Confidential Enquiry into Homicides and Suicides by Mentally Ill People (1994) *Preliminary Report on Homicide*. London: Department of Health.

[8] Department of Health (1993) *Legal powers on the care of mentally ill people in the community*. London: DH.

[9] Department of Health (1993) *Legislation planned to provide for supervised discharge of psychiatric patients. Press Release (H93/908)*. London: Department of Health.

[10] Department of Health (1994) *Guidance on the discharge from hospital of mentally disordered people and their continuing care in the community*. DH: Fleetwood.

[11] Mental Health Task Force (1994) *Priorities for Action*. London: NHSE.

[12] Jenkins, R.J. (1994) The Health of the Nation. Recent Government policy and legislation *Psychiatric Bulletin* **18**, 324–327.

2 Defining Severe Mental Illness

ROBIN POWELL & MIKE SLADE

Introduction

The care of the mentally ill, amongst other groups, has long been identified as a priority for England's health and social services (DHSS, 1975; Royal Commission, 1979). More recent emphasis has been on directing services towards those with most need: the severely mentally ill (Department of Health, 1992). This process, though in large part initiated by government, has been spurred on by recent independent reports highlighting a failure to focus services on the most vulnerable patient groups (Audit Commission, 1994; House of Commons Health Select Committee, 1994; Mental Health Foundation, 1994).

There is no consistent definition of severe mental illness. It is asserted that this deficiency handicaps those who would purchase, provide, or evaluate services for the severely mentally ill. The result is that services for the most severely mentally ill are not being prioritised. Within the United Kingdom this feeling was recently given expression by the House of Commons Health Committee (1994), who recommended that the Department of Health publish an operational definition.

This chapter is the product of an informal working group set up following the publication of that report. Its goal was to identify examples of good practice in defining severe mental illness, and to present them in an illustrative but not prescriptive fashion. It reviewed the available research literature and obtained pragmatic operational definitions from health care providers and social services within Great Britain. It also informally contacted professional bodies, user groups, and governmental organisations for any written definitions [see Table 1]. Of special interest were definitions arising from joint working or commissioning between agencies. The study was conducted during June and July 1994. Information was requested by telephone on definitions of severe mental illness.

Sources of definitions

A review was conducted of some 20 international studies of service provision for people with severe mental illness to determine what definitions were used to identify this group. Guidelines proposed for the United Kingdom by the Department of Health are reproduced in table 2 (Department of Health, 1994). Although there is no consensus, a trend was noted towards including within definitions concepts such as Diagnosis, Duration of illness, and Disability. Some authors wrote loosely of "the 3Ds". Others incorporated measures of service utilisation. Many used exclusion criteria. A helpful survey of this literature is that of Schinnar *et al* (1990).

Table 1:   *National and international organisations contacted for definitions*

Professional bodies

- British Association of Social Workers
- British Psychological Society
- Central Council for Education and Training of Social Workers
- College of Occupational Therapists
- Royal College of General Practitioners
- Royal College of Nursing
- Royal College of Psychiatrists

User groups

- National Association for Mental Illness (MIND)
- National Schizophrenia Fellowship (NSF)
- Schizophrenia, A National Emergency (SANE)

Policy Definitions of SMI

United Kingdom

- Department of Environment
- Department of Health
- Department of Social Services

World Health Organisation

United States

- National Institute of Mental Health

Australia

- New South Wales

Table 2: *Guidelines to distinguish high, medium and low support mental health services from Health of the Nation Key Area Handbook*

Group	Patient Characteristics	CPA	Supervision Register
High support group	Individuals with severe social dysfunction (eg social isolation support unemployment, and/or difficulty with skills of daily living) as a consequence of severe or persistent mental illness or disorder. In particular, individuals with the following difficulties will be identified for high levels of support: • current or recent serious risk to self or to others or of self-neglect • severe behavioural difficulties • high risk of relapse • history of poor engagement with mental health services • little contact with other providers of care • precarious housing (eg bed & breakfast) • need staff:patient ratio of about 1:15	✔	✔
Medium support group	Individuals with a moderate degree of social disability arising from mental illness or disorder, eg those able to work at least part-time and/or to maintain at least one enduring relationship. This group will also include the following individuals: • those likely to recognise, and to seek help when early in relapse • those receiving appropriate services from other agencies	✔	✘
Low support group	Individuals who, following assessment, have been found to have specific and limited mental health-related needs which do not require extensive, multi-disciplinary input. In general such individuals are likely to respond to brief or low intensity intervention. For example: • patients with psychosis in remission • moderately severe personality disorder	✔	✘

Statutory organisations from inner-urban, outer-urban and rural districts were contacted. Twenty organisations responded to requests for details of current practice. These comprised Social Services departments and NHS mental health care providers from the length and breadth of England. Information was obtained on eligibility criteria for access to Care Management (CM), Mental Health Services (MHS), the Care Programme Approach (CPA), and Supervision Registers (SR) [see table 3].

Table 3 *Local organisations contacted for definitions*

Organisation	Criteria supplied for access to:		
	Mental Health Services	Care Programme Approach	Care Management
Barnsley Community & Priority Services	✔		
Bath MHS		✔	
Berkshire SS			✔
Bethlem & Maudsley Special HA		✔	✔
Devon County Council SS & Exeter and North Devon HA		✔	✔
London Borough of Brent SS			✔
London Borough of Enfield SS			✔
London Borough of Islington SS			✔
London Borough of Lambeth SS			✔
London Borough of Lewisham SS			✔
Manchester City Council SS			✔
Norfolk County Council SS			✔
North Birmingham HA, North Birmingham SS, & Mind	✔		
North Derbyshire HA & Derbyshire County Council SS		✔	
North Yorkshire County Council SS and Harrogate Healthcare Trust		✔	✔
Southern Derbyshire Mental Health (NHS) Trust		✔	✔
South Manchester University Health Trusts		✔	
Tameside and Glossop MHS		✔	
Westminster City Council SS			✔

Key: MHS = Mental Health Services
      SS = Social Services
      HA = Health Authority

Results

It was possible to categorise definitions into two main groups: operational and comprehensive definitions. Operational definitions were pragmatic attempts to provide clear inclusion and exclusion conditions for access to services. Comprehensive definitions considered a wider range of factors, often at the expense of discriminatory power.

OPERATIONAL DEFINITIONS

Berkshire social services

Used by local authority and "community teams" to aid in the prioritisation of Care Management resources

Use *Risk-Needs Matrix* with scores from 1 (high) to 8 (low) for the dimensions of need and risk. Any score of 3 or less guarantees access to care management.

Contact person: Julie Gunn, Planning Officer, Berkshire Social Services Department. Telephone: 01734–875 444.

Mental health risk-needs matrix

Nature of needs	Degree of risk				
Physical safety of self and/or others	1 Immediate very high risk to physical safety as a result of mental disorder or deliberate self harm.	2 High risk to physical safety requiring prompt intervention. Support and monitoring under s41 of the MH Act or under Criminal Proceedings Act.	3 Strong indicators of continuing physical risk/inability to maintain a safe environment.	4 Some concerns about physical safety. Risk potential or slight.	
Mental health of self and/or others	1 Severe enduring mental disorder having major effects on self/others. After-care duty following compulsory treatment (s3 or s37 of MHA). Guardianship (s7 of MHA).	2 Comprehensive discharge arrangements (CPA) for those with severe and enduring mental disorder. Precipitation of serious mental health problems in others.	3 Mental health affecting functional abilities and requiring regular monitoring.	4 Some concerns about effect of mental health problems on self and/or others. Regular monitoring required.	5 Unable to fulfil ambition due to mental health problems.

Category	2	3	4	5	6	7	8
Physical health of self and/or others	Severe physical illness as a result of presence of mental disorder, requiring continuous care by others. Carer(s) at breaking point.	Severe physical illness in presence of mental disorder. Assistance from others required several times a day. Carer(s) under severe stress.	Reliable evidence of deterioration in physical health without daily support.	Possible risk of deterioration in health—monitoring needed.	Some concerns about individual's physical health—slight risk of deterioration.		
Opportunities for social and emotional		Loss of daily living skills or level of dependence on others. Requires a high level of social/emotional support and regular monitoring.	Limited daily living or social skills requiring some support from others in order to stay at home. Regular monitoring required.	Reduced quality of life due to limited daily living skills/emotional difficulties. Minimal help required.	Unable to fulfil ambitions due to limited daily living/social skills or emotional difficulties.	Partially unable to fulfil ambitions due to limited daily living/social skills or emotional difficulties.	
Opportunities for social interaction and/or community involvement			Very isolated—contact with family/partner/others absent or damaging.	No involvement outside immediate family/partner/household/neighbours.	Social contacts strictly limited by mental disorder or living situation.	Limited opportunity for social contact.	Intermittent opportunity to enjoy full social contact. May need advice and information to build up social contacts.

London borough of Brent social services
Eligibility criteria for receipt of mental health services

Both

- diagnosed mental illness, or signs that the person is suffering from an initial psychiatric breakdown

And one from:

- recently discharged from a psychiatric hospital or ward
- social care needs that are not being met
- assessment of mental state under the Mental Health Act is requested, likely to be a danger to yourself or to others.
- immediate risk of psychiatric breakdown
- court asks for mental state assessment
- statutory duties requiring Social Services involvement

From "What Service, What Standards?" Brent Social Services, 1994

Contact person: *Judy Jones, Brent Social Services. Telephone: 0181–937 4555.*

Norfolk county council social services
Criteria for prioritising social care needs

Guidelines for assessment:

HIGHEST

acute and immediate risk of harm to self or others, *e.g.*

- situation where without intervention, the individual would require urgent admission to hospital, nursing or residential care, and this is inappropriate
- unforeseen and immediate incapacity of prime carer

HIGH

a rapid deterioration leading to an early breakdown in essential care arrangements; this would include situations such as discharge from hospital, or where hospital admission might be avoided, *e.g.*

- discharge from hospital with a significant lessening of functional independence compared with pre-admission
- people unable to continue to care for themselves without support/ personal care/nursing care
- inability of carer to continue to provide an essential element of care

MEDIUM

a progressive increase in the level of vulnerability which in the immediate future will increase the priority, *e.g.*

- progressive loss in independence owing to deteriorating disability
- where a carer is undertaking continuous or intermittent care which is detrimental to his or her health or well being.

- statutory assessments under Disabled Persons (Services Consultations and Representations) Act 1986, Section 4 and Section 5; and Mental Health Act 1983, Section 117 where there is no perceived need for current services

LOW

little immediate impact, and overall level of vulnerability is unlikely to increase in the short term, but a gradual deterioration may be expected, *e.g.*

- a simple request for a single service to improve quality of life
- request for an Orange Badge or simple piece of equipment

From "Community Care Plan for Norfolk 1993–94" Norfolk County Council Social Services Dept. (1993)

Contact person: *Frances Kemp, Service Development Officer, Norfolk County Council Social Services. Telephone: 01603–223 146.*

Southern Derbyshire mental health (NHS) trust
Eligibility criteria for care programme approach

CONTACT WITH SERVICES

- more than two admissions in the past year
- continuous stay in hospital of more than six months in the last three years
- four admissions to hospital within the last five years, accumulating to one year
- attendance at a statutory mental health day resource for more than one year
- five years continuous contact with mental health services, including out-patients

LEVEL AND TYPE OF INVOLVEMENT WITH SERVICES

- in regular contact with two or more separate agencies or services
- living in special accommodation as a result of mental health problems
- currently prescribed depot/major tranquilliser for over one year
- subject to compulsory detention under the Mental Health Act

LEVEL OF NEED

- major impairment of social functioning or motivation, or daily living skills
- requires a range of services to address their challenging behaviour
- six or more requests for help within the last three months by carer or client
- person at serious risk of self harm, causing harm to others, or severe neglect
- other important needs or concerns

From "Southern Derbyshire Mental Health (NHS) Trust and the Implementation of the Care Programme Approach" Briefing paper to the Department of Health, 1994

Contact person: Trisha Tredwell, CPA Manager, Southern Derbyshire Mental Health Trust. Telephone: 01332–624 594.

COMPREHENSIVE DEFINITIONS

Bath mental health services
Qualifying criteria for entry to care programme approach

- patients being considered for discharge who have been in a psychiatric hospital for more than 6 months, either continuously or cumulatively, during the preceding 12 months
- patients with serious mental illness whose health and social care needs require the attention of more than one agency
- patients being considered for discharge or already living in the community whose lives have been seriously disrupted as a result of mental illness and who would be vulnerable without a care programme.

From Broughton, M & Divall P (1994) "Care programme approach: the experience in Bath", Psychiatric Bulletin; **18**: 77–79.

London Borough of Lambeth Social Services
Qualifying criteria for assessment for care management:

- disabled school leavers (under provision of Sections 5 & 6 of the Disabled Persons Act 1986)
- older people and people with learning difficulties whose social or emotional functioning is seriously affected and/or who may be at risk or exploitation or abuse
- people with severe and/or chronic physical or mental health difficulties, including those in receipt of Middle or Higher Rate Disability Living Allowance
- single people deemed "in priority need" under the Housing Act by Special Needs Housing
- people with multiple disabilities
- people who fall within the scope of the inter-agency "Hospital Discharge Agreement"
- people whose carers are (or are likely to become) unable to continue to care
- people who are unable to care for themselves and who have no available carers
- people who are seriously failing to reach their full personal potential as a result of disability

Contact person: Neil Dhruer, Lambeth Social Services. Telephone: 0171–926 4553.

North Derbyshire Health Authority & Derbyshire County Council Social Services
Eligibility criteria for the care programme approach

At least one main criterion under section one should be met plus one indicator from section two

SECTION 1: History of ongoing mental illness with significant health or social care needs:

- continuous stay in hospital of 6 months or more
- 2 or more admissions within 1 year
- contact with specialist mental health services for more than 1 year
- detained admission under the Mental Health Act on an order of 28 days or more, or repeated admissions on short term orders
- other long term conditions such as dementia, head injury, etc

SECTION 2: Significant level of functional disability associated with continuing severe emotional distress

- source of significant distress to any informal carers
- in serious conflict with neighbours, family, etc.
- distressed by emotional or social isolation
- behaviour likely to result in hostility from the community
- unable or unwilling to co-operate with medical treatment
- experiences distressing psychological symptoms
- has considerable difficulty securing a home
- finds difficulty with basic self-care skills, e.g. washing, dressing, feeding
- has problems in sustaining engagement in activity or structuring his/her time
- unable to manage finances, which threatens his/her domestic situation

Contact person: *Celia Millington, Mental health Planning Manager, Community Health Care Service (North Derbyshire) NHS Trust. Telephone: 01246–552 866.*

A JOINTLY DEVELOPED DEFINITION
North Birmingham Health Authority, North Birmingham Social Services, & *MIND*
Service delivery priorities

- Those illnesses which so impair the individual by psychological or psychiatric symptoms that their normal social functioning is so disrupted they require treatment.

Contact person: *Mrs Mary Bath, Patient Services Manager, Northern Birmingham Mental Health Trust. Telephone: 0121–623 5500 x5602.*

The "SIDDD" dimensions

There was considerable heterogeneity amongst the surveyed definitions. They ranged from "no definition" to complex operational criteria. Most organisations were struggling with the development of definitions and some were collaborating with other agencies. Most definitions shared some common characteristics. These were sorted into five distinct dimensions: Safety; Informal and formal support; Diagnosis; Disability; and Duration [see Table 4]. The acronym **SIDDD** may be helpful as a shorthand for referring to these dimensions.

Table 4: *The SIDDD dimensions*

Safety has four components:
- unintentional self-harm, e.g. self-neglect
- intentional self-harm
- safety of others
- abuse by others, e.g. physical, sexual, emotional, financial

Informal and Formal Support has two components:
- help from informal carers including friends and relatives
- help from formal services such as day-centres, paid staff voluntary services, hospital admissions, medication, and detention under the Mental Health Act.

Diagnosis may include:
- psychotic illness
- dementia
- severe neurotic disorders
- personality disorder
- developmental disorder

Disability with impaired ability to function effectively in the community, which may include problems with:
- employment and recreation
- personal care
- domestic skills
- interpersonal skills

Duration of any of the above for a minimum period

The SIDDD dimensions might be more easily considered diagrammatically. In Figure 1 each SIDDD dimension is represented by the side of a pentagon. Such a multi-axial depiction emphasises the importance of taking into account each dimension. Though not itself a validated scale, it could form the basis for the development of either research instruments or more pragmatic operational definitions for use in the field.

Figure 1   *Pentagon depicting five SIDDD axes*

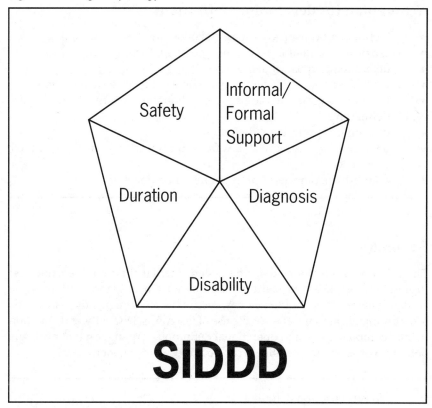

Consultation process

The results of our survey indicate that the best practice in developing a definition occurs where there is simultaneous application of top-down and bottom-up processes at a local level. The top-down process involves consultation with other stake-holders, who may be from the purchaser and provider sides of statutory services, voluntary and private sectors, service users, their carers, and community members. Wide consultation will result in broader acceptability of the resulting definition (and decreased obstacles to its development). A forum is then established in which consultation can occur. Such fora might include "away-days" of all stakeholders, or core stakeholders arranging meetings with the others. Stages of the consultation process include: determining the purpose of the definition; identifying the ingredients of each stakeholder's ideal definition; negotiating to reach concensus on a provisional definition. This definition is then disseminated through the network of interested parties.

The bottom-up process entails developing channels for feedback. This might take various forms, including staff comments and audit procedures. The experience of working with clients will provide useful information on the utility of the definition. Clinical audit facilitates systematic evaluation of the impact on allocation of resources.

Action plan for developing definitions

- identify and consult with local stakeholders
- establish a forum for developing the definition
- determine purpose of definition
- for each stakeholder, identify ingredients of their ideal definition
- through negotiation, combine components to form a provisional definition
- disseminate provisional definition
- develop channels for feedback from frontline staff in the light of their experience
- establish ongoing audit program for amendment of definition

Summary

There is no consensus in defining severe mental illness either amongst professional groups and statutory bodies within England or within the academic literature. Some themes, however, occur more frequently than others. Most prominent amongst these is the use of Diagnosis, Disability, and Duration in both comprehensive and operational definitions. We suggest that no single definition of severe mental illness can be imposed on a national basis.

- No consensus on definition
- Diagnosis, Disability, Duration frequently used
- Suggested framework: *SIDDD*
- Local implementation
- Inter-agency co-operation

The *SIDDD* dimensions for defining severe mental illness comprise five axes:

Safety; Informal and Formal Support; Diagnosis; Disability; and Duration. These dimensions can serve as a basis for discussion between agencies wishing to implement care management. At the local level, inter-agency definitions can be developed by the simultaneous application of top-down and bottom-up consultation. In this way the principles for targeting resources can be implemented in a fashion that is both flexible, relevant to local conditions, and amenable to change.

References

Audit Commission (1994) *Finding a Place: A Review of Mental Health Services for Adults.* London: HMSO.

Department of Health (1992) *The Health of the Nation: Specification of National Indicators.* London: HMSO.

Department of Health (1994) *Health of the Nation Key Area Handbook* (2nd Edition). London: HMSO.

Department of Health and Social Security (1975) *Better Services for the Mentally Ill* (Cmnd 6233). London: HMSO.

House of Commons Health Select Committee (1994) *First Report of the Health Committee: Better Off in the Community? The Care of People Who Are Seriously Mentally Ill.* London: HMSO.

Mental Health Foundation (1994) *Creating Community Care: Report of the Mental Health Foundation Inquiry Into Community Care for People with Severe Mental Illness.* London: Mental health Foundation.

National Institute of Mental Health (1987) *Toward a model plan for a comprehensive, community-based mental health system.* Washington DC: NIMH.

Ritchie, J., Dick, D. & Lingham, R. (1994) *Report of the Inquiry Into the Care and Treatment of Christopher Clunis.* London: HMSO.

Royal Commission on the National Health Service (1979) *Report of the Royal Commission on the National Health Service* (Cmnd 7615). London: HMSO.

Schinnar, A., Rothbard, A., Kanter, R., & Yoon Soo Yung (1990) An emperical literature review of definitions of severe and persistent mental illness. *American Journal of Psychiatry*; **147**: 1602–1608.

3 Developing a Mental Health Focus for Purchasers

TONY GOSS & PETER GLUCKMAN

Governmental policy on mental health has been relatively consistent for some thirty years. The drive to close the long stay institutions and to create care in the community was accepted by most if not all concerned in the field. Yet mental health became a major issue in 1994. Many searching reports were published, including Ritchie *et al* (1994) and Mental Health Foundation (1994), all of which gained widespread media coverage. The image of a system in crises was created. In part this arose from the concerns of the public over incidents of violence towards strangers by the mentally ill (despite the infrequency of such attacks). In part it related to the perceived lack of acute psychiatric beds and of medium secure facilities. Battle lines became drawn in the debate, with organisations such as MIND using the publicity to highlight the deficiencies in community care and to raise issues about the safety of patients both from other patients and from the system that treats them. Others used the opportunity to argue for more psychiatric beds and to force the hand of Government to look at the question of what response needed to be made to the growing concern about the lack of secure services. The impact of the Reed Review (1993) became apparent as those who would formerly have been contained within the criminal justice system became instead the concern of the National Health Service. Also, the first tentative steps were taken in moving to local services those who do not require high security from the Special Hospitals.

In inner south east London all of these debates were apparent and were highlighted by the high levels of identified need in the area. The development of community based alternatives to care in the old psychiatric hospitals is well advanced, with one hospital closed some years ago, another about to close at the time of writing and the third into a phased closure programme which will see our patients decanted by 1997. The impact of the initial transfer of mentally disordered offenders has been large, as would be expected in an inner urban area, especially one which has had a traditionally high usage level at the three Special Hospitals (95 patients in December 1994). However, many of the initiatives taken locally have been driven by the providers of services and it became increasingly apparent that the purchaser must take a far more proactive and leading role in the development of responses to the environment in which we work. The question is how can a purchaser achieve this? In what ways should they operate in order to add a unique and valuable focus to issues that allows "clinical product champions" (with whom we are well-blessed) to create new and innovative services whilst also maintaining at the same time a grip upon resources and an understanding of the need to demonstrate effectiveness. This is particularly true where, should the resources be made available, beds could be increased overnight and where an increase in community activity will not be reflected in less bed usage, merely a drop in admission criteria in terms of severity of condition.

We would argue that the development of a mental health focus for purchasers requires nine key elements. These are set out in Table One. We do not give a particular weight to each of these but rather consider that all must be in place and allowed to interact in order to create the necessary conditions in which purchasers can focus on the areas where their perspective is different and developmental. This does not mean that they are all equal, but that their relative importance will shift over time as local conditions change and different parts of the system require attention. There are, however, certain pre-conditions to the adoption of these key elements. These include but are not restricted to there being trust between the purchaser and providers, adequate clinical involvement in decision making on both sides and a commitment at the most senior levels to working through differences in a way that allows for constructive criticism without recrimination. This is especially true in mental health, where gaining the right levels of service for users depends so much upon there being real Healthy Alliances between the wide range of agencies who are likely to be involved in the commissioning and delivery of care packages. These include crucially the users themselves and their advocates. An indicative range of stakeholders in the process is set out in Table Two.

Table 1: *Key Elements in Creating a Purchaser Focus on Mental Health*

Element	Stakeholders
Flexible approach	All
Long-term planning	All—led by purchasers
Coping with financial uncertainties	All—supported by purchasers
Team playing	All
Working across boundaries	All
Risk taking	Shared, with Purchasers setting framework
BUT finding out what works!!	Purchasers, especially Public Health, linked to local, national and international research
NOT simply transferring but adapting	All
Collaboration where competition isn't relevant	All—led by purchasers

We can examine these key features in turn and point in some cases to the experience of adopting them in practice. The flexibility of the purchaser's approach is vital to creating new responses to new problems. Only by taking on board a view that allows and encourages change can change be engendered. If we simply say that we will continue, for example, to accept only one type of intervention for people in crisis, then we will not build services that are accepted as relevant by significant sections of our community who have rejected them as being unacceptable. This issue relates specifically for us in our locality to people from African and Caribbean backgrounds. We must look for other ways that may be just as effective, if not more so, at targeting particular populations or particular problems.

The significance of long term planning, allowing perspectives to be developed that encompass more than just the current financial year we happen to be in is self-evident. However, in a system which operates within the political Budget making round on an annual basis, it is all too easy to allow the financial imperatives of the moment to be our excuse for not planning for the future. This relates directly to the issue of coping with financial uncertainty. The commitment of purchasers to strategic aims over mid to long term periods, preferably on a shared basis between the key commissioners of services (Health Authorities/Commissions and Social Services Departments at least), must be given. Such planning allows shifts in investment to be planned and adjusted from year to year as resources allow, without losing sight of the bigger picture. Indeed, with a strategy in place (albeit one that is also flexible to allow for new issues that emerge over time), the management of anxiety over the financial position can be eased significantly.

Team playing almost goes without saying, but we believe that it is important to restate it. Lip service is often paid to joint planning and working together but the creation of real teams that can deliver is much more difficult to achieve. The place to start is within the purchasing agency itself. Commissioning teams which contain within them the key skills and attributes must be developed. This means that the often disparate functions of Public Health, contract management, quality, information, and finance must be brought together to create a whole which is far greater than the sum of its parts. Our experience suggests that such approaches do bring benefits and allow all members of the team to gain an understanding of, and a respect for, their various areas of expertise. In mental health, where the boundaries between health and social care and between the various levels of health care (primary, community, secondary, tertiary) are so blurred, it is even more important to be able to adopt such a system. This neatly dovetails into the next element of cross-boundary working. The approach adopted by our Health Commission has been characterised as "respecting the divide where we have to and ignoring it where we can". Whilst this is simplistic, the message is clear—people with mental health problems will have a range of needs, which cross boundaries that health or social services or housing or other agencies put up, whether for good reasons of service or for self-protection. The challenge is to work within the bureaucracies that we inhabit, but to constantly place the interests of the service user at the forefront of our thinking about how we operate those systems to best effect. We have attempted to put aside arguments about who controls and manages resources devoted to the care of people with mental health problems in primary care and to seek instead to commission resources from whoever happens to be best placed to provide such resources as cases demand. Our general practitioners have begun to have a range of services available to them which might include counsellors directly employed within the practice, CPNs employed by a mental health Trust but working with patients from a practice or group of practices, clinical psychologists offering sessions within practices and senior registrars doing outreach work in practices and being used as referral screeners by GPs.

Risk taking, on an advised basis, is one of the most difficult areas for purchasers, particularly in the field of mental health, given the recent exposure in the media. Retreat into safety first policies, designed to protect public bodies from adverse publicity is the easy option. However, if we are to develop services that meet the needs of people in the twenty first century we cannot afford to listen only to those who counsel staying with that which is familiar.

The development of risk management amongst providers has been noted, with many companies entering the field in recent times. Risk management and the associated competence of risk assessment are less well known to purchasers. No doubt a literature will soon emerge, as the experience of purchasers increases. What can be said at this stage is that calculated risk taking must be encouraged and purchasers must be prepared to support providers in adopting such policies. A major feature of risk assessment is likely to be working in new areas which, although new to the particular circumstances, have some evidence of successful implementation elsewhere and this brings us to our next key feature. Finding out what does work in other places and distilling the knowledge of other purchasers and providers must be done. This may involve literature searches, utilising the knowledge and experience of others, and visiting other services to see what actually goes on. Whilst this process can be characterised at times as in some way detracting from core business, it must be accepted as important for purchasers to understand what is going on in the field. This cannot always be done by simply reading the published results which can sometimes overstate the best parts and understate the less effective areas of particular projects.

The biggest mistake that is made, however, by purchasers in such circumstances is taking what is successful elsewhere and seeking to transfer it wholesale into their local context. There is a world of difference between local circumstances and what works in one place will not necessarily work in another. Different demography and need will have an enormous effect upon such matters. It is important to be able to distil from what has been seen those elements which will be capable of transfer and to filter out those which will not. It is also important to ensure that a full picture is brought back from other places. Thus, for example, the simple transfer of successful innovation from the United States that does not take account of the different cultural and historical perspectives and funding systems is doomed to failure. Recent experience of one of the authors is a case in point. Community led services in Madison, Wisconsin, are often held up as a model, with bed numbers per head of population some five times lower than in south east London, State of Wisconsin (1988). However, simply setting up similar health services will not lead to similar outcomes. The system in Wisconsin depends crucially upon the facts that there is no divide between health and social services in the commissioning of care packages and that the community mental health teams have direct control over and access to housing for their clients. These pre-conditions are unlikely to be in place, at least in the short term, in the U.K.

The Health Advisory Service survey of purchasing (1994) referred to later in this book points to the final element that we have identified as assisting in the creation of a purchaser focus on mental health. This is the question of competition or collaboration. It is our view that for the foreseeable future demand for mental health services will outstrip supply by a considerable margin; we operate in a sellers' market. In such circumstances, it seems obvious that the best results in terms of effectiveness and efficiency will be brought about not by forcing competition between providers, at least for mainstream services, but rather by creating collaboration. The role of the purchaser in such circumstances is to encourage collaborative attitudes and innovative ways of working across providers, whilst maintaining a rigorous approach towards quality gains, activity improvements and pressure on costs. We believe that this is the central message of the HAS review and that the adoption of this approach is the mark of mature purchasing. It is eminently more difficult to achieve than the simplistic drive for competitiveness, and brings with it a set of demands upon both purchasers and providers that challenge both sides, but it brings benefits to patients that are long lasting and satisfactory to them.

It is also important that purchasers collaborate where this is appropriate, for example where specialist services need to be purchased on a wider than District basis. Purchasers need to consider the impact of their purchasing decisions in such circumstances upon the whole of the service being offered and not take a purely parochial view.

Table 2: *Potential Stakeholders in Mental Health*

Users and carers

Health Authority/Family Health Services Authority (to be merged)

Provider Trusts

Voluntary Sector Providers

Private Sector Providers

General Practitioners

Other Primary Health Care Team Members

Social Services Department

Housing Department

Leisure Department

Police and Probation

Employment Services

We have identified the elements that we believe are essential in creating a mental health focus for purchasers and we have identified the likely stakeholders in the process. The question then remains—what will the development of such a focus mean for the development of purchaser capability and service delivery? We can refer to some local issues that we believe have benefited from this clear focus.

Firstly, the focus engendered within our Health Commission has enabled us to place mental health as a key priority area. This emerges from the Health of the

Nation targets on the functioning of people with mental health problems and on suicides (Department of Health 1992). However, the simple fact that there are such targets does not necessarily move mental health to the forefront. There is a whole range of pressures which impact upon the thinking of Health Authorities and Commissions in identifying change that will bring health improvement. These include effectiveness data, specific service and investment strategies, contracting pressures, substitution and many others (see Table 3). All of these need to be turned into recommendations that are then value filtered to create priorities for change that are made explicit through purchasing intentions. The primacy of mental health in these influences is greatly assisted, we would argue, by the fact that the requisite preconditions are put in place through adopting the schemata described in this chapter. It has led to the publication of a five year commissioning strategy (1994–1999) for mental health "With Need in Mind" and to a clear idea of the scale of, and likely sources of, additional investment in mental health that will be necessary to achieve a community led and appropriate range of services to meet the very high needs of our local population.

Secondly, and of equal importance, is the fact that the development of such a focus creates both an actual and a perceived improvement in purchaser expertise. Relationships with other agencies and with various professionals within them are eased by the clear indication that the purchaser is operating on a logical basis, with sound information and with clarity of understanding of local needs, the services required to meet them and a shared vision of the future. This, of course, does not mean that there are not disputes and disagreements over detail, nor that there is not still tension between players. However, our conclusion is that the development of a focus on mental health by purchasers makes most of this tension creative rather than negative in its effect.

Table 3

Improved Contracting

- agree speciality specific quality standards
- contracting informed by clinical audit
- clinicians involved in contract monitoring

Improved Purchasing

- purchasers use informed clinical advice
- how does clinical advice change purchasing
- do arrangements command confidence of clinicians

Responsive Management

- providers to stimulate clinical involvement
- providers to review arrangements for clinical involvement
- allow for sufficient business planning support

Motivated Clinicians

- shift away from activity & finance focus
- agree resources for audit and clinical training

References

Ritchie, J. *et al*, *Report of the Inquiry into the Care and Treatment of Christopher Clunis*, North East and South East Thames Regional Health Authorities, February 1994.

Mental Health Foundation, *Creating Community Care*, Report of the Mental Health Foundation Inquiry into Community Care for People with Severe Mental Illness, Mental Health Foundation, 1994.

Reed, J. (Chairman), *Review of Health and Social Services for Mentally Disordered Offenders and others requiring similar services*, Home Office and Department of Health, 1993.

State of Wisconsin, *Report of the Advisory Committee to the Department of Health and Social Services*, State of Wisconsin, 1988.

Health Advisory Service, *Survey of Mental Health Purchasing*, HAS, 1994

Department of Health, *The Health of the Nation*, HMSO, 1992.

Lambeth, Southwark & Lewisham Health Commission, *With Need in Mind: A Five Year Commissioning Strategy for Mental Health*, Lambeth, Southwark & Lewisham Health Commission, September 1994.

4 Population-Based Assessment of Needs for Services

SONIA JOHNSON, GRAHAM THORNICROFT & GERALDINE
STRATHDEE

Introduction

The rational approach to planning services which are fully appropriate for the local population is the systematic assessment of the needs of all individuals identified as mentally ill within each catchment area. This should also include those who have severe mental health problems but are not currently in contact with services. A local case register should then be used to aggregate the needs detected in all these individuals, and services developed to fit them (Wing, 1989). However, planners in many areas do not currently have access to the extensive information this approach requires. A more pragmatic approach therefore has to be taken to assessment of local needs for services by interpreting the incomplete mosaic of data that is to hand.

This chapter discusses how widely available demographic and service use data may be used to assess current local service needs and provision. The methods outlined should not be regarded as more than approximations which can be used as proxies for more detailed local needs assessment. However, they do provide a means of beginning to plan services in a way which is informed by the characteristics of the local population, without having to undertake further local research. As well as using the methods outlined here, service planners may take into account any available reports on local services from bodies such as the Health Advisory Service, or other epidemiological or service-related research which has been carried out locally.

The demographic indicators which we discuss are for the most part readily available in Office of Population Censuses and Surveys (OPCS) data, and in the Health Service Indicators (HSI) published by the NHS Executive. The data on local service provision to which we refer are also usually readily available. However, health purchasers and providers sometimes have surprisingly little access to accurate information about voluntary sector and social services provision. A key initial step in assessing local services will often be collating information already available from disparate sources about current levels of residential and day care provision.

In this chapter, this pragmatic process of assessing local services on the basis of a group of demographic and service use characteristics will be illustrated using the example of an imaginary health catchment area, here called Planningham. Tables 1 and 2 show the main characteristics of Planningham which are referred to in the examples which follow.

Table 1: *Basic information required for population-based estimation of service needs: demographic characteristics of Planningham.*

Demographic Indicator	Figure for Planningham
Population	250,000
Location	Inner City
Jarman Index	39th most deprived of 400 Districts
Ethnic Mix	70% White, 15% Asian 12% Black Caribbean 2% Black African
Homeless known to local authority	1500 Households
Street homeless	175 individuals
Unemployment	17% economically active population unemployed
Suicide rate	16.2 per 100,000 per year
Age structure	Slight over-representation of 25–44 year olds as compared with national age structure

Table 2: *Mental Health Service Provision in Planningham*

Service	Planningham level of provision
Number of people admitted at least once to hospital	1,900 people (1,400 general adult service)
Admissions per annum (including re-admissions)	2,820 admissions (2,110 general adult service)
Number of out-patient attendances	6,500 attendances total
Acute psychiatric beds	170 beds, general adult service
Day centre placements—all functional mental illness	150 places
Sheltered work placements	100 places
Community psychiatric nurses for general adult service—maximum total caseload	200 clients
Places in 24 hour staffed hostels (age 18–65, mental illness)	30 residents
Places in day staffed hostels Group homes Intensive care unit beds Patients in Regional Secure Unit or Special Hospitals	90 residents 25 residents 3 beds 14 patients

The data in Table 2 illustrates an issue which it is important to remember in comparing local data with national figures. There are no standard classifications for collection of service information, and there will often be inconsistencies between data sets in the age ranges and diagnostic categories included. Care is therefore needed to ensure that like is compared with like.

Simple information of the types illustrated in Tables 1 and 2 may be used to assess current local services by four main methods, each with some limitations:

Method 1: Local need may be estimated on the basis of epidemiological studies which give figures for the national prevalence of psychiatric disorders.

Method 2: Levels of service provision which would be expected locally may be calculated from national and international patterns of service use and service provision.

Method 3: Current local services may be compared with expert views on desirable levels of service provision.

Method 4: The validity of estimates derived from Method 3 may be increased by using a deprivation-weighted approach. Estimates of service need may be adjusted on the basis of current knowledge about the relationships of mental health disorders to age, sex, ethnic group, marital status, economic status and other social variables.

Finally, the degree of fit between current service provision and the population's needs should be assessed from a geographical perspective as well as in terms of numbers of individuals who can be provided for. In particular, those demographic variations within catchment areas which may produce especially high levels of need in certain areas need to be considered. In this chapter, each of the above methods is explained and illustrated using the example of Planningham.

Method 1: Using epidemiological studies of the prevalence of psychiatric disorder

An estimate of local morbidity may be derived from community studies of levels of psychiatric morbidity carried out elsewhere in the UK. Table 3 shows the expected numbers of people with psychiatric disorders in our fictional District, Planningham, based on the figures for expected morbidity summarised in the 'Health of the Nation' (Department of Health, 1992).

Table 3: *Estimates of psychiatric morbidity in Planningham based on national prevalence data.*

	Estimated prevalence/ 500,000	Estimated prevalence for Planningham (population 250,000)
Schizophrenia	1,000–2,500	500–1,250
Affective psychosis	500–2,500	250–1,250
Depression	10,000–25,000	5,000–12,500
Anxiety	8,000–30,000	4,000–15,000

Based on Department of Health, 1992.

Survey and case identification data from inner city London suggests that about 0.7% of the population suffers from some form of psychotic disorder (Campbell *et al*, 1990). This would suggest an expected prevalence for Planningham of some form of psychotic disorder of 1,750, compatible with the ranges in Table 3.

Epidemiological data provide an overall estimate of needs in the community. It does not indicate which forms of service are needed: most people with depression or anxiety do not need referral to specialist services. However, for schizophrenia and other psychoses these data are more useful, as it may be assumed that most patients with these severe mental illnesses will need some form of long term contact with psychiatric services. Returning to our fictional District, Planningham's community services accommodate 200 people on Community Psychiatric Nurses' caseloads, 150 people in day centres, and 100 people in sheltered work placements. This might cause concern when considered in relation to epidemiological data. If the estimate that there are 1,750 people with psychotic illnesses in the District is accurate, local community services do not currently have the capacity to provide for more than a small minority of these people.

The local suicide rate is another important epidemiological indicator. Suicide rates have a dual function in service assessment. They may be seen both as an indicator of psychiatric morbidity, and as a marker of service outcome. Suicide rates for each District and national rankings for males and females are available in the Health Service Indicators. The following table shows suicide rates for Planningham and for the country as a whole for 1991/2.

Table 4: *Rates of suicide per 100,000 per year*

	Males	Females	Persons
Planningham	20.1	14.1	16.2
England and Wales	16.9	5.7	11.2

Thus Planningham has a relatively high suicide rate, particularly among women. This cannot be unambiguously interpreted without access to other data. However, it suggests that needs for development of mental health services may be great compared with other areas, either because it indicates high levels of morbidity, or because it reflects ineffective services.

In deciding what form of intervention may reduce local suicide rates, it is important to consider which groups are particularly at risk. For example, Planningham has a large Asian community, and it is important to investigate the possibility that its high rates for women are due to suicide among young Asian women, known to be elevated nationally (Soni-Raleigh and Balarajan 1992).

Method 2: Estimating service need on the basis of national patterns of service use

The work of Goldberg and Huxley (1980, 1992) may be used to compare local service use with national and international data on service utilisation. Table 5 shows the expected Planningham levels of morbidity and of service use, based on Goldberg and Huxley's calculations of the proportion of the population using services at various levels. These figures include the elderly as well as younger adults.

Table 5:   *National and Planningham expected morbidity and service use*

Level of Service	1 year prevalence for population at risk (%)	Expected Levels for Planningham (pop. 250,000)
Adults suffering from mental illness/distress	26–31.6	65,000–78,750
Consulting primary care	23	57,500
Identified by doctors as having mental illness/distress	10.2	25,500
Seen by specialist mental health services	2.4	6,000
Admitted to psychiatric hospital	0.6	1,500

Based on Goldberg and Huxley (1992).

Referring to the figures for Planningham, the number of people admitted at least once to a psychiatric hospital (1,900) is high compared with these estimates of service use. However, the information considered so far gives no grounds for choosing between various possible explanations, including higher than average levels of need, greater than usual willingness to admit, and shortage of services providing alternatives to admission.

Wing (1992) gives the following national figures for patients with mental disorder in contact with services per 250,000 in 1990/1. These figures include people with dementia. Again expected levels of provision for the population of Planningham may be derived.

Table 6: *National figures for service use and expected Planningham figures*

Type of contact	National figures for 1990/1, per 250,000 population	Expected for Planning-ham
No of patients attending GP per annum	64,250	64,250
No of patients attending out-patients per annum	2,858	2,858
Total no of out-patient attendances per annum	8,586	8,586
No of in-patients on one day, stay <1 year	135	135
No of acute admissions per annum	1,095	1,095
No of in-patients on one day stay 1–5 years	93	93
No of in-patients on one day, stay >5 years	70	70
No in Local Authority residential care on one day	18	18
No in Local Authority long term day place on one day	63	63

From Wing (1992).

Planningham again has large numbers of acute admissions compared with rates predicted from national figures (2,820 actual admissions compared with 1,095 predicted). The number of out-patient contacts, on the other hand, is smaller than expected (6,500 actual attendances compared with 8,586 predicted). This pattern could be explained in various ways. One important possibility is that the out-patient service might currently be under-resourced, leading to an inability to respond swiftly to referrals. Alternatively, patients may find the out-patient service geographically inaccessible or psychologically unwelcoming, or local professionals may have limited awareness of how to make referrals to it. If such difficulties exist, the ability of the out-patient service to avert in-patient admissions may be compromised. Wing (1992) quotes other national figures for service use on the basis of the Local Authority Profile of Social Services for 1989/90. Again, these may be extrapolated to give expected figures for Planningham, assumed to be an inner city Borough.

Table 7: *Use of local authority services: predicted service levels in Planningham based on national data.*

	LA residential	Other residential	Day centre
England	0.4/10,000 population	0.3/10,000	4/10,000
Shire Counties	0.2/10,000	0.2/10,000	3/10,000
Outer London	0.5/10,000	0.9/10,000	4/10,000
Inner London	1.2/10,000	2.2/10,000	8/10,000
Planningham	30	55	200

Comparing these figures with the actual provision figures, it appears that Planningham has low levels of day centre provision compared with current national levels (150 actual places compared with 200 predicted from national levels). Looking at residential placements, on the other hand, suggests greater provision than is available nationally (145 places compared with 85 predicted from national levels).

An important disadvantage of national service use data is that they are often based on incomplete or inaccurate returns, especially where they refer to community services (Glover 1991). A good alternative may be use of data from studies in areas such as Salford where detailed case registers recording all service contacts have been kept (Wing, 1989: Fryers and Wooff, 1989).

Service utilisation data do not of course allow for a normative assessment of the services which the health authority *should* have. However, planners may find it helpful to use them to get some idea whether numbers of contacts for particular components of their local services are relatively large or small compared with services elsewhere.

Method 3: What are desirable levels of service provision?

The disadvantage of comparing local services with national data is that national average service use cannot be assumed to represent ideal levels of service provision. It is also unwise to assume that the current balance between service components such as acute beds, residential services outside hospital, day care services and community services is the best possible. The development of ways of determining optimal levels of service provision is still in its infancy, but a number of writers have contributed to the debate.

The 1975 British White Paper suggests targets of 50 District General Hospital beds per 100,000 of the population, together with 35 for the elderly severely mentally infirm and 17 for the 'new' long stay patients. More recently the House of Commons Social Services Committee report on Community Care (1985) noted that 'a smaller number of in-patients beds is now thought necessary for general psychiatric services', and a Royal College of Psychiatrists working party has specified this as 44 acute beds for a population of 100,000 (Hirsch, 1988).

Strathdee and Thornicroft (1992) have set out targets for service provision based on a Delphi method of summarising expert opinion in Britain and on likely prevalences of mental illness nationally. These targets assume that services should as far as possible be community based, with community residential places and day care taking the place of institutional care. Naturally, none of these suggested levels of provision should be taken in isolation—if one component of the mental health services is underdeveloped, this is likely to lead to a higher demand on the other elements in the system (Audit Commission, 1994). Wing (1992) has made similar estimates of targets for general adult residential services. These two sets of estimates are shown in table 8.

Table 8:   *Estimated need for general adult residential provision per 250,000 population. (Wing, 1992, Strathdee & Thornicroft, 1992).*

Type of accommodation	Midpoint number of places	Range	Midpoint number of places	Range
	Wing		Strathdee & Thornicroft	
Staff awake at night				
Acute & crisis care	100	50–150	95	50–150
Intensive care unit	10	5–15	8	5–10
Regional Secure Unit & Special Hospital	4	1–10	5	1–10
Hostel wards	50	25–75		
Other staffed housing				
High-staffed hostel	75	40–110	95	40–150
Day-staffed hostel	50	25–75	75	30–120
Group homes (visited)	45	20–70	64	48–80
Respite facilities			3	0–5
No specialist staff				
Supported bed-sits	30	–		
Direct access	30	–		
Adult placement schemes			8	0–15
Total per 250,000	**394**	**226–565**	**357**	**174–540**

Wing (1992) also provides some figures for targets for day provision by mental health services and for total numbers in contact with any mental health services, again taking account of the prevalence of severe mental illness in the community. These figures appear to include elderly people who have functional mental illnesses. Figures based on his calculations for the full range of provision by the mental health services are shown in Table 9.

Table 9: *Estimated numbers of day and residential places needed for 250,000 population.*

Form of provision	Places per 250,000
Total in contact with specialist services	572–1716
NHS specialist residential care with night staff	82–246
Other residential	115–345
Specialist day care (4+ half days a week)	183–548*
Other active contact with specialist team (excluding those in above categories)	250–750

* Including people in non-NHS residential care, of whom half are assumed also to require day care.
From Wing (1992).

Method 4:   The deprivation-weighted population approach to needs assessment

The above calculations of expected levels of morbidity and of service utilisation in Planningham have not taken into account its particular population characteristics. This is unsatisfactory, as there is strong evidence that social and demographic factors are closely associated with rates of psychiatric disorder.

The association between psychiatric disorders and social class (particularly for schizophrenia and depression) is one of the most consistent findings in psychiatric epidemiology. The Jarman combined index of social deprivation has been shown to be highly correlated with psychiatric admission rates for Health Districts in the South East Thames Region (Jarman, 1983; Jarman, 1984; Hirsch, 1988; Thornicroft, 1991: Jarman and Hirsch, 1992).

It thus seems reasonable to use Jarman scores to make deprivation-weighted assessments of likely local needs for services. Weightings based on Jarman scores may be used to estimate where each District should fall within the national ranges for desirable levels of service provision which are shown in Tables 8 and 9. For example if Planningham has a Jarman score 10% below the top of the national range, a useful approximation of numbers of places needed can be obtained by assuming that the District should have service levels around 10% below the upper end of the national range. The following shows the estimated requirements for Planningham, calculated on this basis from Strathdee and Thornicroft's estimates of ideal levels of national service provision reproduced in Table 8.

Table 10: *Estimated residential service requirements in Planningham calculated on basis of deprivation scores*

Type of Provision	Estimated requirements in Planningham
24 hour staffed residences	139
Day staffed residences	111
Acute psychiatric care	140
Unstaffed group homes	77
Adult placement schemes	14
Local secure places	10
Respite facilities	5
Regional secure unit	9

The same approximation may be applied to Wing's (1992) figures, given above in Table 9.

Table 11: *Deprivation weighted estimates of required day and residential services in Planningham*

Form of provision	Estimated requirement for Planningham, based on Jarman score
Total in contact with specialist services	1602
NHS specialist residential care with night staff	230
Other residential	322
Specialist day care (4+ half days a week)	512*
Other active contact with specialist team (excluding those in above categories)	700

* (including people in non-NHS residential care, of whom half are assumed also to require day care).
Based on Wing (1992).

Fit between current services and deprivation-weighted estimates of requirements

Returning to Table 2, which shows current levels of service provision in Planningham, some of the actual levels of provision may now be compared with the deprivation-weighted estimates of requirements.

Table 12: *Actual levels of services and estimated requirements in Planningham*

Service	Actual level of service	Estimated number required	Gap between actual and required
Acute psychiatric beds	170 beds	140 beds	+30 beds (21% above expected requirement)
Day centre or sheltered work placements—all functional mental illnesses	250 places	512 places	–262 places (49% of expected requirement)
Places in 24 hour staffed residences (18–65, mental illnesses)	30 residents	139 residents	–130 residents (22% of expected requirement)
Places in day staffed hostels	90 residents	111 residents	–21 residents (81% of expected requirement)
Group homes	25 residents	77 residents	–52 residents (32% of expected requirements)
Local intensive care	3 beds	10 beds	–7 beds (30% of expected requirements)
Patients in Regional Secure Unit or Special Hospitals	14 patients	9 patients	+5 patients (56% above expected requirement)

Thus this simple exercise allows us to begin to evaluate the overall pattern of service provision in Planningham, which seems to be a relatively high level of in-patient service provision, but levels of day service and community residential services which are lower than estimates of what is required. Again it must be noted that it is crucial to look at all the elements in local services together. If the acute bed provision were considered in isolation it might be judged to be unnecessarily high. However, if considered in relation to the low levels of community provision, it becomes apparent that reliance on in-patient beds and high admission rates may well be a consequence of undeveloped community facilities. It thus seems unlikely that numbers of acute beds could reasonably be reduced without considerable further development of community services.

Specific local modifying factors

Weighting according to overall deprivation levels is a helpful beginning in planning epidemiologically-based services. However, various other local demographic factors should also be considered in tailoring the overall approach to local conditions. These will be outlined in this section.

a Ethnicity

Ethnicity has a major influence on service utilisation and on the types of services needed. Black Caribbeans are an important group, as several studies have indicated a higher risk than their white neighbours of being admitted to psychiatric hospital (Moodley & Thornicroft 1988) or of being diagnosed as suffering from schizophrenia (Harrison *et al*, 1988: King *et al*, 1994).

It has not been clearly established that Asians have an elevated rate of admission for psychosis (Thomas *et al*, 1993), although King *et al* (1994) argue that elevated rates of psychosis may be general among immigrant groups. However, it has also been found that, despite identical rates of consultation in General Practice, Asians are less likely than the white population to be referred to the psychiatric services, and that psychological disorders in this group may be more likely to go unrecognised (Brewin, 1980), perhaps reflecting linguistic and cultural barriers to service delivery. Refugee communities also have important specific needs. High levels of deprivation and possibly of post-traumatic stress disorders are likely to be found among the various communities of recently arrived refugees in the UK.

Planningham has substantial Asian and Black Caribbean populations, and this will need to be taken into account at all stages of service planning. The presence of the Black Caribbean population may create greater needs for services for the severely mentally ill. For each group, great attention will need to be paid to making services culturally and linguistically appropriate. There may be greater barriers to early access to mental health care than for the white population, so that particular attention will need to be paid to outreach and making services accessible. Distrust of psychiatric services may also be greater than among the white population, so that consultation with members of these communities and effective advocacy services are important.

b Homelessness

Recent research in the UK suggests that the homeless in hostels and night shelters and on the street probably have a rate of mental illness of between 30 and 50%, and that psychoses predominate (Scott, 1993: Timms and Fry, 1989; Marshall, 1989). Conventional psychiatric services often fail to contact or engage the homeless mentally ill, so that specific services are needed. For example, clinics may be provided in places where the homeless tend to congregate or assertive outreach work carried out on the streets.

The extent and location of the local homeless population thus needs to be known in order to plan comprehensive services for the long term mentally ill. Unfortunately, it is often very difficult to obtain an accurate enumeration of local numbers of homeless people, particularly the street homeless. Any 'official' figures, should be treated with caution and enquiries made about the methods used for data collection. It is helpful to ask national and local agencies concerned with homelessness how accurate they think any figures obtained are likely to be, and whether they know of any counts carried out locally. If there have been no thorough local enumerations, this should be a priority.

c Unemployment

Another characteristic of Planningham with specific significance for mental health service provision is the high unemployment rate. Levels of unemployment and suicide rates have been found to be correlated in several Western countries (Pritchard, 1992, Platt *et al*, 1992), and becoming unemployed has been associated with a general decline in mental health (Warr *et al*, 1988). Thus this demographic characteristic again may suggest an increased need for mental health services.

d Age structure

The age structure of the population may also serve as a pointer for service needs. Over-representation in the 20–29 age range may indicate a greater population at risk of developing psychotic disorders. Thus there may be a slightly greater need than nationally for general adult services, and a slightly lower one for services for the elderly mentally ill.

Service needs from a geographical perspective

To meet needs across the catchment area, services should not only provide adequate numbers of places in a range of forms of care, but also locate these services so that they are accessible to their users. The geography of the catchment area thus needs to be considered as well as its overall characteristics. Two principles are important: sectorisation, and the development of services which are highly accessible to parts of the catchment area where particularly high levels of need are likely to be found.

The term sector generally refers to a delineated geographic area with a defined catchment population. Sectorisation, with services for each sector located centrally within it, is likely to be an important principle in ensuring that services are reasonably accessible to people throughout the catchment area. To ensure that services match population needs, it is helpful to examine in detail local maps which include public transport routes, in order to check that local bases are accessible without too much time and effort from every part of the catchment area they serve.

It is also important to consider on an epidemiological basis which parts of the catchment area should be particularly targeted. Attention needs to be paid to providing accessible and well-resourced services with good facilities for outreach work in those areas where levels of overall deprivation are high or where there are large numbers of homeless people or unemployed people. Demographic indicators such as Jarman scores, ethnic mix and levels of unemployment are available for individual electoral wards. It is worth marking on local maps those areas where higher levels of need would be expected, and considering where service bases are located in relation to these areas. In dividing the catchment areas into sectors, variations in deprivation within the area need to be considered—in the more deprived parts of the catchment area, sector populations should be smaller than elsewhere, or else be served by more staff.

Conclusion

This central theme of this chapter is that it is feasible to use currently available information for each local area as the basis for a rational approach to planning mental health services. There is evidence that current mental health services throughout England and Wales are often not distributed in relation to need, however estimated (Audit Commission 1994). It is thus important to develop and apply simple pragmatic approaches to assessment of local population needs. However, more fine-tuned planning of services in each local area will require investment in an information infrastructure that can monitor service performance and continue to provide relevant information to underpin future planning cycles.

References

Audit Commission (1994) *Finding a place: a review of mental health services for adults*. London; HMSO.

Brewin, C. (1980) Explaining the lower rates of psychiatric treatment among Asian immigrants to the United Kingdom. *Social Psychiatry* **15**: 17–19.

Campbell, P. G., Taylor, J., Pantelis, C., Harvey, C. (1990) Studies of schizophrenia in a large mental hospital proposed for closure, and in two halves of an inner London borough served by the hospital. In *'International Perspectives in Schizophrenia'* (ed M. Weller) London: John Libbey.

Department of Health (1992), *The Health of the Nation*. London: HMSO.

Fryers, T. and Wooff, K. (1989), A decade of mental health care in an English urban community. Patterns and trends in Salford 1976–1987. In: Wing, J.K. (ed), *Contributions to health services planning and research*. London: Gaskell.

Glover, G. (1991), The official data available on mental health. In Jenkins R. and Griffiths, S. (eds), *Indicators for Mental Health in the Population*. London: HMSO.

Goldberg, D. & Huxley, P. (1980). *Mental Illness in the Community*. London: Tavistock.

Goldberg, D. & Huxley, P. (1992). *Common Mental Disorders. A Bio-Social Model*. London: Routledge.

Harrison, G., Owens, D., Holton, A., Neilson, D. & Bool, D. (1988). A prospective study of severe mental disorder in Afro-Caribbean patients. *Psychological Medicine* **18:** 643–657.

House of Commons. (1985) Second Report from the Social Services Committee, Session 1984–85, *Community Care*. London: HMSO.

Hirsch, S. (1988) *Psychiatric beds and resources: Factors influencing bed use and service planning*. London: Gaskell (Royal College of Psychiatrists).

Jarman, B. (1983). Identification of underprivileged areas. *British Medical Journal*, **286**, 1705–1709.

Jarman, B. (1984). Underprivileged areas: Validation and distribution of scores. *British Medical Journal*, **289**, 1587–1592.

Jarman and Hirsch (1992). Statistical models to predict district psychiatric morbidity. In *Measuring Mental Health Needs,* (Thornicroft, G., Brewin, C. & Wing, J. K. eds) Royal College of Psychiatrists, Gaskell Press.

King, M., Coker, E., Leavey, G., Hoare, A. and Johnson-Sabine, E. (1994). Incidence of psychotic illness in London: comparison of ethnic groups. *British Medical Journal*, **304:** 1115–1119.

Marshall, M. (1989). Collected and neglected: are Oxford hostels filling up with disabled psychiatric patients. *British Medical Journal* **299**, 706–709.

Moodley, P. & Thornicroft, G. (1988). Ethnic Group and the Compulsory Admission of psychiatric patients. *Medicine, Science and the Law,* **28**, 324–328.

Platt, S., Micciolo, R., Tansella, M. (1992) Suicide and unemployment in Italy. Description, analysis and interpretation of recent trends. *Social Science and Medicine* **34**. 1191–1201.

Pritchard, C. (1992) Is there a link between suicide in young men and unemployment? A comparison of the UK with other European Community countries, *British Journal of Psychiatry* **160**, 750–756.

Scott, J. (1993) Homelessness and mental illness. *British Journal of Psychiatry* **162**, 314–324.

Soni-Raleigh, V. and Balarajan, R. (1992), Suicide and self-burning among Indians and West Indians in England and Wales, *British Journal of Psychiatry*, **161**, 365–368.

Strathdee, G. and Thornicroft, G. (1992), Community Sectors for Needs-Led Mental Health Services. *In Measuring Mental Health Needs.* (Thornicroft, G., Brewin, C. & Wing, J.K. eds). Royal College of Psychiatrists, Gaskell Press.

Thomas, C.S., Stone, K., Osborn, M., Thomas, P.F., Fisher, M. (1993) Psychiatric morbidity and compulsory admission among UK born Europeans, Afro-Caribbeans and Asians in central Manchester. *British Journal of Psychiatry* **163**, 91–99.

Thornicroft, G., Social deprivation and rates of treated mental disorder developing statistical models to predict psychiatric service utilisation. *British Journal of Psychiatry 1991*, **158**; 475–484.

Timm, P. and Fry, A. (1989) Homelessness and mental illness. *Health Trends* **21**. 70–71.

Warr, P., Jackson, P. and Banks, M.H. (1988), Unemployment and mental health, some British studies. *Journal of Social Issues* **44**, 47–68.

Wing, J. (1989). Editor. Health Services Planning and Research. *Contributions from Psychiatric Case Registers.* London: Gaskell.

Wing, J. (1992). *Epidemiologically Based Needs Assessment;* Mental Illness. NHSME, London.

5 The Mental Illness Needs Index (MINI)

GYLES R. GLOVER

Introduction

The prevalence of mental illness is not uniformly distributed. Before the 1990 reforms of the NHS, health authorities covered populations characteristically of around two hundred thousand. The trend since the reforms has been for authorities to amalgamate into larger units with a population base of three to four times that size, with several separate mental health units providing care of geographically defined catchment areas within the overall territory. Within provider units it has become increasingly common for service delivery to be shared between clinical teams often on the basis of geographically defined catchment areas. These arrangements produce resource allocation problems at two levels: how should the purchaser assign resources for mental health care between the provider units and how should the provider units allocate between clinical teams.

Epidemiological Evidence

Epidemiological studies shed some light on these problems. Thornicroft's (1991) exploratory study of prediction of district level admission rates in the South East Thames Region began by reviewing this literature. He identified a range of social variables (lower social class, male gender, single marital status, some aspects of domicile such as living alone, in overcrowded accommodation or in highly transitory neighbourhoods, high residential mobility, living in inner cities, population density and poverty) with established relation to psychiatric morbidity. By a principal components analysis he identified components of general deprivation and social isolation and permanent sickness which were effective predictors of district admission rate.

The problem for resource allocators is to determine the quantitative weight such issues should be assigned. Two groups (Jarman et al 1992; Car-Hill et al 1994) have undertaken work to produce methods of predicting resource requirements on a reasonably wide scale (i.e. wider than a single district) on the basis of independent statistical indicators. None of their conclusions satisfactorily solves the problem.

Some of the difficulties are practical. Two of the studies developed models which, while theoretically relevant, are practically difficult to use below the district level as they are based on data elements not routinely published at lower levels. Some objections are theoretical. The same two studies develop models which make use of data about population ethnicity which categorise Caribbeans and individuals with roots in the Indian subcontinent as a single group despite evidence that the former show a high rate of mental health services use while the latter show a low rate (Harrison *et al* 1988; Glover, 1989; Cochrane, Stopes-Roe, 1981; Ineichen, 1990).

Development of the MINI

A collaborative study of this area was set up between two members of the Charing Cross Westminster Department of Public Health and Primary care and the Research unit of the Royal College of Psychiatrists, with financial support from the Department of Health as part of the first mental health Research and Development programme. The study set out to develop an index of mental health care need which was based on statistical indicators available from census data for the whole country, for all levels from the electoral ward up. Ward level data on admission prevalence from the old North East Thames region were used for the modelling work. This region was chosen in part for the wide spectrum of types of area it encompassed and in part as recent hospital episode statistics were readily available and appeared to be reasonably complete.

The study began by developing regression models of the patterns of admission prevalence rates *within* each hospital's catchment area. Factors influencing these distributions should be relatively independent of the availability of beds, since all patients requiring admission are 'competing' for the same pool of beds. Models for catchment areas showed systematic differences. Prediction was generally more effective in rural and surburban than in inner city areas and the predominant variables differed. Models for groups of catchment areas suggested that admission thresholds in relation to socio-demographic characteristics were higher in suburban areas than in rural ones, perhaps suggesting that the provision of beds in relation to need was sparser in the former.

On the basis of this work a Mental Illness Needs Index (MINI) has been defined. The detail of this work is described elsewhere (Glover *et al* 1995). The index itself is widely available for use within the National Health Service and Local Government. Copies of a computer program calculating the index for any territory definable by its electoral ward composition are available from the Royal College of Psychiatrists Research Unit(*). In addition to calculating the MINI, this programme shows the population structure and the predicted standardised admission prevalence for adults aged 15 to 64; the number of adults likely to be admitted is also calculated.

Two groups have published analyses of the range in of the level of requirements for all the key types of resources for a comprehensive mental health services. Wing (1992) on the basis of an extensive review of research studies (Table 1). Thornicroft and Strathdee (1992) on the basis of a modified Delphi technique (Table 2). In each case, for each type of facility (acute beds, 24 hour staffed residential accommodation etc.), the authors suggest the range of provision required from the least needy district to the most. The MINI program goes on to locate the selected area within this range and to translate the proposed rate of provision into actual place numbers. It is important to note that recent overall NHS Executive (1995) guidance about numbers of secure places needed envisages substantially higher *national* levels of provision than the work cited above. For this type of provision numbers are generally small and purchasers are usually aware of their position.

The Relevance of MINI for commissioners

The relevance of this work for district purchasers is that it provides a simple method for obtaining a first estimate of how a rational apportionment would distribute whatever is the level of resources available to them. Of course this type of method has many problems. A number of local factors, such as clusters of resettled patients, may determine the distribution of need in ways the model could not anticipate. The model is based only on predicting the numbers of people likely to have an admission, not the associated costs, which may vary separately if the cases in some districts are unusually costly to care for.

Finally the model makes no estimate of the number or burden of patients cared for without admission. However the work is intended to provide a first estimate, and this it does. During 1995, the Audit Commission's NHS District Audit Service is examining, mental health services. Issues raised in the Commissions report *Finding a Place* (The Audit Commission, 1994) are the focus of this work, and it is expected that the MINI program will allow users to examine the geographical targeting of mental health services, at the sector, provider and purchaser levels. Finally, it needs to be recognised that these estimates of population-based needs for mental health services may have to be adjusted to allow for specific local circumstances (Table 3).

Table 1: *Estimated service needs (Wing, 1992)*

	Per 250k total pop		Per 100k total pop	
	Lowest	Highest	Lowest	Highest
Wing facility guidelines				
Acute/crisis care	50	150	20	60
Intensive care	5	15	2	6
Reg secure/Sp hosp	1	10	0.4	4
Hostel wards	25	75	10	30
High staffed hostel/rehab	40	110	16	44
Day staffed hostels	25	75	10	30
Group homes	20	70	8	28
Wing client group size guidelines				
Residential care staffed at night	82	246	32.8	98.4
Other residential care	115	345	46	138
Day care	125	375	50	150
Others in spells of care	250	750	100	300
Total	572	1,716	228.8	686.4

Table 2: *Estimated Service Needs (Strathdee & Thornicroft, 1992)*

	Per 250k total pop		Per 100k total pop	
	Lowest	Highest	Lowest	Highest
Thornicroft and Strathdee guidelines				
24hr staffed hostels	40	150	16	60
Day staffed hostels	31	135	12.4	54
Group Home	48	80	19.2	32
Respite care beds	1	5	0.4	2
Acute care beds	50	150	20	60
Local secure beds	5	10	2	4
Regional secure beds	1	10	0.4	4

Table 3: *Specific local factors which may require adjustment of MINI outputs*

Local factor	Example
Service availability	Number of low staffed hostels
	24 hours staffed accommodation
	Court diversion
	Police diversion
	Local psychiatric institutions
	Alternatives to hospital admission
	Extent of voluntary sector provision
Patients characteristics	Homeless persons
Bed management strategies	Senior gatekeeping
	Home based assessment
	Bed manager
Staffing levels	Staff : patient ratio (1:10 to 1:15 recommended for high dependency severely mentally ill)

References

The Audit Commission (1994) *Finding a place. A review of mental health services for adults.* London: HMSO.

Carr-Hill, R.A., Hardman, G., Martin, S., Peacock, S., Sheldon, T.A., Smith, P. (1994) *A formula for distributing NHS revenues based on small area use of hospital beds.* York: Centre for Health Economics, University of York.

Cochrane, R., Stopes-Roe, M., (1981) Psychological symptom levels in Indian immigrants to England—a comparison with native English. *Psychological Medicine*, **11**, 219–327.

Glover, G.R. (1989) The pattern of psychiatric admissions of Caribbean-born immigrants in London. *Social Psychiatry & Psychiatric Epidemiology Soc Psychiatry Psychiatr Epidemiol*, **24**, 49–56.

Glover, G.R., Robin, E., Emami, J., Arabscheibani, G.R. (1995) A needs index for mental health. *Submitted for publication.*

Harrison, G., Owens, D., Holton, A., Neilson, D., Boot, D. (1988) A prospective study of severe mental disorder in Afro-Caribbean patients. *Psychological Medicine*, **18**, 643–657.

Ineichen, B. (1990) The mental health of Asians in Britain. *British Medical Journal*, **300**, 1669–1670.

Jarman, B., Hirsch, S., White, P., Driscoll, R. (1992) Predicting psychiatric admission rates. *BMJ*, **304**, 1146–1151.

NHS Executive (1995) *High security psychiatric services: Changes in funding and organisation.*

Strathdee, G., Thornicroft, G. (1992) Community sectors for needs led mental health services. In: *Measuring mental health services.* Edited by G. Thornicroft, C. Brewin, J.K. Wing. London: Royal College of Psychiatrists, Gaskell Imprint.

Thornicroft, G. (1991) Social deprivation and rates of treated mental disorder. Developing statistical models to predict psychiatric service utilisation. *British Journal of Psychiatry*, **158**, 475–484.

Wing, J.K. (1992) *Mental Illness.* London: NHS Executive.

* MINI is available from:

> The Royal College of Psychiatrists Research Unit,
> 17 Belgrave Square, London SW1X 8PG.

6 How Mental Health Services are Commissioned

The NHS Health Advisory Service survey of commissioning

STUART CUMELLA, RICHARD WILLIAMS AND BOB SANG

Commissioning and purchasing

The term *commissioning* is used in this chapter to denote the strategically-driven process by which health authorities, GP fundholders, and social services departments endeavour to provide effective services which recognise the needs and opinions of the population for which they are intended, and monitor, define and manage the markets for health and social care. *Purchasing* refers to the technical process through which commissioners relate to providers in securing and monitoring the required services. *Contracting* involves summarising this process in documentation.

Figure 1 presents and idealised model of commissioning, in which the results of the regular monitoring and evaluation of services is fed back through strategic reviews, to form the basis for revised priorities and hence an improved purchasing of services. Figure 2 shows the steps that can be taken to balance perceived need, clinical capacity and the views of services users and informal carers, with current provision, in order to generate priorities for service development (Williams & Richardson, 1995).

Figure 6.1: *An idealised approach to commissioning mental health services*

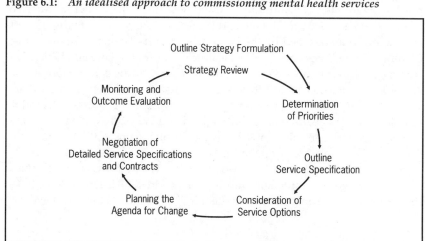

Figure 2: *Determination of priorities*

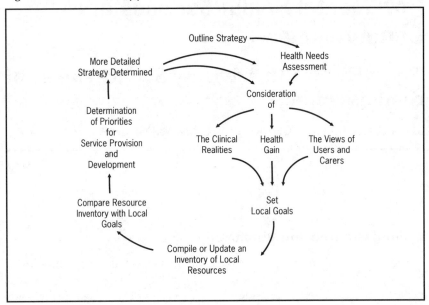

The steps needed to implement effective commissioning for mental health services have been identified in papers presented at the Consensus Meetings organised by the HAS during 1992/1993 (NHS Health Advisory Service, 1994a, 1994b, 1995a, and 1995b; Williams, 1993). Since then, detailed guidance on meeting national objectives for mental health services has been issued by the Department of Health in a *Key Areas Handbook* (Department of Health, 1992a, and 1994), the Welsh Office in a *Protocol for Investment in Health Gain* (Welsh Health Planning Forum, 1993), and the Mental Health Task Force in *Local Systems of Support* (Mental Health Task Force, 1994). Reviews of the needs and provision for people with a severe mental illness have also been published by Thornicroft *et al* (1992), the Mental Health Foundation (1994) in *Creating Community Care*, and by the Audit Commission in *Finding a Place* (Audit Commission, 1994).

Yet there have been few analyses of how DHAs and GP fund-holders implement purchasing for mental health services, and how this is affecting the pattern of mental health services in England and Wales. This chapter summarises results from work commissioned by the HAS, as part of its Thematic Review of the Commissioning Process for Mental Health Services in England and Wales. This comprised three main investigations: *a content-analysis of commissioning documentation* for mental health services produced by DHAs in England and Wales for 1993/4 and 1994/5; *a survey of the commissioning process* in a random sample of twenty health districts in England and Wales, involving interviews with senior managers, clinicians, DHA purchasing teams, GPFHs, and senior staff in social services departments; and an *analysis of commissioning documentation for mental health services in London*. The first two were completed by the Centre for Research and Information in Mental Disability (CRIMD) at the University of Birmingham, and the third by the King's Fund College.

Approaches to commissioning mental health services

The results from these investigations indicate that DHAs adopt radically different approaches to commissioning mental health services. The King's Fund College noted that several of the London DHAs had a reactive approach to commissioning mental health services, in which purchasing plans confirmed the existing pattern of services, with incremental changes to meet problems as they arise. This *historic/incremental model* contrasts with the *rational/incremental model*, in which DHAs take the lead in reviewing and developing new patterns of services; and the *innovative/progressive model*, in which DHAs facilitate changes in the pattern of services in collaboration with providers and other agencies.

Nevertheless, the opportunities for rapid change through commissioning are limited, despite the introduction of market mechanisms. The survey of the commissioning process carried out by CRIMD found that DHAs made only limited use of competitive tendering, employing it mainly for new services (including services reprovided after the closure of the mental illness hospitals), or in a few cases where a provider was seen as chronically unresponsive to DHA requirements. Indeed there is a trend in most districts away from competition for the provision of local mental health services, as DHAs specified clear demarcations of catchment areas for different trusts operating within the same health district, and sought local reprovision of out-of-district specialist services. This trend probably reflects two factors:

- Most DHAs expressed a clear policy objective that mental health should be an accessible community-based service. It was difficult in most areas to envisage how this could be achieved by competing locally-based services.

- Limiting the number of providers helped DHAs reduce the complexity of mental health services, and hence control their demanding annual administrative cycle of contracting and contract-monitoring.

Providers in turn were reluctant to widen their market reach and compete with neighbouring NHS trusts because they lacked spare capacity to treat a larger number of patients, capital to expand services on a speculative basis, or financial reserves sufficient to cushion fluctuations in demand. It is therefore not surprising that most providers chose instead to concentrate on developing a good working relationship with their purchasers, and a reputation for providing a high quality of care.

The content of mental health strategies

In England and Wales as a whole, the analysis of commissioning documentation returned by 90% of DHAs found major variations in the development of mental health strategies. At the time of the survey, just over a third of DHAs (35%) had either completed a mental health strategy or had a strategy in draft form, while a further 10% had completed preparatory work for a mental health strategy (such as an initial review or needs assessment). By contrast, many DHAs had yet to complete a full set of specifications for mental health services. The majority of strategies and purchasing plans focused only on the main psychiatric subspecialties, particularly services for the elderly (90%), alcohol and/or substance misusers (77%), and offenders (68%). Less than a half included specific purchasing plans for psychotherapy (48%), rehabilitation (39%), pregnancy-related disorders (33%), neuropsychiatry and head injuries (19%), or eating disorders (11%). Very few indeed included proposals for homeless people with a mental illness, or deaf mentally ill people.

The survey of the commissioning process identified a number of reasons for delays in developing comprehensive mental health strategies:

- *Lack of expertise.* Managers and clinicians in the majority of the NHS trusts expressed concern about the limited expertise available to health authorities on mental health issues. DHAs were more positive about their expertise, although most depended for detailed knowledge of mental health services on a single member of staff.

- *Lack of information.* Hardly any of the purchasers or providers had adequate information about the numbers of patients in contact with local mental health services, and the outcome of their care. Although health authorities had made extensive use of the mass of data included in the first edition of the *Key Area Handbook* (Department of Health, 1992a), few had been able to complete comprehensive assessments of the specifically local needs for mental health care.

- *Overlapping boundaries.* Mergers of DHAs since 1991 have resulted in multiple overlaps of boundaries between health districts, social services departments, and the NHS providers of mental health services. The survey of the commissioning process found that only 30% in the sample of DHAs shared common boundaries with both a single social services department and a single main provider of catchment area mental health services. Several purchased specialist mental health services (particularly child and adolescent psychiatry and forensic psychiatry) from further providers, while some purchased community and inpatient adult acute services for the same catchment area from different trusts. DHAs reported that such complex patterns of provision made the purchasing task particularly difficult.

- *Lack of co-operation between purchasers and providers.* Some DHAs reported that they now had achieved a 'mature relationship' with their main local provider of mental health services, and were co-operating successfully in developing and implementing strategies. But relationships between some DHAs and providers were somewhat suspicious and distant. The most common complaints from providers were that DHAs had not engaged in a dialogue about mental health strategy, delayed making key strategic decisions, and had no clear lines of responsibility for developing mental health policy. The most common complaints from DHAs were that providers were unresponsive to the needs of users as interpreted by the DHA, and failed to produce adequate accounts of the type and quantity of service they provided. In a few health districts, poor relationships between the main statutory agencies resulted in separate mental health strategies being developed independently by the DHA, the mental health providers, and the Social Services Department.

DHAs were attempting to improve their effectiveness in developing mental health strategies in a number of ways. The survey of commissioning documentation found that 46% were proposing to improve the information available to them about the needs for mental health services in their district. The most common initiatives were to develop more effective methods for consulting expert advisers, professionals, users, and carers (20%), commission surveys of needs (17%), and improve databases (17%).

Implementation

The great majority of DHA commissioning plans and strategies included a commitment to the treatment of people with a mental illness in the community (83%), on a multi-disciplinary (80%) and multi-agency basis (69%). DHAs proposed to implement these principals by developing a pattern of services modelled on those proposed in The *Key Area Handbook* (Department of Health, 1994), and the recommendations of the Mental Health Task Force summarised in *Local Systems of Support* (Mental Health Task Force, 1994). Key changes included:

- Improved staffing for specialist community mental health teams (CMHTs), particularly CPNs and clinical psychologists.

- An expansion in the provision of community mental health centres (CMHCs) to provide local bases for multi-agency community mental health teams. Some DHAs proposed to complete a planned network of CMHCs, while others were still in the early stages of implementing this pattern of care.

- The development of a 24-hour crisis service to provide an alternative to inpatient admission, or the enhancement of an existing service. DHAs usually specified that crisis services would be provided by CMHTs. Over a third (36%) of DHAs proposed that people with an acute mental illness should be treated at home.

Most (60%) DHAs were currently implementing plans to close a mental hospital, and proposed to fund all or part of this expansion of community services from reductions in inpatient beds. But a substantial minority found this option impeded by the need to meet a shortage of acute admission and secure beds. Eight out of the 20 districts in the survey of the purchasing process reported a significant shift in the pattern of acute inpatient admissions over the last three years, characterised by occupancy levels well in excess of 100% (representing the use of leave beds), frequent resort to out-of-district placements, and a doubling in the proportion of detained admissions. The acute bed crisis was experienced in a wide range of health districts, including inner cities, rural areas, and suburbs. Local managers and clinicians in the NHS trusts attributed its cause to major reductions in the number of acute beds as part of hospital closure programmes, greater caution among clinicians about discharge as a result of recent central guidance, and a change in morbidity with a greater proportion of admissions being of patients with a combination of drug abuse and psychosis. Even in health districts not experiencing an acute beds crisis, there was a perceived lack of medium secure and intensive care beds. Places were frequently unavailable for potentially-dangerous patients, and clinicians and managers expressed concern about the risks they were required to take in accommodating such patients in ordinary acute wards.

The immediate response by DHAs to shortages of acute or secure beds was to purchase beds on an extra-contractual referral (ECR) basis, either from out-of-district NHS providers or the private sector, until a local bed became available. This had the effect of splitting a single acute episode between two hospitals and sets of clinicians, while the very process of finding beds and transporting patients consumed hours of staff time. Several DHAs and trusts were therefore developing a long-term response to the crisis. A few districts were proposing to continue the redeployment of resources from inpatient to community services, on the basis that enhanced community services would prevent admissions. But over a quarter (27%) of DHAs were expanding hospital provision for the intensive treatment of people with acute psychiatric disorders. Staff in several DHAs expressed frustration that a more rapid response was not possible because of the slowness of the NHS capital bids procedure and the lack of immediately accessible funds to meet local crises.

Social Services Departments

The array of services for people with a severe mental illness was also affected by the significant expansion in the services for this client group purchased by social services departments. The survey of the purchasing process found that almost all local social services departments had used the Mental Illness Specific Grant (MISG) and the Special Transitional Grant (STG) to generate a wide range of residential, vocational, and recreational schemes, in almost all cases provided by the independent sector. The 'infrastructure' component of the STG had been used to create or expand teams of specialist mental health social workers, and to appoint senior staff with experience of mental illness services. However this expansion has been from a very low base of provision in most departments, and has been concentrated on services for adult non-elderly people with a mental illness.

The impact of fundholding

Although the purchasing policies of DHAs and social services departments were affecting the array of services for people with a severe mental illness, the most important influence on the operation of these services in many districts were the local GP fund-holders. The survey of the purchasing process found that GPFHs purchased mental health services in a very different way from DHAs. Most were content with their specialist mental health services, and usually contracted to maintain the status quo. Changes in contracts occurred where the practice preferred to contract with a single provider for all their registered patients, irrespective of their place of residence, and where the GPFH had historically had a poor relationship with their local psychiatrist. But GPFHs were wary of switching contracts to an alternative provider for fear this would destabilise their local community mental health team. The impact of these changes can be summarised as follows:

- *The shift to practice-based catchment populations.* GPFHs with a practice population straddling the boundaries of different mental health providers or different CMHTs had negotiated contracts for a single CMHT to provide community mental health services for the total population registered with the practice. Some NHS trusts had anticipated this process by shifting from geographical to practice-based catchment populations for their CMHTs.

- *Contracting for more specific referrals.* An increasing number of GPFHs were using the contracting process to specify a right to refer to the psychiatrist, psychologist or other clinician of their choice, in place of referral to a single team or psychiatrist.

- *The development of practice-based mental health teams.* A minority of GPFHs were negotiating with their local mental health provider for a CPNs and other clinical staff to be based at the practice, to provide a local mental health team.

The majority of DHAs (58%) included proposals to improve primary care for people with mental illness, either by additional training for GPs, or by expanding the specialist support to primary care teams from psychiatrists, CPNs, psychotherapists, or counsellors. Several DHAs proposed that enhancing primary care teams in this way would reduce the pressure on specialist services, avoid some inpatient admissions, and contribute to meeting *The Health of the Nation* targets of reducing the number of suicides (Department of Health 1992).

Most GP fund-holders have already implemented these policies for their own practices. All the fundholders interviewed in the survey of the purchasing process had practice based counselling services, or were taking steps to develop such services. In a few cases, counselling was provided by practice attached CPNs under the main contract between the fundholder and the local NHS trust. But it was more common for GPFHs to allocate part of their purchasing fund to employ counsellors, CPNs, or psychologists on a sessional basis. In most cases, GPFHs used general savings from the fund rather than diverting funds from the purchase of secondary mental health care, the exceptions being the GPFHs who had received an allocation of funding for mental health services that exceeded their current use of such services.

Conclusions

The result of these investigations confirm an earlier study for the Clinical Standards Advisory Group, which noted considerable variation between health authorities in the degree to which they use the contracting process as a means of promoting improvements in mental health services (Cumella, 1993). The quality of purchasing plans prepared by some authorities indicated that they had successfully mobilised available expertise and information to generate a comprehensive assessment of the mental health needs of their district, and strategy to implement change in the desired direction. But the gap between the best and the worst was considerable, and its a matter of concern that the majority of DHAs at the time of the survey had yet to complete a mental health strategy.

The problems experienced by many DHAs in developing and implementing a comprehensive mental health strategy result from inherent problems in developing effective purchasing in mental health, given the limited information available about psychiatric morbidity in individual health districts, the absence of evaluative studies of the most effective pattern of mental health services, and the lack of available expertise (Williams, 1993; Master & Perry, 1990; Vanstraelen & Cottrell, 1994). But they may also reflect a need for health and social services to focus on what they can realistically achieve, given the limited staffing resources available to them. Rather than attempting to exercise detailed control over providers by means of elaborate contracts, monitoring schedules, and quality protocols, DHAs should instead focus on what they can do best. This includes four key tasks of developing the public health perspective in mental health, identifying and filling gaps in services, quality promotion, and facilitating the development of joint purchaser/provider strategies.

The public health perspective. Health authorities alone have responsibility for identifying the prevalence of mental illness in their district, for identifying needs among different subgroups in the population, and for promoting policies to improve the effective integration of public health, primary, and secondary care services. This public health perspective can have a major impact on the mental health of the population, by improving the provision of services in primary care teams, and by improving the interface between primary and secondary care. Primary care teams can themselves provide an important source of information concerning the mental health needs of the population (Goldberg & Gask, 1992).

Filling gaps in services. The haphazard development of mental health services in many areas has left gaps or 'underlaps' in services. These have arisen where a specialist service has been the historic responsibility of a distant specialist unit, where services have avoided treating patients with multiple problems (such as learning disability and mental illness, or the psychiatric disorders following head injury), and where patients are due for transfer between services (such as from 'adult' to elderly services). Commissioners should develop an overview of the gaps in the mental health services in their health district, and take action to resolve them by commissioning new services, and negotiating with existing providers.

Quality promotion. DHAs should aim to promote quality among their providers, rather than engage in a futile attempt to monitor a long list of quality standards. Quality can be promoted by ensuring each provider has a clinical audit system which involves all its professional groups and services, and which has a clear and measurable impact on clinical and management practice. This should be supplemented by commissioning a rolling programme of intensive assessments of the main clinical components of the local mental health service, to be carried out by the NHS Health Advisory Service or other panels of experts. These would aim not just to assess quality, but to co-operate with managers and clinicians in identifying how quality can be improved.

Facilitating joint purchaser/provider strategies. Strategies which do not involve the main local centres of expertise in mental health or the people who will be required to implement change are unlikely to be successful. Health authorities should therefore take a lead role in collaborating with local authorities and providers in health and social services, to establish joint strategies for mental health in their district. Purchasers' commissioning strategies and providers' business plans should conform to these joint purchaser/provider strategies. Statutory authorities can not usually predict with any precision the capital or revenue funding they will receive over the next five years, or the demands that will be made on funds from other client groups. In these circumstances, 'big bang' strategies rapidly become outdated. It is more practical to aim for a regularly updated 'dynamic strategy', in which purchasers and providers in the health and social services (in consultation with users and carers) agree the model of health and social care they wish to achieve for people with a mental illness based on evidence of unmet need through the assessment and care management process, and shaped by research into effective care treatment. providers and commissioners need to agree priorities for implementation in the light of funding and other resource restrictions, and a process for regularly updating the strategy (Cumella, 1995).

Strategies need to take account of the fundamental changes in the pattern of mental health services identified from the results of the analyses outlined in this chapter. In particular:

- *The shortage in many districts of acute admission and secure inpatient beds.* This is becoming a national rather than specifically an inner-city phenomenon, and requires urgent action to identify the cause of the crisis in each district, and to rapidly develop additional resources.

- *The increasing diversity and volume of social care services.* This constitutes a major success in recent mental health policy. Yet there are still many districts which provide mentally-ill people with limited access to vocational activities or an appropriate range of supervised housing, and little opportunity to make friends and take part in the ordinary life of the community, despite the proven effectiveness of such services in promoting recovery from severe mental illness (Warner, 1994).

- *The development of primary care services targeted at people with common mental disorders.* This has occurred on an unplanned basis, and there are wide variations between GPFHs in the type of counselling services employed, in the arrangements for professional supervision, and in the types of patients referred. It is particularly important that counsellors are aware of the criteria for referral to specialist services, are professionally supervised, and have sufficient qualifications. There is also a need for the NHS Research and Development Programme to evaluate the impact of primary health care mental health services on the course of common mental disorders, and on referral patterns to specialist services.

Finally the results of these surveys all point to the pivotal importance of commissioning for the development of mental health services. The lesson from

HAS thematic reviews and service visits (Drinkwater, 1995) is that the good commissioners are those which:

- Support, build on, and generalise from successful services.

- Agree explicit aims and objectives with their providers in service specifications.

- Develop mechanisms for regular feedback from patients, carers and their advocates.

- Resist the temptation to impose unnecessary external standards.

- Insist that service providers develop their own explicit standards which are subject to regular review.

- Require service providers to show that they provide regular, team-based, multi-disciplinary training, in addition to uni-disciplinary training.

- Are prepared to accept that effective outcomes result from investment in the development of successful processes, which are the subject of regular review.

These requirements presents commissioners in the health and social services with a major challenge. It is one they must meet if this country is to develop an effective and humane mental health service.

References

Audit Commission (1994) *Finding a Place. A Review of Mental Health Services for Adults.* HMSO: London.

Cumella, S. (1993) *Contracting for Schizophrenia.* CRIMD: Birmingham.

Cumella, S. (1995) *Developing Dynamic Strategies for Health and Social Care. A Manual for Joint Commissioning.* CRIMD: Birmingham.

Department of Health (1992) *The Health of the Nation. A Strategy for Health in England.* HMSO: London.

Department of Health (1992a) *The Health of the Nation. Key Area Handbook. Mental Illness.* Department of Health: London

Department of Health (1994) *The Health of the Nation. Key Area Handbook. Mental Illness. Second Edition.* Department of Health: London.

Drinkwater, C. (1995) Personal communication, published in Williams and Richardson (1995).

Goldberg, D. & Gask, L. (1992) Primary Care and psychiatric epidemiology: the psychiatrist's perspective. In Cooper, R. & Eastwood, R. (ed) *Primary Health Care and Psychiatric Epidemiology.* Tavistock/Routledge: London.

Master, D. & Perry, C. (1990) Contracting for mental health: what is needed? In Jenkins, R. & Griffiths, S. (ed) *Indicators for Mental Health in the Population. A Series of Two Workshops.* HMSO: London.

Mental Health Foundation (1994) *Creating Community Care. Report of the Mental Health Foundation Inquiry into Community Care for People with severe Mental Illness.* Mental Health Foundation: London.

Mental Health Task Force (1994) *Local Systems Of Support. A Framework for Purchasing for People with Severe Mental Health Problems.* Department of Health: London.

NHS Health Advisory Service (1994a) *Comprehensive Health Services for Elderly People.* HMSO: London.

NHS Health Advisory Service (1994b) *Drugs and Alcohol. Current Issues in Services for People who Misuse Substances.* HMSO: London.

NHS Health Advisory Service (1995a) *Comprehensive Mental Health Services.* HMSO: London.

NHS Health Advisory Service (1995b) *Clinicians in Management.* HMSO: London.

Thornicroft, G., Brewin, C., Wing, J. (1992) *Measuring Mental Health Needs.* Gaskell: London.

Vanstraelen, M. & Cottrell, D. (1994) Child and adolescent mental health services: purchasers' knowledge and plans. *British Medical Journal.* **309**, 259–261.

Warner, R. (1994) *Recovery from Schizophrenia. Psychiatry and Political Economy.* Routledge: London

Welsh Health Planning Forum (1993) *Protocol for Investment in Health Gain. Mental Health.* Welsh Office: Cardiff

Williams, R. (1993) *The NHS Advisory Service. A Unique Window for Change. The Annual Report of the Director for 1992–3.* HMSO: London

Williams, R. & Richardson, G. (ed) (1995) *Together We Stand. The Commissioning, Role and Management of Child and Adolescent Mental Health Services.* HMSO: London.

7 Purchasing Mental Health Care for Primary Care

GERALDINE STRATHDEE and RACHEL JENKINS

Introduction

This chapter is intended as a practical aid for GPs and other members of the primary health care team (PHCT) and Community mental health teams (CMHTs) working together to contract for mental health services. The issues involved are equally applicable to GP fundholders, GPs working with DHAs, multi-funds or GP cooperatives. The paper summarises some of the relevant research in the area, draws on models of good practice nationally and makes suggestions for practical steps towards purchasing evidence-based services which improve outcomes. The chapter is presented in three sections. First, the key facts in primary care mental health and the importance of mental health as an issue for primary care in the current NHS agenda is summarised. The roles of the PHCT are reviewed. Second, the range of needs of the mentally ill, both those suffering from the more 'severe and longer term' conditions and those with more transient and common psychological distress are presented. The resource issues which determine service development within the specialist mental health services are discussed. The third section, drawn from examples of good practice describes a range of the practical issues which can inform contracting for evidence based purchasing of services for both the severely mentally ill and the common disorders which present in primary care.

SECTION 1
Key facts in primary care mental health

Working with people with mental health problems comprises a significant proportion of the primary care team's daily work. One-fifth to one-quarter of the consultations in any average daily surgery are by people who have a mental health problem as either their only, or a major reason for the visit[1,2]. Table 1 indicates, by diagnostic group, the likely numbers for the average GP with a practice size of about 2,000.

Table 1: *The Epidemiology of mental health for the average general practice*

Diagnosis	Rates per 1000 population per year	Number of patients in a practice of 2000 per year
Schizophrenia	2–6	4–12
Affective psychosis	3.0	6–7
Organic dementia	2.2	4–5
Depression	30–50	60–100
Anxiety and other neuroses	35.7	70–80
Situational disturbances/other diagnoses	26.7	50–60
Drug/alcohol disorder	2.7	5–6

As the recent National Psychiatric Morbidity survey[3] indicates, the prevalence of mental health disorders is greatest in the inner cities and urban areas. Rates of illness may vary up to four-fold between geographical areas. As Kendrick's study of a number of practices found[4], practices are more likely to have larger numbers of the severely mentally ill where they are near to a large psychiatric institution which is closing down, where the partners have an interest or additional training in psychiatry and where there are a large number of group homes in the practice area.

The shared agenda of primary care and mental health in the NHS

Two of the top priorities for the NHS agenda of the 1990s are the development of primary care led commissioning and purchasing and implementation of community care policies in mental health. Mental health and primary care, perhaps uniquely among specialities share a number of common features. They work on the basis of developing small teams. The primary health care team (PHCT) comprises GPs, practice nurses, manager, receptionists, health visitors and attached professionals. Mental health services in Great Britain operate on the basis of community mental health teams (CMHT) which, although there is a great deal of variation consist of psychiatrists, community mental health nurses, occupational therapist, psychologist, social workers and often support workers. The team provides services for a defined area called a sector (population about 50,000). Because of the multi-factorial nature of the health and social needs of the mentally ill, most sectors were created to achieve co-terminosity with Social Services boundaries. In a number of areas, particularly where practices are large and have well defined boundaries, sector teams are also co-terminus with the practices. In others, notably the inner cities where CMHTs share responsibility with one social services team, the number of practices with which a team must liaise can be as many as forty.

Mental health, in advance of most specialities has led the vanguard to provide the majority of services in the community. The progression to a shared care approach has been incremental. From the first reported attachment of a psychiatrist to a GP practice in the 1960s, mental health disciplines have increasingly moved to undertake sessional work in primary care surgeries. A survey of links between individuals practices and health professionals in 1991 found that 48% of practices had a link with a CPN, 21% with a social worker, 17% with a counsellor, 15% with a psychologist and 16% with a psychiatrist[5,6]. Mental health specialists are also moving to emulate the approaches used by other specialities to improve the quality of care[7]. These include the development of formal shared protocols for specific disease entities such as diabetes and asthma.

The mental health role of the PHCT

The majority of those with mental health disorders have always been assessed and treated only within the primary care setting. Only a small proportion are referred on to the secondary care services. The care of the mentally ill is not just a matter of concern for GPs. All the members of the PHCT have important roles to play. GPs, by virtue of their long-standing knowledge of the families play a crucial role in early recognition and assessment of mental health problems. Their 24 hour, 7 day services are almost always the point of first contact for those in crisis. Continuity of care allows prevention of relapse and a continuing education process which maximises opportunities for prevention, implementation of effective treatments and prevention of unnecessary and expensive hospital admission. Practice receptionists are crucial in setting the style of the practice. A welcoming and understanding attitude to those presenting in distress can be a vital influence in encouraging individuals to seek help at an early stage in their illness or in a relapse.

Practice nurses are increasingly involved in assisting GPs to manage people with depression and anxiety. Health visitors who work with many vulnerable groups such as young mothers with post natal depression, the depressed, isolated elderly who are at higher risk of suicide and attached district nurses and other professionals have their own contribution to make. Practice nurses sometimes administer the depot injections to the long-term mentally ill and can, with training, detect mental state changes and assist in the development of relapse prevention strategies and educational interventions.

SECTION 2
The range of needs for services of the mentally ill

Mental health as a speciality was initially developed on a similar model to that of other medical specialities. However, as research expanded from purely biological aspects of mental health to include the range of psychosocial influences, and as the influence of other treatments beside medication became increasingly recognised, planning for mental health services has become more holistic (Table 2).

Table 2:   *The Range of Needs of Individuals with Mental Health Disorders*

NEEDS	The long term mentally ill	Common primary care conditions
Case-identification & case register recall	+++	+
Crisis intervention	+++	+
Assessment and Consultation services	+++	+++
Medication	+++	+
In-patient, respite and crisis community beds	+++	+
Rehabilitation and continuing care services	+++	+
Family education & support	+++	++
Marital/sexual counselling	+	+++
Behavioural/cognitive therapies	+	+++
Supportive counselling	++	+++
Case management and assertive outreach	+++	+
Physical care	+++	+++
Social skills and stress management	+++	+++
Day care	+++	+
Welfare benefits advice	++	++
Housing	++	++
Legal advice	+	+
Support group/self-help group	++	+++
Information & education: disorders & services	+++	+++

There is often a perception that there is a dichotomy in providing services for the two broad categories of those with mental health disorders. As Table 2 illustrates, individuals with long-term mental health problems do not have such very different needs to those with the more common conditions encountered in primary care. The needs are similar, the variation is in degree.

Setting priorities for CMHTs

The development of mental health services in the UK has, to an extent, replicated models of community services from other countries such as the United States and Australia. The British health care system is almost unique internationally in the strength of its primary health care infra-structure. The vital role of primary care has, to an extent been under-recognised and the conflicts between the large number of 'less seriously ill' in primary care and the priority which needs to be given to the most vulnerable but numerically small for any particular practice has not been explicit. Services have been developed, more often based on available resources in terms of capital and revenue, rather than on a population, needs led basis.

As in the US particularly, many CMHTs in the UK have drifted away from treating those with severe and enduring mental illness. Teams have often existed more in theory than in practice. Rather than an integrated and explicitly managed team, the various disciplines, community psychiatric nurses (formerly called CPNs), psychologists, psychiatrists, social workers have operated as autonomous practitioners[8]. The results of this lack of clarity of structure and organisation are now very apparent. Where CPNs have been attached to primary care, 80% of their case-load has come from the PHCT. CPNs are the cornerstone of the care of the severely mentally ill. Yet in many areas their caseload is comprised of less than 10% of the SMI[9].

The resource issues are difficult[10]. There are approximately 30,000 GPs in the country, each of whom will have 300–600 patient with depression and anxiety at any one time. There are 2000 consultant psychiatrists. Each psychiatrist therefore serves the needs of 15GPs and can realistically help GPs with only a small number of their more severely depressed or disabled patients. Likewise, nationally there is one CPN between 5–10 GPs. In even the best case of one CPN per 5 GPs, with the average number of 7 patients with severe mental health disorders such as schizophrenia or manic-depression who require specialist care, the CPN will have already 35–40 patients. If CPNs are overwhelmed with large numbers of referrals, their ability to undertake skilled care of the SMI is limited to merely injecting depot medication. The vital work of rehabilitation, psycho-education, family education and support, problem-solving therapies, rehabilitation, day care provision and planning and development of services for comprehensive care is lost.

National policy in mental health has been driven by research into effectiveness and by clinical good practice. These combined have led to the recognition that the complex needs of the mentally ill cannot be adequately met by the traditional in-patient, out-patient, day care triad of services. Optimal outcomes and cost-effective use of resources can only be achieved by a *service system* which addresses the range of physical and mental health, social and rehabilitation needs and which is well co-ordinated both at the level of the service components and also at the level of the individual. The components of a comprehensive mental health service system have been described in the Health of the Nation Key Area handbook[11].

At the individual level, the introduction of case management practices through the Care Programme Approach is aimed to build a safety net of services around the mentally ill. This is explained in detail in section 3 but essentially it means that each patient who is accepted for care by the specialist services should be given a named and responsible worker, (a member of the CMHT) who ensures assessment and planning of their health and social needs and regular review.

SECTION 3
Practical issues in contracting: evidence based purchasing

This section addresses the practical issues for contracting evidence based purchasing for both the severely mentally ill and those with the common disorders which present in primary care. The approach taken is to summarise the relevant literature of thirty years of research in this field, combined with examples of how it has been translated into practice in areas of good practice nationally.

Changing the pattern of services: an agenda for informed purchasing

In 1995 a task force set up to examine the way in which clinicians were involved in contracting found that in many areas contracts had been negotiated with minimal involvement of those who would have to deliver the services. Therefore in any strategy to develop a sensible purchasing strategy some arrangements need to be made to meet face to face with those who will provide the services. Table 3 summarises some of the practices in areas where services are better advanced.

Table 3: *Developing a purchasing plan for mental health services*

- meet face to face with the health and social care clinicians and managers who will deliver the services
- check that a needs assessment has been done and understand what the assessed mental health needs mean for your practice
- use your information system to inform and refine local data
- develop a communication strategy
- think about how to adapt other good practice shared care or purchasing models eg diabetes

Purchasing effective communication between primary & secondary care teams

One of the most consistent research findings in mental health is that failure to communicate effectively leads to poor patient care and misunderstandings about the respective roles of primary and secondary care teams. Three decades of research into the communication patterns between primary and secondary care reveal similar depressing findings[12] that vital information to inform decision making is not communicated in the referral and assessment letters, that there is a lack of clarity about roles and responsibilities. Tables 4 and 5 translate into a series of practical action points the lessons learnt from three decades of research. Paying attention to the purchase of a communication and information strategy both at the services level and the level of the individual patients may save a great deal of frustration and improve patient care. Table 4 proposes some elements which should be purchased at the services level.

Table 4: *Communication and Information strategy 1: the service level*

Basic information PHCTs need to know about local mental health services

- An organisation chart of the mental health services with sector names, boundaries, key clinical and management staff

- A brief summary of the needs assessment for the area including number of the mentally ill on the CPA, deprivation indices, services planned

- Sector team names, roles and contact numbers

- Directory of Services provided, both at level of CMHT and tertiary specialist services

- Information booklets of therapies available

- Named contacts to advise on appropriate referrals

- Process by which primary care will be updated eg regular Trust newsletter, meetings, training events

Purchasing a communication and information strategy: the referral level

By virtue of their long associations with their patients GPs are ideally placed to provide information on the background and relevant history of the patient at referral. Table 5 illustrates the consensus among specialists about the information they most value in referral letters from primary care.

Table 5: *Communication strategy 2: the referral level*

What community mental health professionals need in referral letters

- Background family and social history

- Details of presenting problems

- Interventions tried and outcomes

- Reason for referral

- Role expected of CMHT professional

- GP request to maintain or transfer responsibility

Analyses of referral letters reveal that adequate information is presented in only a very small minority of instances. Clarity about what is expected from the referral and the roles which you want secondary services to play significantly improves the chances of a more successful outcome.

Table 6: *Communication strategy 3: the assessment level*

Communications from mental health professionals to PHCT

- Clear management plans with objectives and outcomes

- Indication of suicide risk

- What the patient has been told about their condition

- The prognosis and likely continuing disabilities and influence on patient lifestyle

- The role GP and PHCT are expected to play in the management plan

- The role specialist staff will play and who will be responsible for doing what and within what timescale

- Prescribing and monitoring roles and responsibilities

Table 6 summarises the communications which GPs have indicated they would find most helpful in further management of their patients. In some centres clinicians have developed proformas to include this information. Others prefer the flexibility of clearly defined paragraph headings which contain the items of information.

Purchasing crisis intervention services:

One of the most remarkable consensuses to develop in recent years has been the attitudes of users of mental health services, carers and GPs towards the response they would value in a crisis (Table 7), particularly the desire for access to an experienced practitioner who understands their problems. The majority of mental health crisis response services are based in accident and emergency departments with junior staff or domiciliary services by consultant psychiatrists.

Table 7: *Issues to consider in contracting for crisis services*

Issues to consider in contracting for crisis services

- Agreed timescale of response eg 24–48 hours

- Opinion from an experienced practitioner

- Home assessment and outreach where appropriate

- Telephone advice help line

- Crisis service for parasuicide assessment

- Rapid access to a MHA assessment from an ASW

Outpatient and assessment services

Until the move to develop more community oriented mental health services the majority of assessment services were either undertaken in hospital out-patient clinics or in consultant domiciliary visits. In many areas a number of different locations for assessment are now available. These may be at community mental health centres, district general units, in primary care surgeries or in the home. Wherever the venue, Table 8 draws on the research evidence of how the format, structure and content of the consultation can maximise outcomes[13].

Table 8: *Issues to consider in contracting for assessment and out-patient services*

Issues to consider in contracting for assessment and out-patient services

- Referral-appointment interval
- Referral procedure and criteria for members of the CMHT to include psychiatrist, CPN, psychologist and others
- Location of assessments
- Assessment and feedback interval
- Content of written communications to include stated objectives of management
- Predicted response, complications and side effects
- 6-monthly review of plans for longer-term patients
- Clearly stated role of GP and specialist in treatment
- Clarification of prescribing responsibilities

Contracting services for the severely mentally ill

Because of the major workload for GPs in tackling the large number of people with depression and anxiety, primary care professionals often ask why community mental health teams prioritise the severely mentally ill. In few other areas of health care are decisions to prioritise the most vulnerable and most needy a contentious issue. However in mental health the large number of those with less severe and enduring problems result in a major workload for the GPs. The consequences of failure to prioritise the needs of the SMI are multiple. They include suffering and neglect of the most needy and vulnerable and increased suicide rate in a group whose standardised mortality ratios (SMRs) are already 2.5 times the normal. The stigma associated with mental ill health is likely to increase with possible violent incidents. The resource implications are significant and include inappropriate use of expensive hospital beds (a growing concern for total fund-holders), inability to maximise resource use in the community as opposed to hospital and increased consultation rates in primary care of the SMI, their families and carers.

Table 9:   *Commissioning services for the SMI*

The PHCT role in SMI

- Set up a joint case register similar to diabetes
- Support for CPN focus on SMI
- Agree frequency of regular physical care reviews given that 45 per cent of the SMI have severe physical morbidity
- Assertively get to know your patients' keyworkers
- Develop a mechanism of verbal/physical input into CPA care planning reviews
- Discuss the consequences of expensive new psychotropic drugs
- Agree protocols for group homes/hostels
- Agree a named liaison CMHT worker for each practice

The CMHT role in SMI

- Joint case register with PHCT
- CPA assessment and care plans
- Keyworker co-ordination with PHCT
- Development of the range of appropriate hospital, rehabilitation and other community services including sheltered housing, work rehabilitation, mental health interventions

---

Table 9 proposes a number of practical issues to consider in commissioning services for the practice SMI population. Evaluation of models of services are at an early stage in this country[10].

The Care Programme Approach and primary care

Individuals with mental health problems, especially where these are severe and enduring require a range of physical, psychological, social and other interventions as indicated above. It is internationally accepted that the development of comprehensive community psychiatric services can only be achieved by a system which effectively co-ordinates all these aspects of care. The concept of case management has been found to achieve the best results. This is extensively used in modern psychiatric practice and by the introduction of the Care Programme Approach[14]. This aims to ensure that, for the most severely disabled patients, one key worker or organisation takes responsibility for co-ordinating:

- the assessment of the health and social needs
- agreeing a care plan with the patient
- appointing a key worker who will usually be a nurse, social worker or other member of the CMHT to co-ordinate care
- organising and co-ordinating a regular time for review.

What does this mean for the primary care professional?

The specialist psychiatric services will liaise with the GP of a patient on the CPA to co-ordinate care. This may include inviting a member of the PHCT to care planning and review meetings to assist in the formation of the care plan. If a member of the PHCT is unable to attend such meetings the keyworker will either phone or write to the practice, find out the views, represent them, and give or send a copy of the care plan arising from care plan or review meeting. The keyworker will, as a matter of good practice inform the PHCT of any changes in the patient's key worker and inform the GP of emergency and out of hours contact numbers & crisis plans.

In turn, the Primary Health Care Team may will find it helpful to inform the specialist services of relevant changes in the patient's condition which may include the frequency and reasons for consultations, expressions of suicidal intent, effects of, or changes to, medication or other treatments; feed in information about the patient for care planning purposes, even if unable to attend the meeting itself, know how to get hold of the specialist services in a crisis (as many severely mentally ill people will seek help from their GP first) and inform the CMHT of any relevant changes or pressures on the families or carers which may adversely affect the patient.

Purchasing services for common mental health morbidity in primary care

In the case of the majority of mental health morbidity in primary care two questions need to be asked:

- How best can the community mental health team help the PHCT

- How best can the primary care team develop their skills and use their time to deal effectively with the large case load.

The Department of Health has sponsored a number of initiatives in primary care in order to attempt to respond to these questions and learn lessons which can then be adopted in local settings. These are described in detail elsewhere[10] and include the development of a 'model general practice', nurse facilitator[15], audit of depression and primary care cascade learning process. Many of the projects are now completed and in the process of reporting. Table 10 draws on some of the early conclusions.

Table 10: *Commissioning services for the common mental health conditions*

CMHT role:

- Provide PHCT with Resources directory of all statutory and other mental health resources locally

- Agree Referral criteria to each team member

- Develop joint good practice protocols for common conditions

- Employment and supervision of counsellors, psychologists

- Attached liaison team member to every practice

- Communications strategy and training for PHCT

- CPN job description

- Joint crisis intervention/respite

The PHCT role:

- Make sure you have a Resources directory of all statutory & non-statutory services

- Agree referral criteria with CMHT

- Consider employing nurse facilitators

- Commission training from the CMHT

Increase training of PHCT in:

Practice nurse:

- recognition and management of depression, stress management

- mental state assessment and relapse prevention

- administration and review of medication

- assessment of tardive dyskinesia

Health visitor:

- recognition and prevention of depression in young mothers/children

District nurse:

- recognition of depression

References

1. Shepherd, M., Cooper, B., Brown, A. & Kalton, G. *Psychiatric illness in general practice.* Oxford University Press 1966.
2. Sharpe, D. & Morrell, D. (1989). *The psychiatry of general practice* In: Scientific Approaches on Epidemological and Social psychiatry. Essays in Honour of Michael Shepherd (P Williams, G Wilkinson & K Rawnsley, eds) Routledge. London.
3. *National Psychiatric Morbidity Survey* (1995). Office of Population and Census Surveys. HMSO.

⁴ Kendrick, A. (1991). *Role of general practitioners in the care of the long-term mentally ill*, British Medical Journal, **302**: 508–510.

⁵ Strathdee, G. & Sutherby, K. (1995). *Liaison psychiatry and primary health care settings.* In Multiprofessional Co-operation in Community Mental Health Care. Edward Arnold Publishers.

⁶ Thomas, R. & Corney, R. (1992). *A survey of links between mental health professionals and general practice in six district health authorities.* British Journal of General Practitioners **42**: 358–361.

⁷ Strathdee, G. & Kendrick, T. (1995). *A General Practitioner's Guide to Good Practice in the Care of Individuals with Long-term Mental Health Disorders.* No. 4. In Strathdee G. & Phelan M. (eds) Maudsley Practical Clinical Handbook Series.

⁸ *Finding a Place.* Audit Commission (1995) HMSO.

⁹ White E. (1990). *The 3rd Quinquennial National CPN Survey*, Dept. of Nursing, University of Manchester, Manchester.

¹⁰ Jenkins, R. (1992). *Developments in the primary care of mental illness—a forward look.* International Review of Psychiatry. **4**, 237–242.

¹¹ *Health of the Nation Key Area Handbook: mental illness.* (1993) HMSO.

¹² Pullen, I. & Yellowlees, A. (1985). *Is communication improving between general practitioners and psychiatrists?* British Medical Journal, **153**: 663–666.

¹³ Strathdee, G. (1990). *The delivery of psychiatric care.* Journal of the Royal Society of Medicine **83**: 22–225.

¹⁴ Kingdon, D. (1994). *The Care Programme Approach.* Advances in Psychiatric Treatment **1**, 41–44.

¹⁵ Armstrong, L. C. (1995). *Mental Health Issues in Primary Care.* A practical guide, Macmillan Press Ltd.

8 Should Fundholding General Practitioners Purchase Mental Health Services?

MICHAEL PHELAN, ERIC BYERS, DAVID TOD, CHRIS THOMPSON,
NICK BOSANQUET, TONY KENDRICK

Introduction

It is ten years since Maynard (1986) first suggested that GPs should be able to purchase health care for their patients from their own budgets. The idea was described in detail in the White Paper 'Working for Patients' (Secretaries of State, 1989), which specified that practices could choose to be allocated a budget to purchase health care for their patients. Regional Health Authorities were given the responsibility of setting budgets for each practice within the fundholding scheme. The scheme was rapidly incorporated into Government legislation, and has proved popular with many GPs. Fundholding is now a major element of the NHS, with 35% of the population in England and Wales being registered with GPs holding their own budgets. This proportion continues to increase as the size of eligible practices falls from 11,000 to 7000 patients.

Kendrick (1994) has provided a clear description of the rules and financial arrangements for fundholding GPs. Briefly, practices are given a budget for practice based staff, prescribing and hospital and community services. The mental health budget covers home visits and clinics run by community psychiatric nurses and community mental health teams. Significant exclusions from the scheme include: self referrals, voluntary services, highly specialised services, emergency admissions or referrals, in-patient care, hostel care and day care. In a small number of practices 'total fundholding' is currently being assessed, and may soon be introduced more widely. Under this scheme GPs are allocated a larger budget and are responsible for purchasing a far wider range of health care for their patients.

Fundholding has attracted committed supporters as well as fierce opposition. Ham and Shapiro (1995) express concerns about the continued expansion of fundholding, and the need for a full appraisal has been highlighted (Coulter, 1995). What is clear is that fundholding has had, and will continue to have, a profound effect on the organisation of mental health services within the NHS. A debate was organised to highlight the main issues and test the opinion of conference delegates.

The motion proposed was:

'This house believes that Fundholding General Practitioners are better able to purchase mental health services than health authorities'

The motion was introduced by Mr. Eric Byers, Chief Executive of The Bethlem and Maudsley NHS Trust.

I have been asked to set the scene without pre-empting the outcome of the debate. So my few comments are going to be about my concern for the National Health Service, and its structure. The purchaser provider split is here to stay, and indeed may extend into other aspects of public sector management. There is a considerable power shift within the NHS, and we can look forward to a primary care led health service.

GP fundholders find themselves acting as providers and as purchasers simultaneously. It is not clear how far down the purchasing road they will be allowed to travel. I am concerned that as purchasers will differ, there is considerable potential for fragmentation of services, with differing priorities between different perspectives. There is a risk of a lack of national strategy. While carrying out structural changes, it is vital to remember that most people within the NHS are committed to the ethics and basis of the service. Anyone who has been involved in joint planning will understand how difficult it is for people from different organisations to retain a common culture and generate something productive in terms of joint working.

We need to ask ourselves to whom are GPs accountable? What skills do they have in the areas in which they have moved and are moving? And what skills do they need to help them? Finally someone has to put it all together if we are to ensure equity of access, consistent quality, and open accessible services for everyone.

The motion was proposed by Dr. David Tod, General Practitioner and President of the National Association of Fundholding Practices.

A major difference between general practice and hospital based medicine, including psychiatry, is that GPs have longstanding relationships with their patients and families. I have looked after families for thirty years; their children and grandchildren, their nervous breakdowns, their psychiatric admissions and the ensuing problems. One of the conclusions that I have come to is that by and large we have failed to meet the mental health needs of the population.

One of the advantages of fundholding is that we now have some money to allocate where we think it best be spent. With money you can buy people, time and expertise. When a patient comes to see me it is with the knowledge and belief that I will do something for him or her that day, not some time in the future. When fundholding was introduced, my practice decided that one of the areas of care which was lacking was in the field of the less severe mental illness. Our local teaching hospital could not cope with the volume of referrals, and so we set about thinking about applying our fundholding budget to mental illness. We increased the number of practice based counsellors over three years. We now have four counsellors, and there is no waiting list to see them. Supply matches demand. During the last year the counsellors saw 226 new referrals, compared to 60 seen at psychiatric out-patients. Figures for the previous year were 160 and 48 respectively.

As we have established this service there has been an increase in the number of referrals to psychiatrists. This might be because the presence of the counsellors has encouraged the partners to think about asking for a second opinion from the psychiatric services.

By providing this service we are meeting an unmet need. Most of the patients referred have had two or more years of unemployment, great social stress as well as medical and psychiatric problems. That unmet need is now quantified in our practice and met. We are the people who have been able to fund this, from acute hospital and other budgets, with no cost to the mental health service, and to the benefit of our practice population.

The motion was seconded by Professor Nick Bosanquet, Professor of Health Policy, University of London.

I approach this subject with a great sense of urgency and concern. Mental health services are in a crisis of over professionalism and over dominance by the medical model. Recent surveys in South London, and elsewhere, demonstrate the failure to provide day to day social and personal support. The Mental Health Foundation have recently stated that 'there is no comprehensive strategy from the government for people with severe mental illness, insufficient resources, diffused responsibility, lack of understanding of severe mental illness and enormous pressures of organisational change' (Mental Health Foundation, 1994). If that is the current situation then the practical, realistic answer is that the fundholding scheme can contribute a new dynamic, a new vision, a new momentum and a new willingness to improve local services.

Fundholding is here to stay, and it can radically change and improve standards and quality of service available to patients all over the country, not just in the more prosperous areas. Fundholders have already demonstrated that in many cases they have a strong interest in developing better services for mentally ill people. When trying to provide a service which can react to the very real needs and crisis of severely mentally ill people quickly, you must place that service in primary care. Such a service can not be placed in secondary care, and it is unrealistic for there to be separate services, funded separately from the main primary care network, particularly when prescribing is very much under the control of the GP, and his or her team.

Fundholding practices have demonstrated a willingness to develop local services, to use prescribing more effectively and to use prescribing in combination with other kinds of care to prevent the dangers of addiction and long term dependence. The fundholding scheme is not perfect, but it is adaptable. It could be expanded to cover social care with a social care budget, and it could be given a housing dimension with teams having responsibility for helping people improve their housing situation. Family doctors are ready to play a larger role as co-ordinators, leaders, and agents for people with mental illness. Any other solution risks the sidelining of services for mentally ill people as the role of the fundholders increase. The evidence is that the acute services improvements won by fundholders have very quickly spread to other areas. District Health Authorities, as purchasing organisations, often spending £250–300 million will not concentrate on a particular service for a relatively small group of people. It is fundholders who are showing the drive and concern to improve local services. They have reduced referrals to psychiatric services and provided more accessible services.

Fundholders are there ready to fight for improved services for mentally ill people. They are keen to provide a focus for accessible, effective local services, and in working in partnership with different professionals. Fundholders have provided the focus and driving force to bring about real changes in acute services, let them do this for some of the most neglected and forgotten groups of patients, for whom current systems of care are failing miserably.

The motion was opposed by Professor Chris Thompson, Registrar, The Royal College of Psychiatrists.

There are four main arguments against fundholding, none of which should be taken to be a criticism of any individual GP fundholder, all of whom I have no doubt are in the scheme because they think it will offer the best for their patients.

(1)   Fundholders serve only part of the population, on average one third and at most 80% of any health district. This introduces bias in the resourcing of health care to those particular GPs who are fundholders. Dixon (1994) has shown in the North Thames region that GP fundholders are getting a larger slice of the NHS cake than non-GP fundholders. There were so many inducements to join the scheme, in terms of management, computing and so on, that this seems likely to be true throughout the country. Because of the constraints on list size in the early days, fundholders tend to be in the more affluent and well organised practices and situated in relatively affluent areas. They, therefore, have fewer mentally ill people than non-fundholding practices. Centres of cities and deprived areas tend to be staffed by more single handed practices and these are the places where people with mental illness are more likely to be found. So, the creation of the fundholding scheme, by drawing away resources from other purchasers has been a disadvantage to people with severe mental illness.

(2)   Fundholders purchase only part of any given service, that part they are allowed to purchase under the scheme. This introduces bias into the way they purchase. Mental health services comprise six recognised specialities of psychiatry, with at least three other sub specialities. There are at least five professional groups apart from psychiatrists involved in mental health care in more or less integrated services. Each of the professions and specialities has its own skills and its own roles to play in patient care. Not all are relevant to every patient. The complexity is such that mental health services are at least at the same level of abstraction and complexity as 'physical health services'. No one would propose that fundholding GPs are better able than district health authorities (DHAs) to purchase physical health services without an enormous amount of qualification and I anticipate that no one will wish to endorse the motion that they are better able to purchase mental health services—not at least without very great qualification which would change the scheme itself.

(3)   There is clear evidence that GP fundholders need to be reintegrated into the purchasing plans of health authorities, if public health plans are to be effective (e.g. Health of the Nation). Integrated services have long been a goal, with seamless transitions from NHS to local authority and voluntary sector care. The Department of Health has told fundholding GPs that they should 'discuss issues of the Care Programme Approach with other local purchasers','ensure the providers of psychiatric services operate the Care Programme Approach' and that they must be

'integrated into the planning of community care with the DHA, FHSA and social services'. This is supposed to be achieved through joint commissioning, but to what extent can fundholders be drawn into genuine joint commissioning and remain close to the original concept of fundholding? What then is the point of fundholding?

(4)   The training for purchasing for GP fundholders is less vigorous than that which is now being offered to purchasers in district health authorities. 40% of recently trained GPs and only 25% of all GPs have had any postgraduate psychiatry training whatever, so they are not necessarily well informed about mental health services. In contrast the DHAs have a well established cadre of public health doctors and a network of advice from professionals.

Seconding against the motion was Dr. Tony Kendrick, Senior Lecturer in General Practice and Primary Care, Division of General Practice, St. George's Hospital Medical School.

Although GPs have a contribution to make in the purchasing process we have the wrong perpsective to purchase the whole range of mental health servcies. We are largely reactive in our assessments of need of patients. About 14% of our patients in any one year will have 'conspicuous psychological morbidity' (Shepherd, 1981). GPs want help to deal with these large numbers of people, at least one or two of whom attend every surgery. In contrast it is relatively few patients who require specialist psychiatric referral, and very few (12 on an average GPs list in any one year) who present with severe and long term problems that require hospital admission. These long term patients are often apathetic and undemanding and so their needs for care may not be so immediately obvious to GPs.

From a population perspective these patients become a more salient problem. Amongst 250,000 people you can expect to have 1500 with a severe mental illness, 22 of whom will kill themselves each year (out of 27 expected suicides for the population as a whole). Purchasers need to take at least a district-wide perpsective and target services at the long-term mentally ill if we are to tackle suicide.

Published evidence suggests that fundholders have been more successful in getting better services for their patients, and to explore what aims fundholders had for mental health services in our area we held a meeting for fundholders in 1993 at St George's (Kendrick, 1994). They told us that they would like to end sectorisation and so be able to choose between consultants, obtain direct referral to CPNs, employ counsellors in their practices and maybe ask consultants to hold clinics in their surgeries. How would these changes affect the provision of services in relation to needs?

In a national survey of 1500 GP practices we found that the presence of on-site psychiatric help was associated with large practices, training practices and budget holding practices, but not socio-demographic factors such as location or proportion of ethnic minorities which would predict the amount of psychiatric morbidity (Kendrick et al, 1993). If GPs have direct referral to CPNs, there is evidence to indicate that they will tend to use them as 'counsellors' for patients with minor psychiatric morbidity (Wooff & Goldberg, 1986), and as a result divert them away from caring for people with long-term severe mental illness. CPN counselling did not seem to offer advantages over usual GP care in a controlled evaluation of counselling for minor psychiatric problems (Gournay & Brooking, 1994). In addition, our data from 16 practices in the

South West Thames Region demonstrates that the practices in the more deprived areas have a higher prevalence of chronic schizophrenia, whereas it was the practices in the less deprived areas that were already more likely to have attached CPNs, and were more likely to have become fundholding. Fundholding is therefore likely to worsen the mismatch between needs and the provision of services for the long-term mentally ill.

Fundholding is not extending into the inner city areas, and it is an obstacle to overcoming the present health care inequalities. It is hindering the development of epidemiologically-based, needs-led mental health services.

Discussion

Following the above presentations the audience expressed their opinions and questioned the speakers. It was pointed out that there were conflicting statements about whether fundholding practices increased or decreased referrals to secondary psychiatric services. Concerns were expressed about the lack of active patient participation in the planning, running and monitoring of practices. This was contested by the proposer of the motion who stated that participation groups were increasingly being established by fundholding practices, and that Community Health Councils had an active voice in the whole process. Fears were expressed that fundholding GPs might throw patients off their lists if their care was costly. This was hotly contested, and the proposer of the motion said that in his practice patients would only be discharged after a great deal of soul searching. Prof. Bosanquet stressed that fundholding was now spreading into all areas and that it was now providing real opportunties to improve services in deprived inner city areas.

Dr. Tod summarised his case by stating that in his practice fundholding had allowed them to develop services during the last 5 years that could not be developed during the previous 35 years, and that he believed this would have significant benefits for people with mental illness. In summarising the case against the motion Prof. Thompson emphasised that fundholding fragmented care, and resulted into priority being given to patients with less severe illness over those with more severe problems.

When put to the vote the motion was defeated, with 80 people voting against, 9 for, and 30 abstentions.

References

Coulter, A. (1995) General practice fundholding: time for a cool appraisal. *British Journal of General Practice,* **45,** 119–20.

Dixon, J. (1994) Can there be fair funding for fundholding practices? *British Medical Journal,* **308,** 772–775.

Gournay, K. & Brooking, J. (1994) Community psychiatric nurses in primary health care. *British Journal of Psychiatry,* **165,** 231–238.

Ham, C. & Shaipro, J. (1995) The future of fundholding. *British Medical Journal,* **310,** 1150–1.

Kendrick, T. (1994) Fund-holding and commissioning general practitioners *Psychiatric Bulletin*, **18,** 196–199.

Kendrick, T., Sibbald, B., Addington-Hall, J., Brenneman, D. & Freeling, P. (1993) Distribution of mental health professionals working on site within English and Welsh general practices. *British Medical Journal*, **307**, 544–546.

Maynard, A. (1986) Performance incentives. In Health Education and General Practice (Ed. G. Teeling-Smith) London: Office of Health Economics.

Mental Health Foundation (1994). *Creating Community Care.* London: Mental Health Foundation.

Shepherd, M., Cooper, B., Brown, AC. & Kalton, G. (1981) Psychiatric illness in general practice. 2nd edition. Oxford: Oxford University Press.

Secretaries of State for Health, Wales, Northern Ireland and Scotland (1989) *Working for patients.* London: HMSO

Wooff, K. & Goldberg, D.P. (1988) Further observations on the practice of community care in Salford. Differences between community psychiatric nurses and social workers. *British Journal of Psychiatry*, **153,** 30–37.

Footnote:

The accountability framework of fundholding is outlined in: Department of Health (1994). *Towards a primary care-led NHS; an Accountability Framework for GP Fundholding.* London. Dept of Health.

9 General Practice and the Purchasing of Mental Health Services

FEDELMA WINKLER and ANDREW BURNETT

Introduction

Major changes are taking place within primary care and particularly within general practice. The health service of the future will be primary care-led. What impact will this have on mental health services, its users and its providers? This chapter explores what is understood by a primary care-led NHS, the changes that are taking place and discusses developments in GP purchasing.

The philosophy behind a primary care-led NHS seeks to emphasise the benefits of health care delivered in or close to people's homes. It is the extension of community care policy to all NHS services. It is driven by the development of new technology and by a belief that it will benefit patients. Similar levers enabled community care policy developments. But the difference here is that general practice is being used as the catalyst for change.

As with community care, there are few who would argue that this is not the right policy. The problems are those of transition, the capacity of the primary care sector to provide re-located services, the co-ordination of services and the ability to achieve service shifts within required time scales.

General practice and community mental health services

The key feature of a primary care-led NHS is that is based *in* general practice. This is of particular significance to community mental health services. Up to now these have developed alongside general practice but have not been based upon it. So the degree of general practice involvement has varied with the interest of the individual GP.

This separation reflects the different organisational structures of general practice and community mental health services. GPs are self-employed—they are independent contractors, not employees. They have a nationally agreed contract for the provision of general medical services to those people who register with them. How they organise the provision of care and their practices is, literally, their own business.

People can register with a general practice of their own choice. 'Competition' for patients should stimulate practices to improve their services. However, the main levers for change have been alterations to the national GP contract and payment systems. Patient choice alone has produced few changes.

In contrast, other professionals in the rest of the NHS work in a salaried service and are part of a hierarchical structure. This means that changes in service provision can be implemented by changes in the deployment of staff and resources. For example, as large hospital institutions closed more people had to be cared for in the community. This meant that community mental health services had to be established.

Traditionally, few GPs took responsibility for what happened to their patients whilst they were in hospital. The development of community mental health services occurred separate to general practice and without reference to it. A lack of responsibility for patients using such community services has therefore continued.

This situation has suited both sides. GPs felt relieved of an obligation to provide services for a group of high-user patients. Hospital-based providers felt able to remain 'in-control'. Although one quarter of GP consultations have a mental health component, few practices have developed practice-based mental health services. For example, one survey found that only 9 out of 369 practices actually had developed protocols for caring for people with long term mental health problems.

Mental health providers have developed services based on geographical areas rather than GP practice populations. These services have been organised within boundaries that are meaningless to 'natural communities' and to the efficient provision of primary care. The social and health services aligned their boundaries and hospital catchment areas were retained, but without reference to GP practice populations. Patients move in and out of such boundaries of course—and many with chronic severe mental illness are notoriously 'mobile'. But people frequently retain registration with their general practitioner when they move. The GP may thus provide the one and only continuous relationship that people have with health and social care professionals. Service users see GPs as their access point to health and social services; GPs are perceived as being close to the population, coming to know two to three generations of families, and their central role in the referral process enhances continuity of care. The lack of a close relationship between the mental health services and general practitioners may go some way to explain why half of those with severe mental health problems cease to have contact with specialist services and may end up with no care at all. Significantly, one quarter of people with schizophrenia come into this group.

There are benefits and losses for the patients in a 'separate' community care/ general practice system. In theory, people can be cared for by *either* their own GP *or* a community team. People registered with GPs who offer an inadequate service are assured of services from their local mental health service. On the other hand, people who wish to get their care from a less stigmatising GP service can also do so. But divisions between these services lead to people falling into its cracks. This encourages what Balint referred to as a "collusion of anonymity"—where there is a lack of communication and a lack of shared responsibility between professionals, each assuming that the other is doing what is required. When this happens, GPs and the mental health services can each blame the other.

Since the introduction of the 1990 revised GP contract and the NHS reforms dramatic changes have taken place in general practice. Indeed, they are the most significant changes to have occurred to general practice since 1948 with the introdution of the NHS itself. Care is moving from hospitals back into general practice. Practices are developing services for specific groups of patients and hospital based staff are providing care at GP premises. To a limited extent this has been occurring in a few practices since the 1970s. Community psychiatrists have been providing some practice-based 'clinics' in addition to wider domiciliary and crisis intervention services. But since 1990, practice-based services have expanded in number and variety and GPs are themselves providing a much broader range of services. GPs are developing joint-care protocols and taking their patients back from specialists. For example, 90% of Kent GPs provide care for asthma and for diabetes using county-wide care protocols. Kent FHSA supports training programmes for this care which involve GPs, their staff and hospital-based specialist teams.

The main issues of primary care and mental health services are summarised in box 1.

Box 1: *General practice and community mental health services*

- the NHS is shifting to a primary care (GP)-led service

- GPs are independent contractors—not NHS employees

- the majority of mental health problems occur in the community and are dealt with in the community

- community mental health services have developed separately to general practice

- GP practice-based services are increasing in their number and variety, but rarely involve integrated mental health services.

It remains only the exceptional GP practice which develops comprehensive care programmes for people with mental health problems. The Blackthorn Medical Centre is one such practice.

The Blackthorn Medical Centre

The Blackthorn Medical Centre is a four doctor GP practice on the outskirts of Maidstone, Kent. Not accidentally it is adjacent to a former large psychiatric institution. The practice set out to develop ways of meeting the needs of those suffering long term mental health problems. Their aim is to give motivation, self confidence and self esteem to people through shared activities and a range of therapies. This is achieved through the creation of a community centre integrated with a general practice that provides rehabilitation through social integration and working together.

People undergoing rehabilitation at the Blackthorn Centre are known as co-workers. With equal numbers of men and women, itself an unusual feature, all have chronic, severe mental illness or chronic neurotic and/or personality problems. Many are patients of the practice but referrals from other GPs and consultants are taken as well. The GPs carry full clinical responsibility for the co-workers. Practice staff include an art therapist, a counsellor, a eurhythmy therapist, an aroma therapist and a music therapist. They are funded by Kent FHSA and the Blackthorn Trust—an organisation established to provide support for the centre. Other funding comes from a wide variety of sources—from statutory organisations and charitable donations. Co-operation on funding between purchasers and providers is a key characteristic of this service.

The activities in themselves are not unique: developing and caring for extensive gardens, baking bread, preparing and serving food in the restaurant and creating a range of products for sale. It is the spirit, the range of therapies and the active involvement of practice staff and co-workers in joint activities that makes this centre successful. The resulting interchange enables the development of outside connections from a 'safe base' and creates permeable boundaries between trust and community.

All co-workers are assessed using standard instruments such as the brief psychiatric rating scale, the Beck depression inventory and the Spielberger state-trait anxiety inventory to enable quantification of progress. A review by the Sainsbury Centre for Mental Health identified that co-workers expressed improvements in their feelings of self-worth and social integration. They appeared stronger and more able to trust and more ready to take on responsibility. The Sainsbury review also identified that the Blackthorn Centre's activities meet standard community service principles; see box 2.

Box 2:   *Community service principles*

Community mental health services should be:

- local & accessible

- comprehensive

- flexible

- consumer orientated

- empowering

- racially & culturally appropriate

- focused on strengths & skills

- normalised & incorporating natural community spirit

- meeting special needs

- evaluated & accountable

The report suggested that the Blackthorn Centre did not provide a fully comprehensive community service because there was no overnight accommodation or respite care facility. But the centre is flexible and provides co-operative care across boundaries. For example, one co-worker is actually an in-patient at a psychiatric hospital. She is better able to cope with this (as is the hospital) by being at the Blackthorn Centre during the day—an example of primary care providing respite care for a hospital facility.

Through joint working with complementary therapists, all on the same site, the GPs in this practice have a developed substantial insight into the appropriateness of different types of therapy for their patients including 'everyday' general medical services patients. Thereby they identify problems that previously they might not have recognised, and, more significantly, they can now provide more appropriate management. Previously, their therapeutic armamentarium would have been psychotropic medication, referral outside the practice or placebo.

It is likely that GP-led purchasing will result in more GPs developing as specialist providers of mental health services. The Blackthorn Centre provides a model of how it can be done in a way which contributes value to the whole community.

Counselling services in general practice

The major change to mental health services provided in general practice that has recently taken place is the expansion of counselling. By the end of 1992 up to one third of practices reported having access to counsellors. However, one third of these 'counsellors' were actually community psychiatric nurses (CPNs).

This leads to two concerns. There is the possibility that redefining the CPN role as a counsellor will diminish the necessary services needed by those with severe, chronic mental illness. Also, there is concern that many CPNs do not have appropriate training in counselling, with few providing counselling under appropriate supervision. Nonetheless, there is evidence that counselling is of benefit in general practice. Mechanisms are be needed to ensure its adequate provision. An example of this is given later.

General practice will need help in developing its infrastructure to deal with the scale of the work being transferred to it. Health commissions and GPs will have to develop ways of managing this transition.

Primary care-led purchasing

Current NHS Executive policy is to shift purchasing power from health commissions to general practitioners over the next five years. This will have profound implications for mental health services. It is imperative for mental health commissioners, providers and GPs to work together now with users and community groups to ensure that the current trend of prioritising services for the less severely ill does not disadvantage those most in need.

GPs will continue to be independent contractors. Great skill will therefore be needed to blend the activities of large numbers of small purchasers into a coherent whole. The user movement in mental health is strong and growing. In the past, such user-groups have not been involved at a practice level. Skill and resources will therefore be needed to ensure that the user voice is involved in decision making at practice- and supra-practice level.

There are various models for the shift of purchasing to GPs:

- **GP fundholding**—practices receive a budget to purchase a range of health services

    - standard fundholding for hospital and community services

    - community fundholding, exclusively for community services

    - total fundholding, currently being piloted, where the budget allocated is for purchasing *all* health services for the population of the fund

- **health commission brokerage**—where the commission enables GP purchasing through acting as broker and by negotiating with providers for services which practices then purchase

- **GP co-operatives**—where large numbers of practice join together and work with the local health commission to determine service provision strategies

- **locality commissioning**—service users, GPs, social services and health commissions working collaboratively to commission at a local level

Each of these models is now described with reference to developments in Kent.

1   GP fundholding

Fundholding was introduced partly as a way to control disparate GP referral patterns by creating more accountability through budgetary responsibility. It was also introduced to enable innovation in health care commissioning and provision. Primarily it is based upon individual practices, or consortia of practices joining in a single fund, purchasing a limited range of health care for the patients of that fund. The method has indeed led to innovation in service provision and a greater choice of providers.

Initially, fundholders were only able to purchase out-patient mental health care and so the extension of fundholding to include community nursing and mental health services is particularly significant. Mention has been made of mental health service 'sectorisation' paying no heed to GP practice catchment populations. The ability to negotiate contracts direct with providers has resulted in some fundholders purchasing mental health services from teams which are dedicated to their whole practice population. The advantages for the practice are obvious. Fragmentation of care between the single practice team and two or more different community teams is avoided. There is also greater freedom for the GP to refer to different consultants, as they can with other specialties. But, in the short term, such a system can fragment the services supplied to other, non-fundholding, practices as teams re-align. Also, closer working between the practice and local authority services is required and fundholding, of itself, does not address this. However, neither of these difficulties is reason to avoid such developments.

The introduction of fundholding led to other changes in the provision of mental health services. In the north of Kent people were previously referred to a consultant in an out-patient clinic for assessment and referral-on for appropriate therapy. They had to wait for an appointment with the consultant and then again for an appointment with the therapist. Fundholding practice patients are now assessed on receipt of a referral to the mental health unit and offered the most appropriate treatment facility in the light of this. This service is now being extended to non-fundholding practices. Thus the innovations of fundholding are not necessarily confined to the patients of fundholding practices.

Fundholding GPs are providers *and* purchasers of care. They are thus better able to blend primary and secondary care for patients. The expression 'seamless care' has been used in referring to developing 'ideal' services, but the best garments are *tailored* to fit requirements. Fundholding is one way of developing bespoke services.

Fifty-five per cent of Kent GP patients are now registered in fundholding practices and the number is set to increase. Additionally, several Kent practices are involved in local pilots of 'total fundholding'. Whilst fundholders cannot purchase in-patient mental health care yet they are likely to do so in the future. 'Total fundholding' will indicate how this can best be achieved.

2 Health commission brokerage

In response to identified need Kent FHSA promoted a counselling service through general practice. This was developed in addition to services provided by community mental health teams and non-statutory organisations. Its significance for commissioning is the role of the FHSA as broker. The authority was concerned to ensure wide access for patients to a quality assured service, relevant to identified needs and provided *within* a general practice setting.

A provider was identified by the FHSA, following a two-year pilot study that demonstrated their capacity to run a practice-based service to an agreed standard. This overcame two of the most difficult problems of introducing new services through general practice—identifying suitable providers and 'practice induced' service variation. The variation found in general practice can be reflected in the services purchased because different practices will commission variations of the same general type of service. This is a particular risk with counselling because of a lack of agreed qualifications and professional standards and the diversity of opinion in service requirements. The FHSA role therefore also ensured quality and it standardised service specification.

The FHSA costed the service and agreed a price with the provider. To make the most effective use of counsellor time practices joined into groups to provide a 'patient base' in multiples of 11,000 per 50 counselling sessions per year. The scheme included fundholders and non-fundholders for practices were sub-contracting counsellors as providers of general medical services. Thus, groups of practices that are otherwise separate jointly contract with one provider for counselling sessions. The contractual relationship is between the practices and the provider, but the FHSA maintains a detailed monitoring role.

The service specialises in providing therapy for addictive behaviours, particularly use of tobacco, alcohol and/or psychotropic medication. Importantly, it also provides the doctor with an *alternative* to prescribing. Referrals are made using strict criteria and reports are sent to the referrer at the conclusion of therapy. In the first six months of the scheme 34% of the referrals were for those taking psychotropic medication, and 28% were for people drinking excessive quantities of alcohol. Ninety per cent of available counselling time is utilised for therapy: the numbers of people being referred is increasing and the 'did not attend' rate is dropping. Regular meetings between counsellors and practice staff ensure that each counsellor is a fully integrated member of the practice team and not 'just there' to provide therapeutic 'nihilism'. The scheme's success is indicated by an increase in demand from other practices and a local district health authority piloting its own practice-based counselling scheme.

3   GPs working together in co-operatives

In many parts of the country, but particularly Kent, GPs are establishing out-of-hours co-operatives. These are corporate bodies whose members are exclusively local GP principals which provide a large on-call rota service. A significant factor for the development of primary care-led purchasing is the infrastructure that these organisations create. GPs, who have previously worked in relative isolation, are now working together in large groups providing general medical services. Co-operatives create an esprit de corps and provide a basis for co-working, postgraduate education and service development. Indeed, one Kent co-operative formed the basis of a fourth wave GP multi-fund of 19 practices caring for 140,000 patients.

The co-ops are also providing an infrastructure for the purchasing and the providing of other services. One co-op provides social services' out-of-hours child protection services. Another is working with a local community mental health team to develop a 'rapid response resource' for psychiatric crisis intervention. Another is looking at providing medical cover for a variety of community-based services including 'hospital at home' and a nurse practitioner-led minor injury unit. The lead of one co-op to provide a practice nurse bank service is being followed by others and interest is developing in the possible development of a co-op based GP locum service.

Thus, the relative professional isolation of general practice is beginning to break down and the potential to commission, within a strategic context, across individual boundaries is developing.

4 Locality commissioning

Another method of GPs working together is exemplified by 'locality working'. Localities are identifiable areas that can be defined by geography; administrative boundaries; natural communities; or functional areas, such as groupings of GP practice catchment areas. Throughout the country there is a variety of different models developing commissioning by, for or from, localities but none is yet complete and directly transferable elsewhere.

There are three aspects of locality commissioning:

commissioning BY a locality

Through a representative group, a locality should identify its needs and the services required to meet such needs. These can then be prioritised, with knowledge of all available resources and the effectiveness and efficiency of service provision. Commissioning intentions may thereby be developed. These might involve shifting resources from one provider to another, or from one group of service users to another, i.e. apportioning services to meet prioritised needs within available resources.

Locality commissioning intentions should then be fed into health authority purchasing plans. Here, they can be adapted to fit with national and local priorities and with the commissioning intentions of the other localities in the district. Account must be made of services being *purchased* by GP fundholders as well to ensure equity and avoid fragmentation.

Until budgets are devolved to a locality (as they are to GP fundholders), this process can only be notional, for ultimate responsibility remains with the budget holder.

commissioning FOR a locality

Some services, e.g. residential care for mentally disordered offenders, are too expensive and/or too rarely needed for a locality to sensibly account for them in its commissioning intentions. Such services must be commissioned for the locality by an agency covering a larger area.

commissioning FROM a locality

Other localities and/or health authorities can purchase services in a locality either for the people living in that locality or those outside it from providers in the locality, e.g. NHS trusts, non-statutory organisations, GPs and the private sector.

The underlying concepts of fundholding are developed further where fundholding and non-fundholding locality groups work in association with commissioning authorities. Such arrangements can beneficially influence service developments in a strategic context. In East Kent a model of locality commissioning is developing and involves service users, fundholding and non-fundholding GPs, social services and the district health authority. The localities are based on aggregations of GP practice catchment populations, with a 'GP forum' in each locality. Fundamentally, the localities were defined by the GPs, for only in this way could a representative GP forum be established. Practices that felt they had an affinity with an area, perhaps because of use of a local postgraduate centre or because of fundholding groupings, amalgamated to create each locality. From each GP forum GP representatives have been elected to a locality commissioning team. Here they are beginning to work with the other members of the locality team: a community health council (CHC) representative, a local senior manager from social services, a consultant in public health medicine and a 'locality commissioner' from the health authority. Each locality team is expected to identify local needs, review resources and develop locality commissioning intentions that should then be fed into health authority purchasing plans. In this way, services users (through the CHC) and GPs (who are seen as one of the informed advocates of service users) can start to develop a bottom-up approach to health service purchasing. See box 3.

Box 3: *Issues concerned in locality commissioning*

- localities can provide a local focus for needs assessment and service commissioning
- localities can be based upon:

  electoral ward boundaries

  natural communities and/or geographical areas

  GP practice catchment populations
- locality commissioning should involve all major stakeholders in health care
- locality commissioning is an evolving process: no one model is applicable everywhere

---

This model is congruent with GP fundholding by being based upon GP practice areas and through its involvement with the GP forum. This can enable a synergistic relationship between the two types of health purchaser. The figure indicates how this process is seen to fit into the NHS purchasing system.

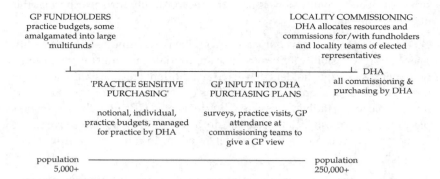

GP FUNDHOLDERS
practice budgets, some
amalgamated into large
'multifunds'

LOCALITY COMMISSIONING
DHA allocates resources and
commissions for/with fundholders
and locality teams of elected
representatives

DHA
all commissioning &
purchasing by DHA

'PRACTICE SENSITIVE
PURCHASING'

GP INPUT INTO DHA
PURCHASING PLANS

notional, individual,
practice budgets, managed
for practice by DHA

surveys, practice visits, GP
attendance at
commissioning teams to
give a GP view

population
5,000+

population
250,000+

Figure: *the purchasing spectrum*

The East Kent model will not work everywhere. In places such as Leeds, where a large population living in a relatively small area is registered with GPs all over the city, an alternative way of involving stakeholders in the commissioning process is required. However, such an area could become one locality, sub-divided into natural communities, and the model adapted accordingly.

The particular relevance of locality commissioning to developing the purchasing and providing of mental health care is that it focuses commissioning into local areas. And it is in 'local areas' where mental health problems occur and are predominantly cared for. The specific needs of particular areas can be better identified and the services provided for them can be better targeted.

Box 4: *The ways in which primary care-led purchasing will develop*

Primary care-led purchasing will develop in the following ways:

- more GPs will become fundholders

- fundholders will purchase an increasing range of services, particularly of mental health services

- fundholders, non-fundholders and commissioning authorities will increasingly purchase collectively

Conclusions: issues for mental health service purchasers

Over the next five years purchasing power will move towards GPs. This will occur as more become fundholders on a practice or a locality basis. Purchasers, current providers and users should expect to see GPs using their purchasing power to develop practice-based services and to be purchasing from an increasing range of providers. Opportunities to change existing patterns of care to better meet users' needs will be created by this.

But there is also the possibility that the service could become further fragmented. This could decrease further the access of vulnerable users to services. Health commissioners have the responsibility for ensuring that this does not happen.

On the other hand, GPs, as purchasers, could make continuity of care a reality. They have responsibility for provision of appropriate care to all those registered with them. As budget holders they have an additional responsibility to ensure the purchase of appropriate services. This has the merit of one person being responsible for an individual's care. Thus registered GP rather than a person's place of residence will dictate access to care in future. This could improve choice for patients because GPs have greater freedom to move away from block contracts.

The danger is that GPs may choose not to register people with severe mental illness, especially the 'revolving door regulars'. GPs might also choose to use their resources to provide in-house services for those with less severe mental health problems, for example. This could aggravate the tendency observed amongst health authorities, providers and existing fundholders to provide services for the less severely ill.

Health commissioners have the task of developing GP purchasing and this includes acting as a 'broker' to enable consistency and quality. In the transition period this will require a significant strategic and developmental role. Health commissioners will need to identify interested practices with capacity and expertise to provide comprehensive mental health services. Critically, development work with practices and the drawing-up of shared care protocols between mental health services and GPs need to be written into contracts now.

Similarly, educational programmes must reflect the shift back of care to general practice. Practice staff need to be skilled and to develop competencies so that an integrated service can be provided to those with serious mental health problems as they already are to those with other long term problems. Everybody, and above all the users of the service will lose out if the development investment in practices does not take place before the shift to GP purchasing.

Providers will need to develop a different relationship with GPs. Acute general specialties have learned to work more closely with GPs than in the past. This has been achieved by a change in the way they work and in the location of services. Mental health teams will have to make similar changes. Health commissioners with a developmental approach can facilitate this change.

The major responsibility of the health commission will be to ensure that services are purchased appropriately for all patients. They will have a responsibility to ensure that the voice of the user is listened to by GP purchasers when contracts are placed. This will require them to ensure that user-advocacy groups are funded to represent the interests of users.

Primary care-led purchasing means a major shift in the way resources are allocated. There are only weak systems of accountability in place. These will have to be strengthened and more effective ways of involving the community are required. Major investment will be needed in the organisation of general practice if it is to successfully take on these new, major responsibilities.

Box 5: *Issues for purchasers of mental health services*

- over the next five years purchasing power will move to GPs

- a greater range of services, from more providers will be purchased—many will be practice-based

- GP purchasing must be developed to increase: expertise, strategic thinking and to reduce inappropriate variation and fragmentation

- skills must be enhanced to integrate services so they are comprehensive

- the voice of the service-user will be paramount to ensure the development of relevant major investment is required to support primary care-led purchasing.

References

NHS Executive, *Developing NHS purchasing and GP fundholding: towards a primary care-led NHS*. 1994, Health Publication Unit.

Shepherd, M., Cooper, B., Brown, A., Kalton, G. (1966) *Psychiatric illness in general practice*. Oxford University Press.

Fry, J. Special features of general practice (primary care) and ethical implications. *J Med Ethics* 1980; **6**: 23–5.

Fry, J., Stephen, W.J. Primary health care in the United Kingdom. *Int Hlth Services* 1986; **16**; 485–95.

Regier, D.A., Burke, J.R., Manderscheid, R.W., Burns, B.J. The chronically mentally ill in primary care. *Psych Med*. 1985; **15**: 265–73.

Pilgrim, D., Rogers, A., Mental health service users' views of medical practitioners. *J Int Care*. 1993; **7**; **2**: 167–76.

Balint, M. *The doctor, his patient and the illness*. 1957 Pitman Press.

Strathdee, G. Delivery of psychiatric care. *J. Roy Soc Med* 1990; **83**: 222–5.

Strathdee, G. Establishing psychiatric attachments to general practice: a six stage plan. *Psych Bull*. 1992; **16**: 284–6.

Sibbald, B., Adington Hall, J., Brenneman, D., Freeling, P. Counsellors in English and Welsh general practices: their nature and distribution. *Br Med J* 1993; **306**: 29–33.

Spiers, R., Jewell, J.A. One counsellor, two practices: a report of a pilot scheme in Cambridgeshire. *Br J Gen Prac* 1995; **45**: 31–3.

Butler, J. *Patients, policies and politics—before and after Working for Patients*. 1992 Oxford University Press.

Hutchinson, A. Explaining referral variation, *Br Med J* 1993; **307**: 1439.

Burnett, A.C. Locality commissioning: a partnership with fundholding. In: *Fundholding—a practice guide*. Pirie A., Kelly-Madden M, (eds) 1994 Radcliffe Medical Press.

Audit Commission. *Finding a place: a review of mental health services for adults.* 1994 London HMSO.

0 A Local Authority Perspective on Purchasing Mental Health Services

CHARLES WADDICOR & MARY HANCOCK

Introduction

This chapter is divided into three parts. The first part will outline the key steps in purchasing mental health services from a Local Authority perspective. The second part will examine some of the potential problems of jointly commissioning services, and the third part will deal with issues that remain to be addressed in purchasing services.

1 Key steps in joint commissioning mental health services from a local authority perspective

We start from the assumption that there is general agreement that it is better to approach the question of commissioning and purchasing services **together**, in co-operation with other agencies. Therefore from a perspective of the Social Services Department, it is important that commissioning should be done in conjunction with the Health Authority, Family Health Services Authority, Housing Department, Adult Education, Leisure Services and representatives from voluntary organisations. Indeed, there are many different models being pedalled up and down the country as to how to approach the question of joint commissioning.

The model outlined in this chapter draws heavily on an article by Knapp, Wistow and Jones, entitled "Smart Commissioning".

"Smart" is an acronym which splits the commissioning function into the following five separate tasks:

- Shared vision

- Managing the market

- Agents of change

- Role of users and carers

- Tactical/Strategic balance

(i) The first task starts with the joint commissioners getting together to identify a **shared vision** or common purpose. At this stage, joint commissioning must blend the technical requirements, such as assessment methods, and financial monitoring, with the social values which recommend community care, such as responsiveness and ease of participation. These values need to be clearly understood and owned by all participants.

(ii)   The second task is described as "**Managing the Market**". This involves knowing what the population's needs are—how large, for example, is the relatively small number of severely mentally ill in the population? How much larger is the group of people with neurotic and depressive illnesses well-known to GPs? What is the ethnic mix, the size of the population, its age profile, the prevalence of homelessness, the supply of local housing and leisure facilities? Finally the needs profile must take into account whether there are any planned long-stay hospital closure programmes which are going to impact on the local population.

Having identified population needs, the commissioners are expected to manage the market to create the necessary supply of services. It is generally accepted that it is important and appropriate at this stage to involve providers.

The Mental Health Task Force, when looking at purchasers in London, found that, in general, purchasers were over-dependent upon providers to form and identify the shape of future services. This may be partly because few Health Authorities had an experienced senior officer responsible for purchasing mental health services on the Board.

(iii)   The third component of Smart Commissioning involves the **change agent**. This recognises that it is not simply enough to bring purchasers together to identify a way forward and to communicate that to existing providers. It acknowledges that there has to be some pressure for change on both purchasers and providers to respond to the needs of users and carers in the population. This change agent may take the form of outside pressures from other agencies, a hospital closure programme, the need to identify savings within the Local Authority, or the appointment of one or two additional staff to work with purchasers to develop strategies and then with providers to ensure they are carried out. In Sutton, for example, one officer has been appointed, who report to the Joint Commissioning Group. She works with purchasers initially to identify what needs to change in existing provision, and then with providers to implement these changes.

(iv)   Fourthly, Smart commissioning notes the important **role for users and carers**. They can often provide an opportunity to break through the professional dead-lock as well as being an important source of information about the value and effectiveness of services.

(v)   Finally, the model refers to the importance of a **tactical/strategic balance** between macro commissioning and micro purchasing. In other words it is illustrating the importance of keeping an eye on both what GP fund holders and care managers wish to buy as well as the proposed shape and composition of larger scale services such as residential care and day time activities.

In addition to these five Smart tasks, the process of commissioning normally includes three other steps not covered by this model. These are:

Agreement of Contracts with Providers

Monitoring and Reviewing

Changes to the Contracts, in the light of the information from the Reviewing and Monitoring process.

This then is the main approach traditionally seen to joint commissioning, and there are many examples of services where Local Authority social services departments, Health Authorities and Family Health Service Authorities, GP fund holders, users and carers and the voluntary sector are working collaboratively covering most, if not all, of these steps.

2   Potential problems with commissioning

There are three important potential problems with commissioning services for Mental Health from the perspective of the Social Services Department.

(i)   Resources

Financing services is probably the biggest single difficulty confronting those charged with implementing social policy changes. Firstly, while it is not necessarily the case that more resources are required to do the job, it is important that those resources currently in the system do stay in the system, and are therefore ring-fenced (ie. used to continue providing services for seriously mentally ill people). The issue of ring-fencing is a difficult one. Where joint commissioning has worked well, the trust that needs to exist between the purchasers has often been established by agreement to ring-fence spending in this area.

Secondly, the resources and finance must flow from those providers who are coming to adopt a smaller role in the provision of services, to those providers who are increasing their responsibilities as new services develop. This is also a challenging area. It is clear that from a number of studies where services are put into the communities to support people in their own homes, the biggest beneficiaries in terms of cost reductions are NHS Hospital Trusts. For example, Beecham, as part of the PSSRU in Kent, found that the Daily Living Programme pioneered by the Maudsley Hospital produced substantial cost savings in the length of time people had to spend as in-patients in hospitals. This cost, however, was, to some extent, transferred to local authorities and, in particular, social services departments. For the system to work, therefore, Joint Commissioning must ensure that resources flow from the providers who gain from the change in service character to those who are shouldering more of the responsibility. This puts a considerable responsibility onto purchasers to ensure this happens.

(ii)   Time Scales

The second potential problem area deals with the issue of time scales. Although there are pressures on purchasers and providers to make the necessary changes to service provision—closing old long stay hospitals, developing new community based services—there is a wealth of experience now which underlines the importance for purchasers not to under-estimate the length of time it takes to set up the new services in the community before beginning the process of closing the traditional hospital supports. In one North East London Authority that the Mental Health Task Force London Project visited, it found that the District Health Authority had a plan for closing the local psychiatric hospital, in which they assumed that local providers could set up community mental health teams in a matter of weeks, to coincide with the closure of hospital beds. In authorities where community mental health teams are working effectively, such as Wandsworth, in South London, it has been shown that these teams need time to work out the areas of responsibility, opportunities for re-training and re-learning skills, and the chance to deal with joint management issues. They also need the opportunity to build up and establish contacts in the community which will lead to better support and services to seriously mentally ill people. The development of new residential provision with Housing Associations can take anything from two to three years before a project has moved from inception to completion. Therefore, closing hospital provisions at the same time as developing new services in the community can quickly lead to difficulties and friction between providers and purchasers.

(iii) Service balance

The third potential problem area with commissioning deals with the difficult question of agreeing the appropriate service balance. To illustrate this we will contrast the experience of GPs, with NHS Trusts and Social Services. Relatively few general practitioners play a major role in supporting seriously mentally ill people in the community. Consultant psychiatrists, community psychiatric nurses, social workers and residential care workers provide most of these services. The general practitioner on the whole sees few seriously mentally ill people in his/her surgery. However, general practitioners see very many more people with depression and neurotic obsessive disorders. From the point of view of the district health authority and the local authority, the over-whelming issue is to provide services for severely mentally ill people. From the point of view of general practitioners, these groups are very important as they constitute a large proportion of the patients they see on a regular basis. The difficulty for the commissioners is how to acknowledge and meet the needs of GPs and GP fund holders, without potentially upsetting long term plans to re-provide a long stay hospital, and to meet the needs of the seriously mentally ill in the community. Health Authorities can play an important part in ensuring that the needs and aspirations of GPs are considered, and, with local authorities, in explaining the importance of their long term re-provision programmes, to General Practitioners.

3   Further purchasing issues

From a Local Authority perspective, there are four remaining issues to be addressed in purchasing services for seriously mentally ill people.

(i) Distribution of resources

Are the national resources available going to those authorities in the greatest need? The changes that the Government announced to the Standard Spending Assessment which provides the basis for Government funding to local authorities in 1993, have led to a slight adjustment of resources towards more deprived authorities. However, the Standard Spending Assessment formula, and the current way in which the weighted capitation formula for health authorities is calculated, does not fully take into account the actual needs of mentally ill people in the particular authority.

They both work on an assumption that the numbers of mentally ill people in the population will be roughly similar and that their needs will be broadly the same. However, mental illness is exacerbated by a whole range of factors, some of which are associated with levels of social and economic stress in the community. In this respect, we consider it important that the Department of Health's review the working of the weighted capitation formula for funding distribution. In addition, the recent proposed changes by the Department of Environment in its funding of local authority housing departments, may reduce the weighting given to the number of homeless people in each authority. This change needs to be carefully watched in case it may lead to loss of resources to those authorities who have large numbers of homeless people which themselves contain as many as 30 per cent of people with mental health problems. Resources need to go where the need is.

(ii) Public and political expectation

There is quite rightly a very high public and political expectation about the quality of results that can be achieved from the social policy changes being attempted in the area of community care. There are pressures to provide services in a more cost effective and efficient manner, together with the need to change from long stay institutional care to community based provision **and** to protect patients and other members of the community in the process. Mistakes and errors of judgment which result in death and injury are often associated with a claim that community care is not working and that the hospital closure programme should be halted or reversed. It is important to set out realistic time-scales for these changes and to promote a general understanding that in the area of risk management nothing is 100% certain. From a local authority perspective the issue is similar to the question of how society wants social workers to protect children from abuse. On the one hand it does not want children taken away from parents unnecessarily, but on the other it will not accept children being abused and injured. The path between these two extremes is sometimes impossibly difficult.

(iii) Services for the mentally ill from ethnic minority groups

There is widespread evidence that services are failing people who are mentally ill and from an ethnic minority. In general black and ethnic minority groups are under represented amongst some users, except where a voluntary organisation has been established and funded to provide services to these groups. However, black and ethnic minority users are over-represented in acute psychiatric wards. In some districts, they are alarmingly over-represented in locked wards and in medium secure forensic services. This is particularly true for Afro-Caribbean men. In one district in London all five people in the locked ward of the hospital Trust were Afro-Caribbean and male. In another, 11 out of 19 places in a medium secure regional forensic unit were occupied by Afro-Caribbean men. These were not districts with very high proportions of black and ethnic minority people in the population. Not only does the system seem to be failing to divert black people from acute in-patient beds, but quite possibly, it is perceiving black men in particular as threatening and challenging and moving them rapidly into locked wards and forensic beds.

(iv)   The role of local authorities, GPs, carers and the voluntary sector

Many people who are mentally ill are living in the community: and often with considerable support from carers, and from Local Authority services, including housing, leisure, and adult education. Although Health Authorities and Trusts are the significant fund holders and spenders on services for seriously mentally ill, local authorities, GPs, carers, and the voluntary sector play an important part in supporting the majority of the seriously mentally ill. So although in 1993 £2.1b was spent by health authorities and the trusts on supporting people who were diagnosed as suffering from schizophrenia, compared with £200m by local authorities and GPs and the voluntary sector, the DHAs only supported 32% of the number of known sufferers, whereas the remaining 68% of schizophrenic people were living at home, in residential accommodation funded by local authorities, or in hostel accommodation. From the point of view of the patient or person with the serious mental illness, whilst they value and understand the importance of medication and advice, studies have shown that they also value and need the support from services which are managed by the local authority, the general practitioner and the voluntary sector: services which include housing, daily occupation, social contracts and income.

In conclusion, Joint Commissioning is the way forward for Local Authorities and is becoming more common. Challenges remain for commissioners in producing the balance between hospital and community resources, in getting the timescales right for closing down hospital services and developing new community-based services. Local Authorities should continue to develop their commissioning skills, particularly in conjunction with other agencies, in order to effectively support people suffering from mental illness in the community.

1 Housing and Mental Health: A Brief Guide for Commissioners

MIKE FARRAR, JUDITH YOUNG and VANESSA MALIN

Introduction

1   This guide is aimed at those organisations responsible for the **commissioning** of mental health care. Its primary audience is therefore Health Authorities, Fundholding General Practices and Local Authority Social Services Departments. However the guide may also be relevant to Housing Departments, Probation and other Criminal Justice Agencies.

2   It is usefully considered in conjunction with the *Health of the Nation Key Area Handbook on Mental Illness (DoH 1994)*[1] which sets housing in the context of a comprehensive mental health service and a number of associated papers and documents such as; *Housing for People with severe Mental Illness (Corp and Levi 1996)*[2]; *The Housing Component of Mental Health Services (Prior 1996)*[3]; and *Local Systems of Support (Mental Health Task Force 1994)*[4] which provide detailed guidance primarily for **service providers** on the development of specialised accommodation for those with severe mental illness.

Accommodation and mental health—the links

3   **Accommodation and mental health are linked.** It is essential that Health Authorities understand the need to address housing issues if they are to commission an efficient and effective service response for people with mental health problems/illness. Table 1 identifies the link between housing and mental health drawing on a number of recent reports and research findings.

Table 1:   *Links between housing and mental health*

- Bad housing or inappropriate accommodation can lead to the development and/or the exacerbation of mental health problems/illness (Dooley 1993)[5].

- Many people have their accommodation threatened or lose accommodation as a result of the onset of mental health problems/illness[6].

- Inadequate housing is particularly common among people with mental health problems/illness (Audit Commission 1994)[7].

- Many people who are homeless have mental health problems/illness. Mental health morbidity may be up to eleven times greater amongst the homeless/roofless and eight times greater amongst those people in Bed and Breakfast accommodation than in the general population (Arblaster, 1993)[8].

- Users of mental health services cite 'an appropriate place to live' as a fundamental component of their needs (Mental Health Foundation 1994)[9].

- Interventions which tackle either mental health or housing conditions alone were found not to prevent subsequent service failures, while only 10% of clients who showed improvements in both mental state and accommodation subsequently defaulted from care (Wing, Lelliot and Craig 1995)[10].

Accommodation and mental health—the principles

5   There are a number of principles that need to be considered in order to ensure an appropriate range of accommodation and support is available for those with mental health problems.

- Users of mental health services should have a choice as to the type of accommodation they would wish to have, although this must be considered in light of the degree of risk posed to themselves and others.

- Assessment of an individuals accommodation needs should be a central component of any overall assessment of mental health need, including those associated with the care programme approach and care management requirements.

- The provision of a mental health service should be available to all people irrespective of where they may be accommodated.

- People providing accommodation for people with mental health problems/illness (eg carers, landlords/ladies etc) should be entitled to expect appropriate mental health support and training.

- Individuals who exhibit co-morbidity, particularly where this includes, housing, mental health and substance misuse problems, should receive a planned and coherent service response based on a general assessment of need rather than isolated, sporadic and uncoordinated interventions.

Accommodation and mental health—a model for understanding and responding to need

6   Many models have been proposed in order to understand the relationship between accommodation and mental health. Most presuppose that an individual's ability to sustain independent living decreases with the severity of their particular mental health problem/illness. As such the individual may move up and down the range of accommodation according to the onset of illness or stage of rehabilitation. An example of such a model was proposed by the Kings Fund (1988)[11].

Accommodation		Desired Consumer Direction
a	Person receives required services in own home; supported by regular social network	↑
b	Home environment and/or social network augmented by another agency (package of services to maintain person in own home)	↑
c	If person is unable to live in own home then an ordinary home with a built in support can be devised	↑
d	Professional services available if requested—in ordinary home (ie sheltered accommodation)	↑
e	Professionals on site 24 hours but not getting all services from this site	↑
f	All services provided on site	↑

(Braisley, Echlin, Hill and Smith, 1988)[11].

7   In reality a number of factors serve to confuse the ideal position as set out in the model and individuals may move in and out of stages on a less planned basis. For example some groups, such as those with schizophrenia, may find shared housing solution counterproductive, making better therapeutic progress in single occupied facilities.

8   From a commissioning perspective it may be more valuable to develop categories of people according to the nature of the commissioner's response to their need.

People requiring support to stay in their own or general rented accommodation:

Description

People who are at the onset of an illness or mental health problem for whom the task of maintaining their own home is becoming increasingly difficult;

People who are returning to independent living as an ongoing process of rehabilitation;

People for whom short but frequent admissions to in patient care may affect their income and ability to maintain accommodation.

Potential responses

Essentially support may be required at a basic practical level such as;

- Carer support (and respite)
- Help with financial matters (eg paying rent)
- Advocacy with banks/building societies
- Gardening and maintenance of property
- Ensuring access to housing advice and support
- Advocacy with neighbours, if required
- Offering ordinary housing workers some mental health input
- Befriending schemes and help to access social groupings/activities
- Providing emergency contacts for use in the event of crisis.

Commissioner activity

In order to ensure the necessary inputs are available, commissioners may wish to consider actions such as;

- more detailed assessment of carer needs
- contracting/funding non statutory agencies (eg MIND, CAB) to provide advocacy
- contracting/funding non statutory agencies to provide practical support schemes (eg Crossroads, Citizens Volunteer Bureaux)
- purchasing house advice and support workers (either HAs, GPFHolding consortia or Local Authority Housing Departments)
- building and maintaining alliances with community development groups (eg tenants associations, local social or self help groups).

People requiring 'respite' or 'asylum' from existing circumstances on a short stay basis to enhance their ability to sustain independent living and prevent an acute admission

Description

People for whom a recent 'crisis' in their mental health has led to a placement on a short stay basis.

People whose crisis or offending is associated with a mental health problem and has led to a temporary placement in a refuge, probation hostel or local authority accommodation.

Potential Responses

Dedicated accommodation for the groups in question is rare yet recent studies have shown that at least 1/3 and in some cases up to 70% of those in acute psychiatric beds are inappropriately placed of which a significant proportion would have been prevented from an admission had experienced crisis intervention services and/or crisis diversion places been available (Royal College of Psychiatrists 1994).

The ability of non NHS workers such as those in probation hostels and refuges to provide an effective crisis response may be dependent on their ability to recognise and support those with mental health problems. This ability will be enhanced by routine inputs to basic and post basic training on mental health, in addition to having rapid and easy access to specialist mental health support.

Commissioner activity

Commissioners should access the local profile of admissions to acute psychiatric beds in order to consider the option of investment in crisis intervention approaches.

Commissioners may wish to review the current links between contracted mental health services and potential non NHS services providing crisis intervention, to ensure that the training and support needs of non specialist staff are being provided for and unnecessary admissions avoided.

People who are returning to independent living as part of their rehabilitation

Description

People whose mental health problem/illness requires specialised accommodation with mental health support.

People whose experience of long stay hospital accommodation has led to a placement as a component of their rehabilitation.

Potential responses

- Accommodation to meet the needs of the group (s) in question would be most likely provided by a variety of agencies (eg Housing Associations, Voluntary Agencies, Probation Services, NHS providers).

   The effectiveness of such placements may depend on

- the quality of the specialist mental health service/input available to residents

- the match of accommodation to consumer choice

- the mix of clients within the facility

- the support for generic staff in terms of training and consultation from specialist services.

Commissioner activity

Commissioners should acknowledge that the range of provision required to meet individual needs will necessitate the involvement of a variety of agencies and funders. Local Authority Social Service and Housing Departments will be the key agencies in securing this range. Commissioners should seek to:

- ensure there are coordinated structures for social service and health service planning
- improve their liaison with Local Housing Departments
- increase their understanding of national policy on special needs housing and local housing strategy
- access housing advice through the use of secondments, shared training, shadow schemes or direct employment of housing advice workers.

Commissioners may face difficulties if they are involved directly in purchasing or developing accommodation. These relate to a recognition that the nature of such provision may change in relation to user needs over time (eg users moving through 'group homes' demanding a more outreach orientated service and leaving difficult 'voids' to fill; older users requiring physically adapted environments; changes to treatment/care interventions dictating different responses for new clients). As such, useful criteria for commissioners when selecting providers might include:

- provider ability to demonstrate shifts in models of care and staffing profiles
- provider portfolio on a range of service inputs
- provider training and recruitment programmes
- provider history of developing 'outreach services'
- provider history on risk assessment and management
- provider openness to working in a problem-solving relationship with commissioners.

Some commissioners may opt to retain flexibility through the purchasing of buildings and care separately from different agencies, allowing change of care provider without losing access to physical accommodation.

People who are accommodated in specialised environments organised primarily in response to specific mental health needs

Description

People in specialised therapeutic communities.

People in secure accommodation whilst being treated for mental health problems/illness.

Young people in specialised facilities provided by education, social services or criminal justice system.

Potential responses

It is important to ensure that the period of care in specialised settings is an integral element of the individuals overall care plan. Specialised placements, especially at some distance from an individuals district of residence, should not constrain the continuity of care offered. Similarly people with mental health problems/illness discharged from prisons should have access back into local mental health services through responsible discharge planning.

The provider of the accommodation should not be assumed to be able to meet all the mental health needs of the individual and Commissioners may seek to ensure that any mental health input is agreed. This may be particularly relevant for young people in specialist education accommodation or being looked after by the Local Authority.

Commissioner activity

Commissioners may wish to review/audit relevant cases periodically with providers to ensure arrangements for assessment, mental health input and discharge planning are acceptable.

Commissioners may wish to consider the current contractual arrangements they hold with specialised placements to ensure that an effective system of quality control is in place.

People with mental health problems/illness but without accommodation

Description

People who have been rejected or ejected from existing accommodation as a result of their mental health problem/illness or the degree of challenge posed to staff.

People who have become itinerant as a consequence of their mental health problem/illness.

People whose homelessness has caused or exacerbated their mental health problem/illness.

People who have mental health problems and have been temporarily accommodated by Local Authorities in bed and breakfast or hostel accommodation.

Potential Responses

It is essential that homeless mentally ill people have access to mainstream primary care and specialist mental health services. Much will depend on the ability of those services to engage with and build the trust of those individuals concerned, many of whom may have a poor perception or experience of statutory agencies.

Accident and emergency services provide an important access point to health care for homeless mentally ill people and could be encouraged to recognise and utilise this role.

Advocacy may be necessary not only to promote access to health care but also to other statutory agencies such as benefits agencies, housing departments and social services.

Homeless mentally ill people who experience a high level of co-morbidity with drug and alcohol problems, deliberate self harm and personality disorder are likely to make great demands of generic services. Good communication between these and specialist services will be essential if an effective intervention is to be made.

On a similar basis, the children of homeless mentally ill people are vulnerable to greater levels of health problems and need to be enabled to access primary care and specialist childrens services where appropriate.

Commissioner Activity

Commissioners can enable such responses by:

- actively promoting registration of this group by General Practitioners

- commissioning outreach orientated services specifically geared to work on identifying and working with this group (non statutory agencies may well be placed to offer this type of service)

- developing local needs assessment work to define the nature and extent of the problem locally

- commissioning liaison roles in accident and emergency departments to ensure continuity of care once individuals have presented for help

- ensuring appropriate implementation of supervision registers and the care programme approach/care management to facilitate responsible and timely flows of information on itinerant people.

Conclusion

Accommodation and Mental Health—Opportunities for Health Gain

9   Although little specific research has been carried out into health gain, mental health and housing it is suggested that there are a number of opportunities for Commissioners presented by the following:

- greater basic practical support to enable more people with mental health problems/illness to retain and maintain their own accommodation

- earlier advice being made available on housing matters users, carers, mental health providers and Commissioners

- increasing the housing element of assessment arrangements to ensure that accommodation needs are considered at the earliest opportunity

- improving the liaison between Commissioners and Local Authority Housing Departments to harmonise housing and mental health strategies

- reviewing and enhancing the mental health component of basic and post basic training for residential staff and housing advice/support staff from non health organisation

- providing early mental health support to housing managers in order to prevent homelessness.

References

[1] Department of Health (1994) *Health of the Nation Key Area Handbook*—Mental Illness 2nd edition. London: HMSO.
[2] Corp and Levi (1996) *Housing for People with severe Mental Illness.*
[3] Prior C (1996) *The Housing Component of Mental Health Services*, Chapter in *Purchasing Mental Health*: ed by Strathdee, G. and Thornicroft, G. HMSO London.
[4] Mental Health Task Force: NHS Executive (1994) *Local Systems of Support Heywood.*
[5] Dooley (1993).
[6] Mental Health Foundation (1995/6) *Housing and Mental Health*
[7] Audit Commission (1994) *Finding a Place—A Review of Mental Health Services for Adults*. London: HMSO.
[8] Arblaster L. (1993) *Homelessness and Health Yorkshire RHA*
[9] Mental Health Foundation (1994) *Creating Community Care*. MHF London.
[10] Wing, Lelliot and Craig (1995).
[11] Kings Fund College (1988).
[12] Royal College of Psychiatry Research Unit (1994) MILMIS Study.

2 Writing a Strategy[1]

HELEN SMITH, DAVID KINGDON, EDWARD PECK

Introduction

Over the past two decades, a disproportionate amount of time has been devoted to the act of writing mental health strategies; disproportionate, that is, to the amount of time and attention given to eliciting and understanding the needs of those who use the services and their carers. Since 1976, when it became a requirement for mental health services, much has been written about the development of strategies in health and social services but progress in formulating effective strategies has been disappointingly slow. It was 1984 before most Districts made serious attempts to develop strategic plans and, by 1988, a majority had some form of strategy in place[1]. However, the process of formulation and their content varied greatly with very few providing comprehensive strategies with clear aims and objectives and costed plans to achieve them.

It is unsurprising, therefore, that, despite all this planning activity, little has actually changed in service provision. Service users and their carers continue to report that services are at best patchy and at worst, irrelevant to their needs. This is particularly true for users and carers from minority groups. A frequent criticism, from users, their families, some staff groups and voluntary agencies, of traditional approaches to planning and consultation, is that they feel passive recipients of someone else's plan. The strategy is written to meet the needs of users, *as perceived by planners and managers*, distributed to a range of people and amended in light of comments, In other words, those who are most significantly affected by the service are always responding to someone else's ideas about what should be on offer. The result is that many users and carers feel alienated from a process which is often also characterised by poor joint working between health and social services. By the time these large, monopolistic agencies turn to those at the receiving end of services, the views of users and carers may exert little influence and consultation becomes tokenistic.

Analyses of how to effect change through strategic planning have tended to focus on factors external to the planning process, such as how to ensure proper representation of various interest groups. Whereas these are clearly important, it may be that many planning processes are themselves inherently flawed. Much planning activity focuses primarily on writing the strategy or plan, to the extent often, that the plan becomes the end in itself rather than the means to achieve improvements in services. It is rare for the procedure of writing a plan, in

---

[1] This chapter is based on an article by 'Smith H (1995) *Strategic Planning of Mental Health Services* Community Care Management & Planning Journal, Vol. 3, No. 1. Parts of the original article are reprinted here with kind permission of the Editor.

itself, to change people and circumstances and to produce an imperative to action and implementation. It was to assist in changing this situation that the Centre for Mental Health Services Development (CMHSD) was established by the Department of Health in 1991 (with additional support from the Mental Health Foundation) to work with districts, and others, in the development and implementation of effective strategies.

The CMHSD has approached this task by developing strategic planning processes which by their very nature, aim to make change unavoidable. This has included looking to other countries, notably the United States, for inspiration and ideas. Such processes are described in this chapter. They seek to turn the rhetoric of a 'needs-led' approach into practice outlining the crucial steps which can, in themselves, change the way participants in the planning process think about mental health services.

Learning from the US experience

A proven effective approach to planning is that of a 'search conference', an approach well established in the United States. In the mid-1970s, the National Institute of Mental Health (NIMH) looked to develop a vision of a comprehensive mental health service. Since 1978, a series of national, regional and state conferences 'encouraged dialogue and collaboration amongst representatives from interest groups with a stake in mental health, i.e. users, families, managers, professionals, researchers, planners and policy makers'[2]. A search conference involves gathering together the major stakeholders in a service with the stated purpose of 'searching' for the answer to the questions: 'What do people want from the service?' and 'What are they prepared to do to achieve it?' The 'search' takes place within a framework where contributions are sought from people who directly use the services or care for those who do, including those from local black and minority ethnic communities, alongside those who work within the services as professionals or managers.

The NIMH used a framework to structure the planning done in a search conference, based on service functions: that is, they defined eleven components of a comprehensive service and required all states to develop services to deliver these functions. These are[3]:

- client identification and active outreach
- mental health treatment
- physical health and dental services
- a range of crisis response services, including alternatives to inpatient care
- housing
- income support and benefits entitlements
- peer support (self advocacy; tenants association; user-run clubs, etc.)
- family and community support
- meaningful occupation, including employment
- protection of rights and citizen advocacy
- individual planning/care management.

These service functions are the essential components of the national Community Support Services initiative for people with more severe and long term mental health problems[4]. Local mental health services are required to organise the service components listed above into a comprehensive mental health system, through individual case management, joint planning with other agencies, careful monitoring and evaluation. The value of this approach is that it does not depend upon a national 'blueprint' of services, something which is both culturally and practically unacceptable in the States; rather, it defines what services should be *achieving* for users and leaves it to local discretion to decide how these achievements are to be delivered.

Using the stakeholder approach in Britain

Two components seem to underpin the success of this approach in the States: firstly, the involvement of a wide range of people in the planning of services. The CMHSD search or 'stakeholder' conferences in this country have included not just the statutory and voluntary agencies, users and carers, but also representatives from minority groups, GPs, housing departments, the police, the probation service, and even Adult Education and Leisure where they have a particular interest or involvement. Secondly, search conferences structure planning in terms of quality standards and outcomes for users and carers, rather than simply in terms of a list of services. The CMHSD process structures the work in terms of categories of needs. A useful starting point is to consider what sort of help people are seeking. The evidence from user consultation exercises is that people are looking for a service, rooted in an understanding of their culture or background, which might include help:

- with emotional problems
- to get them through a crisis
- to learn new skills
- to have a full life during the day
- to get and hold down a job
- with information about any illness they may have
- with choosing between the services and treatments available
- to get a reasonable income
- to find somewhere to live
- to make and keep friendships
- to link with others of the same race/culture and/or gender
- to find someone to speak on their behalf if necessary.

This is not an exhaustive list, but does encompass most of the significant needs of people who use mental health services. This approach is based on understandings of need rather than on clinical notions of diagnosis. There are similarities to the principles which underpin normalisation, a philosophy which has been influential in the planning of services for people with learning difficulties[5]. There are also similarities to the approach taken by the Research Unit of the Royal College of Psychiatrists in developing 'Health of the Nation' Outcome Scales which have emphasised the importance of social care needs as well as symptomatic measures[6]. Clinical diagnoses in psychiatry have not, as yet, proved useful in determining needs or outcomes or even resource utilisation.

In order to respond to the range and variety of people's needs, services have to address each of the following categories of need:

Access into the service—the service needs to identify local people who require support and ensure that the service is visible, easily accessible and acceptable to men and women from all cultural and ethnic backgrounds. This requires effective working links with other agencies, particularly primary care, social services, the criminal justice system and the voluntary sector, ease and immediacy of access to services and assertive outreach to people who have traditionally mistrusted and/or not used services (such as homeless people or young African-Caribbean men).

Individual Planning—each person requires a comprehensive assessment of her or his needs, as required by the Care Programme Approach/case management, based on a thorough understanding, where appropriate, of the unique health and social care needs of women and people from minority groups. A care plan should use the combined resources of the individual's social network, mental health services and other statutory, voluntary or community services. Effective, integrated care planning systems are the underpinning of a comprehensive service.

Support in Ordinary Living—the service crucially needs to identify those people who need a high degree of support to ensure that their fundamental needs are being adequately met. For some people, this will mean help with securing permanent accommodation and an adequate level of income through benefits. People may also need the support of a befriending or advocacy service. Assistance may also be needed to register with a Primary health Care Team and a dentist for general health care.

Growth and Personal Development—services have a responsibility for the enhancement of the quality of people's lives by: supporting them in developing useful skills; receiving specialist treatment for particular mental health problems; encouraging people to pursue their interests; and assisting them to be empowered to take control over their lives. Services will need to be innovative in their approach to counselling, the use of adult education, the development of interpersonal and domestic skills, enabling people to seek and enjoy new experiences such as photography, cooking, instrument playing, British and other foods and so on. Employment or meaningful occupation is essential if people are to have fulfilling lives; users consider this to be a priority area of development for services which do not currently offer active re-employment programmes. The failure to replace employment schemes provided by the traditional mental hospitals, even though these were largely woefully inadequate, has resulted in people living isolated and directionless lives in the community. The few effective schemes that exist[7][8] demonstrate that, even with high levels of general unemployment, partnership with Local Placement, Access and Employment Teams and other employment agencies can be successful.

Needs in Crisis—any comprehensive mental health system relies on its capacity to respond immediately to people who experience a severe, sudden decrease in their ability to function. The aim is to ensure the safety of the individual and others and to enable people to remain in their own home, if they so chose, or to return to it as soon as possible. People who wish or require asylum away from their home need to receive it in settings which are as ordinary as possible and which seek to maintain links with family and friends.

These five groupings can be used as a framework to categorise peoples' needs. Clearly, not all users will have needs in all categories but each category of needs should be provided for in the overall planning of services. This approach is in contrast to the traditional ways of planning, based on population 'norms' which often result in a standard configuration of existing services. The uncritical extrapolation of estimates given in 'Better Services for the Mentally Ill'[9] to local situations has led to gaps in provision in many areas and both over and underprovision of acute hospital facilities, often to the neglect of community services including residential accommodation. For example:

'In a given area with a population of 30,000, about a hundred people (0.4%) are expected to have a diagnosis of functional psychosis and one in seven (4–5000) will have neurotic disorder: planning has often proceeded on the basis of assumptions about *service* response—15 acute beds, 70 day hospital/day centre places, 300 out-patient appointments and so on. However, this is *not* information about people's needs: for example, how many of the 100 people with psychosis need help in finding a job? In making friends? In using the Adult Education or leisure services? In shopping and caring for themselves adequately? In finding decent accommodation?'[10]

The effects of 'needs-based' planning

The liberating effect of actually identifying *need* can be seen in the many innovative strategies produced through the stakeholder process. For example, a traditional approach to a crisis is usually to define an acute emergency as where people need intensive levels of medical, nursing and therapeutic support in order to maintain their personal safety and the safety of others. This approach identifies the response to needs (intensive medical input, etc.) but not the needs themselves and leads mostly to hospital-based services. The stakeholder approach identifies the needs of people in terms of: 'accommodation and food; 24-hour observation; prolonged assessment; medication; respite from family; respite for family; problem solving/advice; counselling; company; rest and safety; stress relief; help with self-care; detoxification; relief from responsibility'[11]. This approach has led to the setting up of 24-hour crisis services, crisis phonelines, home-based crisis care, crisis beds in CMHCs, 'brief hospitalisation' programmes, community treatment units, respite/sanctuary houses and intensive day care, alongside more conventional requirements such as acute in-patient wards, secure units, 'hospital hostels' and community teams.

Managing the process

The overall review and development of a strategy is usually co-ordinated by a Steering Group, consisting of a range of stakeholders. The tasks of a Steering Group are typically to draw together the work of stakeholder conferences and project groups, draft the strategy, cost it, and set priorities. The composition of the group varies between districts but, certainly in a major review of services, it is chaired by a representative of the purchasing agency. The relationship of the Steering Group to health and local authorities and to other mental health planning and operation groups, e.g. joint care planning teams and any specific inquiry teams, needs consideration to avoid duplication of effort.

User and carer participants may need extra support in order to fully participate in the strategic review process at all levels. They will certainly need travel and carer expenses and should be offered payment for their involvement where a significant amount of their time is involved (after all, it is likely that they are the only people participating in an unpaid capacity). Philpot[12] identifies a number of strategies which maximise the effectiveness of user involvement, including clear communication from agencies, training and administrative support for users and carers and dedicated workers to facilitate their involvement. User consultants can be used (as in reviews facilitated by the CMHSD) to support and develop local user groups to participate fully in the review.

In the CMHSD process, the work arising from the stakeholder conferences is carried forward in more detail in project groups, which focus on a defined theme such as developing services to meet needs in crisis, and in 'focus' groups of particular stakeholders such as GPs or people from minority groups. These groups take the needs outlined in the stakeholder conferences, quantify levels of need locally, consider good practice from this country and elsewhere, assess the adequacy of local service responses and develop new ones. This requires the bringing together of information on both the resident population and current service usage, although careful interpretation of such information is needed as it can frequently mislead. It can only represent how current services respond not how they would or could respond if reconfigured to meet the needs of the population.

Data interpretation is particularly problematic and controversial in relation to usage of acute in-patient beds. The evidence from reviews of specific incidents (e.g. the Ritchie Report) and general circumstances (e.g. the Select Committee and the Mental Health Task Force) is that the reduction in inpatient bed numbers has outpaced the development of alternative services to meet the needs of people with severe mental illness; this has meant that patients who could be supported in their own homes or staffed accommodation outside hospital, are instead 'trapped' on acute wards paradoxically preventing admission of others with similar needs at an early enough stage to allow their admissions to be brief and successful in terms of return to their previous setting. Many inner city districts are now increasing their acute in-patient provision; however, it is not clear whether this expansion is part of a planned longer term development of alternative services, necessary to meet the needs of users and carers, or a short term 'fire-fighting' response.

National policy aims will need to be integrated into local strategies and this may conflict with what is essentially a 'bottom-up' approach to planning. However, in practice, current policies have been concerned to remedy the problems of previous policies, which have not been successful in meeting the needs of people with severe mental illness and great emphasis is placed by the DoH on a 'needs-led' approach. The Care Programme Approach/case management involves assessment of both health and social care needs of

128

individuals and identification of shortfalls in provision. Supervision registers are a first step to the development of person-based comprehensive mental health information systems, focusing on those most vulnerable and in need. 'The Health of the Nation' mental illness key area handbook sets targets to improve health and social functioning of mentally ill people and, more specifically, to prevent suicide by improved risk assessment and managements, recognition and treatment of depression and by reducing access to means.

The stakeholder approach has been used by the CMHSD in a large number of districts but what has it achieved for users and carers and for those working in services? The essence of a community-orientated mental health service is to support people, as far as possible, in their own communities. The stakeholder process will be successful if it results in a range of different types of support and care settings which enable users to be helped in the least restrictive/most facilitative setting possible. Government initiatives have emphasised the *co-ordination* of care, for example: the CPA/case management initiatives established the importance of individual care planning and 'seamless' care between agencies; the Patient's Charter has enshrined the right to a named nurse to provide a focus for care; supervision registers focus on the co-ordination of care for very vulnerable patients. However, the involvement of users and carers in the stakeholder process focuses planning not just on the co-ordination of services within particular parts of the 'service system' but also on the *integration* of the service system across different levels. Planning for an integrated service needs to be undertaken at three system levels[13]:

At an individual level: that is, care planning led by a keyworker who co-ordinates all individual planning, accesses the range of different services and agencies and regularly reviews individual care. All agencies need to develop a common approach to assessment and care planning which ensures that users receive an equal focus on both treatment and support in independent living. This becomes more crucial with the increasing number of care purchasers: care/case managers, GP fundholders and the health authority/social services.

At an agency level: that is, clear objectives and ways of working for each service component including primary care services and housing departments, which ensure that all services have a common community focus. For example, targeting of clients in relation to severity of need; clarity of working practices (e.g. an emphasis on providing practical support within a person's own environment); clear policies and procedures for individual care planning, keyworking and joint working with other agencies; clear lines of responsibility and accountability from senior management to practitioners.

At a district level: that is, developing a comprehensive range of voluntary and statutory, secondary and primary, community-based, specialist and inpatient services to enable all service users to achieve their maximum potential for independent living, systematically planned and delivered on the basis of identified health and social needs. Work at this level will encourage the proliferation of independent sector services. Many people can benefit from self-help groups and other associated techniques[14] supported by counselling and psychotherapy services. Because of the gap between what is currently provided and that aspired to, development of services should target those whose needs are greatest and progressively extend to others.

Community mental health teams: a case study of integration

The importance of integration across the three levels defined above can be seen in relation to community mental health teams (CMHTs). Many authors have noted their lack of focus[15] and how this can actually militate against effective patient care[16]. Indeed, Galvin and McCarthy[17] argue persuasively that multi-disciplinary teams are inherently unworkable and not able to deliver an effective service. Despite this, CMHTs are universally viewed as integral to modern mental health care in all the strategic reviews facilitated by the CMHSD and the review of Inner London services by the Mental Health Task Force[18], resulting in a development of new or strengthening of existing CMHTs. This has occurred through identifying users' needs and then determining the best service response rather than saying: 'We must have CMHTs, now what are they to do?' A much clearer sense of their role has been achieved through defining their role at individual level (what do they actually *do* for users?) at service level (target group, clear lines of management and clinical leadership, responsibility and accountability etc.) and at district level (what role do they play in the full range of statutory, voluntary and informal services used by any individual). This approach has ensured CMHTs a level of integration throughout the service system which has greatly enhanced patient care.

Conclusion

There is no blueprint for strategy development. However, the key guiding principle is that both the process and the final strategy must be directed and belong to local participants especially those who will use and provide the service. Planners, managers, or consultants can suggest options, advise based on their experience and knowledge and help local people in making decisions adapted to local circumstances. The process should be stimulating, even enjoyable, and involvement in the planning process should change individuals' approach to mental health services and to service users. People who use mental health services and their families and friends have waited long enough for services to effectively and comprehensively meet their needs, effective strategic planning is an essential step in attaining that goal.

References

1. Kingdon, D.G. Mental Health Services: a survey of strategic plans. *Psychiatric Bulletin*, **13**, 77–78, 1989.
2. Turner-Crowson, J. Long term strategies for system change: The US community support programme (CSP) *J of Mental Health*, **1**, 90–92, 1992.
3. Anthony, W. & Blanch, A. Research on community support services: what we have learned. *Psychosocial Rehabilitation Journal*, **12**, 3, January, 1989.
4. Stroul, B. (1988) Community support systems for persons with long term mental illnesses: Questions and answers National Institute of Mental Health Community Support Programme, Rockville, MD; National Institute of Mental Health.

5   Brown, H. and Smith, H. (eds) Normalisation: *A Reader for the Nineties.* London: Routledge, 1992.

6   Department of Health. Health of the Nation. *Mental Illness Key Area Handbook.* 2nd Edition. London: HMSO, 1994.

7   MIND. *Action Pack on Employment and Mental Health.* London: MIND, 1992.

8   Mental Health Task Force. Meeting need. *Leisure and Unemployment.* NHSE Video, 1994.

9   DHSS. *Better Services for the Mentally Ill.* London: HMSO, 1975.

10 Peck, E. and Smith, H., Contracting in Mental Health Services Bristol: *NHS Training Directorate,* 1991.

11 KEYHOLE, Alternatives to Acute Hospital Admission: *A bulletin for managers, planners and commissioners of mental health services* Bulletin No. **1**, May 1991. Published by the Kings Fund Centre, 126, Albert Street, London, NW1 7NF.

12 Philpot, T. Managing to Listen: *A guide to user involvement for mental health service managers.* London: Kings Fund Centre, 1994.

13 Smith, H. *Conference Presentation on Achieving Innovation in Community Mental Health Services,* Kings Fund Centre, July, 1994.

14 Tyrer, P., Sievewright, N., Murphy, S., *et al.* The Nottingham study of neurotic disorder: comparison of drug and psychological treatments. *Lancet,* **2**, 235–240, 1988.

15 Sayce, L., Craig, T. and Boardman, A. The Development of Community Mental Health Centres in the UK. *Soc Psychiatry Psychiatr Epidemiol* **26**, 14–20, 1991.

16 Patmore, C. and Weaver, T. *Rafts on an Open Sea HSJ,* **11** October, pp1510–1512, 1990 and Patmore, C. and Weaver, T. *United Fronts HSJ,* **18** October, pp1554–5, 1990.

17 Galvin, S. and McCarthy, S. Multi-disciplinary community teams: Clinging to the wreckage *J of Mental Health,* **3**, 157–166, 1994.

18 Mental Health Task Force. *Priorities in Action.* London: NHSE.

3 Core Components of a Comprehensive Mental Health Service

GERALDINE STRATHDEE & GRAHAM THORNICROFT

Introduction

This paper sets out the sources of information will assist purchasers in defining what constitutes the components of a mental health service. First, the basis on which a service system should be planned is described. Second, the components of a comprehensive mental health service are outlined. Third, the mechanism to ensure effective working of community mental health teams as the vehicle for service implementation are summarised.

Determinants of the core components of a mental health service system

The fundamental basis of modern day community mental health provision is that services should focus on the needs of those with mental health disorders, and should be provided, as much as possible in local, accessible settings. Table 1 illustrates some of the important issues to be considered in determining the necessary range of services. Underpinning these are the need to involve users and carers at all stages of the development of services and to give priority to those with severe and enduring mental illness.

Table 1: *The basis of developing the core components of a comprehensive mental health services system*

- understanding the range of needs of individuals with mental health disorders
- agreement on organisational principles underlying the provision and delivery of mental health services
- knowledge of service structures which improve clinical, social, satisfaction & cost outcomes
- use of proven effective interventions
- knowledge of examples of good practice and feasible implementation

Fig 1 outlines the wide range of needs of those with mental health problems, (Stevens & Gabbay, 1991)

Figure 1: *Need, demand and supply: influences and overlaps*

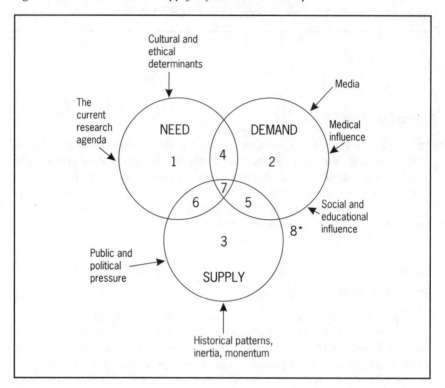

This illustrates that no one agency or service alone is likely to be able to provide the wide range of interventions needed for a comprehensive care package. Several agencies may need to be involved for the most vulnerable and may include primary and secondary health care providers, social services, housing and welfare benefit agencies, self-help and carer support groups. This presents a major task of co-ordination both at the level of the individual care plan as well as at the wider service system level.

The principles of community psychiatric services

However organisations and individuals may argue about the range of services needed there is little disagreement on the principles which should underpin the move to community services. These are that:

Services should be local and accessible and to the greatest extent possible delivered in the client's usual environment.

Services should be comprehensive and address the diversity of needs of individuals with mental health disorders.

Services should be flexible by being available whenever and for whatever duration. There should be a range of complementary models which provide individuals with choice and vary, depending on need, at any point in time.

Services should be consumer-orientated that is based on the needs of the client rather than those of providers. Achieving this balance is one of the major difficulties to be overcome in resource allocation. Central, highly resourced facilities, for example hospital based units, may appear more efficient and effective in terms of easy movement of staff between wards, training, information gathering and reduction in staff isolation but inflexible in addressing patient's needs.

Services should empower clients by using and adapting treatment techniques which enable clients to enhance their self-help skills and retain the fullest possible control over their own lives. This can take place at both the individual level and at all stages in the planning and development of a service. By integrating an educational component into treatment, users of services can determine the strategies in terms of medications and manipulation of social environments which enable them to take part in secondary and tertiary prevention. At the services level, clients should be actively involved in planning and policy making decisions and be represented on all relevant committees.

Services should be racially and culturally appropriate (see chapter 20). Mechanisms to ensure provision of appropriate and acceptable services include use of culturally appropriate needs assessment tools, representation on planning groups, cross-cultural training for staff, use of indigenous workers and bilingual staff, identification and provision of alternative basic facilities and evaluation of the provision against accepted indicators.

Services should focus on strengths   They should be built on the skills and strengths of clients and help them maintain a sense of identity, dignity and self-esteem. Patients should be discouraged from adopting the sick-role and the service from developing an environment organized around permanent illness with lowered expectations.

Services should be normalized and incorporate natural supports by being in the least restrictive, most natural setting possible. The natural work, education, leisure and support facilities in the community should be used in preferences to specialised developments.

Services should meet special needs with particular attention being paid to those with physical disabilities, mental retardation, the homeless or imprisoned.

Services should be accountable to the consumers and carers and evaluated to ensure their continuing appropriateness and acceptability and effectiveness on agreed parameters.

THE CORE COMPONENTS OF A MENTAL HEALTH SERVICE SYSTEM

It is well recognised that the traditional triad of in-patient, out-patient and day care services will not ensure that the most vulnerable people receive a services. The necessary components of a comprehensive community mental health service system have been set out in the Health of the Nation Key Area Handbook (1994) and endorsed by users, carers and professionals. These service structures are those which have demonstrable impact on health and social outcomes, quality of life and satisfaction and are reiterated in Table 2.

Table 2: *The components of a comprehensive mental health service system*

1 Identification and needs assessment systems
2 Care Programme Approach integrated with care management
3 Hospital and Community beds and bed management
4 Case management and assertive outreach
5 Day care, rehabilitation, education and work opportunities
6 Crisis response
7 Assessment and consultation
8 Carer and community education and support
9 Primary care liaison
10 User advocacy and community alliances

However, despite the consensus, several diagnostic enquiries over the past few years have found that implementation is far from easy (Audit Commission, 1994, Mental Health Foundation 1994, House of Commons Select Committee Inquiry into the care of the severely mentally ill). The priority given to mental health at a national level has rapidly moved up the political agenda. Integrated health and social community mental health teams (CMHT) have been seen as crucial in driving community care forwards. However, in many areas setting up the CMHT has been seen as the end, rather than the beginning of the process needed for implementation.

Identification and needs assessment of the severely mentally ill

At all level in the development of the core components of comprehensive service there is a need to establish strategic and operational plans. These must be underpinned by a systematic analysis of the service needed. This involves, in each local area, over a one to three year timetable, the establishment of a data base of the number and needs of individuals with SMI in the area. The OPCS national morbidity survey (1995) has produced surprising findings of wider variation in the prevalence of psychosis in England than has previously been identified. This varies from 0.2% in affluent areas to 0.9% in more deprived areas.

Of those with psychiatric morbidity, it is likely that only a proportion will be in contact with the specialist mental health services, Between 25–40% may be in contact only with their GP, social services, the housing agencies, police, local churches or user groups. A co-ordinated strategy between agencies is needed in order to develop an identification component of the service. This requires joint strategic planning and operational working between health, housing, social services and voluntary sector staff.

Table 3: *Sources of contact of people with SMI*

1	**Mental Health Service Contacts**
	Outpatient attenders
	CPN case-load and depot clinic patients
	Mental Health Act data
	Domiciliary visit records
	Crisis attenders eg A/E attenders
	In-patient audit data
	Residents of long-stay institutions
2	**Primary Care Team Contacts**
	Practice register diagnosis of psychosis
	Repeat psychotropic drug prescriptions
	Frequent emergency and other consultations
	Hostel/group home/sheltered residence populations
	CPN attenders
	Health visits case notes
3	**Social Service Contacts**
	Area social worker case-loads
	Care management recipients
	Housing department clients causing concern
4	**Voluntary Sector and other Agency Contacts**
	Residents of sheltered accommodation
	Individuals presenting to churches in distress
	Individuals causing local beat officers concern
	Imprisoned and homeless people
	Probation officer case-loads
	Drop-in and other casual facility users
	User groups

Table 3 indicates the likely contact points of people with SMI. In many services nationally the implementation of the Care Programme Approach (CPA) and care management have been used as the vehicles to agree a local inter-agency definition of SMI (see chapter 2), and audit the number of SMI in contact with the service compared with that expected from the epidemiological data.

Needs assessment for rational service planning

Having identified individuals with SMI in the area, the next step is the introduction of a system of needs assessment. In services where CPA and Care Management have been integrated, the agreed inter-agency definition of the priority group for services has facilitated agreement on the categories of needs to be assessed. The routine collection of a clinical data set and care planning assessment and review is vital and when incorporated into the CMHT culture has the following effects: it ensures that services are developed based on the aggregated needs of patients, it informs the case for resources, it facilitates multi-agency co-ordination of services planning and delivery, it is vital at a national level for the mental health agenda.

Despite the many standardised assessment instruments in mental heath, remarkably few are used in routine clinical practice. This discrepancy may be because, although many instruments are helpful in monitoring symptoms they do not lead directly to inform decision making or management plans. In general, any innovation which is seen as a time-consuming addition to, rather than an integral part of, routine clinical practice is unlikely to succeed. Newer instruments are a first stage in combining research validity with practical application. These include the Health of the Nation Outcome Scales and the Camberwell Assessment of Need (Phelan *et al.* 1995).

Case management and assertive outreach services

To meet the complex needs of people with SMI case management as a service or at least a technique is essential in drawing together all the necessary services into one coherent package of care. In practice, case management for the long-term mentally ill has developed into a range of techniques that can be described along 12 different axes (Thornicroft, 1990), which aim to ensure that patients with long-term psychiatric disorders receive consistent and continuing services for as long as they are required. Studies have compared a number of models of case management which offer acute home-based care with hospital care (Test & Stein, 1980; Hoult *et al*, 1984; Muijen, *et al*,1992).

Despite differences in the models and evaluative methodologies used, these and several other studies confirm a decrease in hospital admissions, improvement in clinical outcomes and social functioning and greater patient satisfaction from acute home-orientated care. However case management cannot be regarded as a panacea for success. The lessons from the USA is that 'in many settings the response to the lack of basic services for clients has been to let them eat case management' (Goldman, 1981). It is only effective where those practising employ effective intervention techniques and where it is supported by an adequate infra-structure of resources.

Hospital & community beds

People with schizophrenia account for 60% of all in-patient bed use in mental health units. The context of the current funding distribution is that in some areas as little as 10%, and on average only 25%, of the total mental health budget is available to community work. This makes it essential that use of hospital beds, the most expensive resource is necessary, high quality and based on sound therapeutic reasons. A great deal of controversy has surrounded the number, use and management of acute mental health beds. The success of community based services is crucially related to the nature and availability of accommodation with appropriate levels of support and to developing a wide range of hospital and community beds. These should range from responsive and community-sensitive secure facilities for mentally disordered offenders, through acute hospital beds, 24 hour staffed units in hospital hostels and community places for the new long stay, especially those with mild to moderate challenging behaviours, and a range of community beds for crisis diversion, quarter-and half-way hostel purposes, respite facilities to residential and permanent accommodation, (see chapters 11 and 16).

In developing the core services, however it is essential that two major problems identified in a large number of services nationally are addressed. These are the failure to plan accommodation for the newer and younger people with severe and enduring mental health disorders and the revolving door syndrome of such patients into acute hospital beds. Lelliott and Wing's (1994) study of the new long-stay found that 61% of patients were considered to be inappropriately placed in hospital beds, 47% required a community based residential setting, and of these over half were in hospital because no suitable community placement was available. Several analyses of acute bed unit use indicate that: 30–70% of those in the beds are 'revolving door regulars', well known to services, that a significant proportion had been readmitted within three months of discharge and due to a lack to provide of high support community accommodation and effective discharge planning mechanisms.

Crisis response services

Individuals with SMI are vulnerable to environmental stressors which may result in exacerbations of symptoms and relapse, and episodes of acute illness. Successful mental health services must aim to provide support and help for the client, family members, and others to cope with the emergency while maintaining the client's status as a functioning community member to the greatest extent. Studies of users, carers and GPs produce almost interchangeable findings. All want crisis services to be available at a single point of telephone or face to face contact. They would value services on a 24-hour, 7-day basis, manned by experienced and known mental health professionals and providing crisis diversion facilities as a viable alternative to hospitalisation. Nationally this type of service is provided by a limited number of teams. Even when the SMI are in contact with specialist mental health services it is often the GP or casualty staff with limited training who provide the majority of crisis care. Shifting services from routine work hours to more comprehensive care has to be done on an incremental basis with appropriate care taken to ensure adequate safety and risk management training for staff.

Day care and rehabilitation programmes

In a comprehensive review, Holloway (1988) defines three possible functions of the day hospital for the severely mentally ill; an alternative to hospital admission when acutely ill; provision of support, supervision and monitoring in the transition between hospital and home; source of long-term structure and support for those with chronic handicaps; site for brief intensive therapy for those who require short-term focused rehabilitation; an information, training and communication resource. Wood also stresses the importance of user consultation and the formation of formal liaison with all local providers of work, education and day care, (see chapter 18).

Assessment and consultation service

Until the past few decades the majority of consultation services were conducted in hospital outpatient settings. Evaluation of these services indicates dissatisfaction with communication patterns, clinical and referrer outcomes and up to 45% non-attendance. The response of many clinicians, uniformed by policy or research considerations was to work on a sessional basis in primary care centres. Early criticisms of the clinics was that they would result in psychiatrists serving only the worried well. The evidence refutes this. They provide a service to groups of the SMI who previously dropped out of contact with the specialist services ie. women with long-term disorders, young men with schizophrenia, the homeless with psychosis and those with paranoid disorders who felt stigmatised by attendance at a hospital site (Tyrer, 1984).

In many community services community psychiatric nurses were the first to develop attachments to particular general practices. Where the nurses have been hospital based and work as members of the secondary care term, 80% of their referrals are from psychiatrists and individuals with SMI form a considerable proportion of their workload. In other organisations, nurses, although employed by secondary care services are attached to particular general practices, the referral pattern shifts with 80% of their referrals coming direct from GPs. Caseloads tend to be large, composed of patients with neurotic and adjustments disorders. Although the caseloads of both the hospital based and primary care based CPNs remain similar in terms of the numbers of individuals with SMI, the mean time in contact with psychotic patients is a third of the time spent with non-psychotic patients and almost entirely limited to the administration of injections.

Community services and effective interventions

Much of the traditional training in mental health focuses on the development of clinical skills at the level of the individual client. Few initiatives address the major service development training agenda and the implementation into practice of the lessons learnt from rigorous and systematic research. This particularly relates to the teaching of effective intervention skills in community mental health teams. An analysis of the skills of the community workers and funding dedicated for training in acquiring new skills are essential for community care to succeed (Conway *et al.* 1996). Table 4 is not comprehensive but outlines some of the most important core skills which community workers should possess.

Table 4:   Training in core interventions

Core interventions for people with severe mental illness

Housing with adequate support
Welfare benefits and financial advice
Physical and dental care
Medication
Psychoeducation programmes
Behavioural-Cognitive therapy for psychotic symptoms
Identification & development of coping strategies
Crisis Contracts
Family problem solving therapy & lowering EE
Rehabilitation
Practical skills and support
Day care
Work and education

Psychosocial interventions

In a recent comprehensive review researchers found up to 45% of the severely mentally ill do not apply for or receive their entitlements to welfare benefits. The provision of welfare benefits to provide an adequate standard of living is a major priority for service users. 'Motivation' to attend for day care programmes or out-patient clinics is likely to increase when the choice between spending money on a bus fare to attend has to be made against buying food is no longer an issue. Likewise having permanent, affordable, comfortable housing is important in achieving a stable mental state free of worries about rent, damp, harassing neighbours etc. Craig's (1994) studies of the homeless has shown that outcomes are improved when care programmes include interventions which address housing needs.

Physical health and dental care

Co-existing physical morbidity is common in patients with SMI. In a study of long-term day centre attenders, Brugha et. al. (1989) found that forty-one percent suffered medical problems potentially requiring care. Annual physical review as a minimum should be arranged with the GP by the patient's keyworker. The development of consensus guidelines for the management of long-term mental health disorders are evolving and should be of practical implementation value (Strathdee & Kendrick, 1995; Tylee, 1995).

Medication and psychoeductional programmes

Medication is an important element in the management of many of those with SMI in the acute and longer-term phases of their illness. It can however be toxic in misuse and produce long-term irreversible side effects. It is important that practitioners familiarise themselves with good practices in medication prescribing, regular review, tailoring of both medication type and dosage to the individual needs of patients which will alter between acute and continuing care phases and monitor side effects. The publication of recent good practice guidelines in the prescription and administration will have assisted practitioners address these issues and incorporate good practice and mechanisms for monitoring it into their CHMTs (Thompson, 1995). Where easily accessible psychoeducational packages of information on conditions, treatments, (preferably developed jointly with users and carers) collaboration with treatment is enhanced and relapse prevention increased.

Family and carer education, support and therapies

Adequate, early treatment, associated with client, family, and staff education and training can prevent the onset of many crises (Birchwood *et al*, 1989). For example, for reductions in family disruption, physical and mental disorders, and perceived burden after structured family interventions. Because of the episodic nature of the illness, however, there will be instances that require acute care and rapid response crisis stabilization services. The need to see the individual in the context of his or her family environment is well understood. Six controlled studies have illustrated the impact of wider intervention packages on relapse rates in households with high EE. Successful programmes contain the following features: a problem focused approach to reduce expressed emotion and stress in the home environment, an educational component, long-term application for six to nine months, involvement of the patient in the family treatment, well trained intervention staff and close liaison with members of the clinical team and other agencies, (Kuipers & Bebbington, 1988).

Effective leadership, management and organisation of CHMTs

It can be argued that in the British development of community services we have too slavishly followed other countries in their failure to move towards community care as integrated teams involving all disciplines and agencies. The effective care of patients with SMI requires the skills of nurses, occupational therapists, psychologists, social workers and psychiatrists. No one discipline working autonomously has the range of skills required if clinical and social outcomes are to be improved. The development of such practices in this country has resulted in many of the criticisms of the national reviews described above. Both the Audit Commission and the Mental Health Taskforce London studies found that the development of community service which targeted the SMI was most advanced in those areas where there were integrated health and social CMHTs with clear management structures and when the organisational issues outlined in Table 5 have been clarified.

Table 5: *Core organisational issues in the organisation of CMHTs*

Multi-disciplinary and inter-agency integrated working

Acute generic CMHT or dedicated specialist team members

Sector specific case-managers or central rehabilitation service

Control over hospital beds

Team member responsibility for development of service components

Operational policy to allow focus on SMI

Acceptable policies for the care of the non SMI

In the majority of services CMHTs are generic ie they provide care to both new referrals, those requiring acute care and also those with SMI. Unless effective management systems are in place to ensure a continuing prioritisation of the most needy and vulnerable, the drift towards treating the less ill is well described. Services have developed a number of organisational formats to prevent this trend. In some areas a dedicated case management and assertive outreach team serves a limited number of those with SMI across several sectors. Within generic sector teams there are a number of strategies. Agreed case-loads/case-mix are regularly monitored to ensure that the proportion of those with SMI remains high. An additional strategy is the appointment of specialist case managers or rehabilitation experts within the generic team. For them to develop or retain specialist expertise they have dual membership of both their generic sector team and a district wide rehabilitation service. In areas where the prevalence of SMI is high, sectors have divided their total pool of staff resource to form two sector teams, one providing acute care while the other provides case management and specialist rehabilitation services which emphasise normalisation and community integration. Whatever the arrangement case-loads must be realistic, requiring of the order of one case manager for fifteen patients requiring assertive outreach and high levels of input. The ratio extends to one to thirty-forty where the individuals in the caseload have had comprehensive assessments, well developed care plans, are stable, engaged and trusting of services offered, rehearsed relapse prevention and crisis contracts and well supported by a range of community agencies.

Conclusion

The development of an operational policy is a re-requisite for the effective working of any CMHT (Ovretveit at al., 1986) serves as a useful basis for both team building and service development. Onyett has described the management techniques which ensure focused working of CMHT's. In Britain psychiatry we have a consensus about the range of services we need to offer, the interventions we recognise as effective and the outcomes we hope to achieve. Effective organisation and management of CMHTs is an essential building block to the future. There is no standard blueprint. Success depends on a shared vision at local level, alliances forged between community agencies and solutions developed based on local strengths and resources.

References

Audit Commission (1994). Funding a Place, HMSO, London.

Birchwood, M., Smith, J., Macmillan, F., Hogg, B., Prasad, R., Harvey, C. & Bering, S. (1989). Predicting relapse in schizophrenia: the development and implementation of an early signs monitoring system using patients and families as observers, a preliminary investigation. *Psychological Medicine*, **19**, 649–656.

Brugha, T. S., Wing, J. K. & Smith, B. L. (1989). Physical ill-health of the long-term mentally ill in the community. Is there an unmet need? *The British Journal of Psychiatry*. **155**: 777–82

Conway, M., Shepherd, G. & Melzer, D. (1996). Effectiveness of interventions for mental illness and implications for commissioning. In Thornicroft G & Strathdee, G. *Commissioning Mental Health Services* (1996). HMSO, London.

Craig, T. (1994). *The Homeless Mentally Ill Initiative. An Evaluation.* London HMSO.

Department of Health. (1994) *The Health of the Nation. Key Area Handbook. Mental Illness,* 2nd edition. HMSO. London.

Goldman, H. (1981). Defining and counting the chronically mentally ill. *Hospital and Community Psychiatry.* **32**, 21–27.

Holloway, F. (1988). Day care and community support. In Lavenders, A. & Holloway, F (eds). *Community Care in Practice*, Chichester: Wiley.

Hoult, J., & Reynolds, I. (1984). Schizophrenia: a comprehensive trial of community oriented and hospital oriented psychiatric care. *Acta Psychiatrica Scandanavica* **69**, 359–372.

House of Commons Health Select Committee. (1994) *Better Off in the Community? The Care of People who are Seriously Mentally Ill.* HMSO. London.

Kuipers, E. & Bebbington, P, (1988). Expressed emotion research in schizophrenia – thearetical and clinical implications. *Psychological Medicine*, **18**, 893–909.

Lelliott, P.; & Wing, J. National audit of new long-stay psychiatric patients. 2:Impact on services. *British Journal of Psychiatry* 1994, **165**: 160–169.

Mental Health Foundation (1994) *Creating Community Care.* London. MHF.

Muijen, M., Marks, I., Connolly, J. & Audini, B. (1992) Home based care and standard hospital care for patients with severe mental illness: a randomized controlled trial. *British Meical Journal*, **304**, 749–754.

Ovretweit, J. (1986). Case responsibility in multi-disciplinary teams (BIOSS). London. *Good Practices in Mental Health.*

Phelan, M., Slade, M., Thornicroft, G., Dunn, D., Holloway, F., Wyles, T., Strathdee, G., Loftus, L., McCrone, P. & Haywood, P. (1995). The Camberwell Assessment of Need (CAN): the validity and reliability of an instrument to assess the needs of people with severe mental illness. *British Journal of Psychiatry*, **167**, 589–595.

Stein, L., Test, M. (1980). Alternative to mental hospital treatment. I Conceptual model, treatment program and clinical evaluation. *Archives of General Psychiatry*, **37**, 392–397.

Stevens, A. & Gabbay, J. (1991). Needs assessment, needs assessment. *Health Trends*, **23**, 20–23.

Thompson, K., Phelan, M., Strathdee, G. & Shiress, D (1995). *Mental Health Care; a guide for housing workers*. London: PRiSM and Mental Health Foundation.

Thornicroft, G. (1990). The concept of case management for long-term mental illness. *International Review of Psychiatry*, **3**, 125–132.

Tyrer, P. (1984). Psychiatric clinics in general practice: an extension of community care. *British Journal of Psychiatry*, **145**: 9–14. Chapt 13 ref.

4 Commissioning and Managing Hospital and Community Beds

GERALDINE STRATHDEE, SARA DAVIES, MAURICE PERRY and KELLY THOMPSON

Introduction

This chapter aims to provide the reader with a knowledge base to assist in the commissioning and planning of the range of hospital and community beds which are an essential part of any comprehensive mental health service system. A number of fundamental tenets underpin the work presented. Beds or places whether in hospitals or the community are a very important part, but only one part, of a total mental health service system. Their planning and development will be influenced by the range of other resources available. The number and nature of beds is inextricably linked to the presence or absence of the other key service components. Local levels of morbidity and provision across the different sectors are also major determinants of bed requirements. Bed use in any area is likely to be affected by the availability of levels of acute and non-acute, hospital and community based, statutory and non-statutory provision.

The majority of research in this area has focused on acute bed numbers and there is no agreed formula which takes into account the factors outlined above. The successful development of beds in any area must be underpinned by a systematic and comprehensive analysis of the number of individuals with mental health disorders who are likely to require a bed of whatever type. The process of securing the most cost-effective solution in any area is best informed by a thorough analysis of what is already available and planned by all agencies including health, housing, social services, voluntary and independent sectors. This chapter therefore needs to be read in the context of chapters 11, 13 and 16 on the core components of a mental health service system and the housing perspective.

This chapter cannot comprehensively review all the issues surrounding the provision of 'beds'. Firstly, there is a review of the research and audit information on current costs and levels of mental health beds. This focuses on presenting some of the key findings in the national picture of bed provision, describes some of the major concerns surrounding this important service component including the difficulties encountered in the provision of acute bed services and the current lack of appropriate provision for the new long stay. It summarises the factors which influence bed requirements and examines and reviews current patterns of bed use. It examines the evidence on bed number calculations for any local area and reviews methods to audit bed use. Alternatives to hospital bed use and effective evidence based methods for bed management are described. A checklist for use by purchasers to assist in planning, commissioning and auditing bed use more effectively summarises the work.

Numbers and costs of mental health beds

Until the community care movement of the 1960s and beyond, the majority of psychiatric care in this country was provided in the large psychiatric institutions. The policies of the last four decades have consistently advocated a move to develop local, accessible and community orientated services (Health of the Nation Key area Handbook: mental illness, 1993). The number of psychiatric in-patient beds has fallen from 149,700 in 1955, through 89,000 in 1978-79 to around 50,000 in 1991-2 (Thornicroft & Bebbington, 1989). Despite this, the majority of the mental health budget is still spent on the in-patient component of care. In 1992/3 the total amount spent on mental health services in England was £2.6 billion. This consisted of £1780m for in-patient care, £160m for out-patients, £120m for day patients and £250m for community services. This excludes specific primary care or residential costs (Clinical Standards Advisory Group on Schizophrenia 1995). The appropriate and effective use of beds is therefore essential in any mental health service commissioning strategy.

The relationship between bed provision and use and mental ill health

There are clearly difficulties in the current national development of the range of hospital and community beds and concern has grown that the planning and development of appropriate beds for the community care policies has been inadequate and inappropriate. The situation raises a number of key questions. Have the old long stay patients from the institutions been discharged to inadequate provision and ended up in prison or exploited? Have the mentally ill merely become homeless in the absence of a range of beds? Are there too few acute beds in many areas or is the use of these beds rendered inappropriate because of inadequate development of other options? How do the current policies on development of housing with support for special needs groups impact on the mentally ill?

Various studies have attempted to answer these questions. The Mental Health Task Force Survey of English mental hospitals: (Davidge et al, 1993) found that 53% of beds were still for long-stay clients, 43% could be defined as short-stay and 4% as secure. The overall number of beds and residential places had decreased slowly from 92,000 to 85,000 between 1982-1992 and from 1992-1993 there had been an increase of 2000 to 87,000. However there had been a change in the distribution of providers with 63% of beds provided by the NHS and an increase in private sector provision both for acute care and residential places.

In their survey of adult mental health services, Faulkner et al (1994) undertook a comprehensive examination of bed provision nationally. They found little correlation between need and provision and little association between the range of services and bed numbers. There was no association between residential care provision and the number of acute or long-stay beds in any area. The number of residential beds had no strong association with socio-demographic or service variables. They identified a significant increase in the independent sector provision of beds which almost exactly parallels the reduction in long-stay beds. Higher levels of community beds were associated with the presence of community based continuing care teams with no associated reduction in the number of acute beds.

Community housing with support

The use of hospital beds, as indicated above, is influenced by many factors starting with the level of housing in the community. The relationship between mental ill health and the provision of housing is well researched. At one end of the spectrum are the homeless. 450,000 to 750,000 homeless people in the UK suffer from serious mental illness; as many as 66% of the homeless in London suffer from schizophrenia and in direct access hostels this figure rises to as many as 75%. In a major study of homelessness, Craig (1994) and his colleagues in four clinical teams set up to deal with the homeless reported that, for 88% of clients, the first episode of homelessness occurred after the onset of mental illness and in a third of cases, the loss of accommodation was a direct result of mental health problems.

However, it is not just the number of housing places which is important. The levels of support must be equally appropriate. The Mental Health Foundation report (1994) recorded a situation where nearly 25% of the homeless mentally ill had been in general needs housing before they became homeless, but were unable to retain their places due to mismanagement, eviction due to arrears, and lack of mental health care and support from psychiatric services. Even when special teams are set up to provide mental health care, without adequate attention to housing factors, 20% of the homeless seriously mentally ill fall out of contact with psychiatric outreach teams (Craig 1994). Interventions which tackle either mental health or housing conditions alone were found not to prevent subsequent services failures, while only 10% of clients who showed improvement in both mental state and accommodation subsequently defaulted from care (Meltzer *et al*, 1991).

Acute bed use and pressures

In the past few years concern has grown about the lack of provision for the 'new long-stay' i.e. those individuals with severe and enduring mental health disorders who have never been institutionalised. In the first enthusiasm of community care such a long-term group were thought to be rendered a problem of the past by virtue of new treatment systems. There is accruing evidence that these patients, in fact aggregate at a rate of 1-2/100,000 per year (Lelliott & Wing, 1994) and are the ones who are most often inappropriately placed. Acute bed occupancy rates have been recorded at between 90 - 130%, (the variation being partly explained by the inclusion or exclusion of patients on leave from beds at the time of the census). In their analysis of services both in London and forty districts nationally (Lelliott, 1995; Lelliott & Wing, 1994) found that nearly 65% of patients in acute psychiatric beds could be in non-hospital settings, if appropriate supported accommodation was available. 33% acute beds were taken by "new long stay", 14% patients could be with families or living independently, if support was provided and 50% patients who could not be transferred because a suitable facility did not exist or suitable facilities were full or no facility could be found to accept the degree of disability. Other explanations for the unacceptable high occupancy rates of acute beds included: a lack of adequately supported sheltered accommodation in the community, increased incidence and relapse rates among ethnic minorities (King *et al*, 1994) a reduction in available admission beds in some areas (Mental Health Taskforce, London, 1994) and the increased demand for admission beds placed by former long-stay patients resettled in the community.

Corroboration has come from a one day census of acute and low-level secure patients was carried out across all in-patient units in North and South Thames regions (1994). The study found that 42% of the patients had schizophrenia, black people were over represented (15.3% patients were black compared to 4.3% of the population, 10% were homeless. Over a quarter had been in hospital for more than three months and almost half had been admitted to a psychiatric facility one or more times in the previous year, just under a quarter more than twice. More than half had not been assessed for Local Authority care management even though in almost half, inappropriate placement was regarded as the main reason for their remaining on an acute ward. The most frequently recorded services required for safe and appropriate discharge were supported accommodation, group homes and in-patient rehabilitation.

Factors influencing bed use

Table 1 demonstrates the complex interplay of factors which determine bed use. The relative roles within each area will be determined by local circumstances.

Table 1:   *Factors affecting bed usage*

- individual related factors
- available service components
- use of bed management strategies
- staffing levels
- treatments offered
- organisation of the mental health services
- local inter-agency provision

Individual determinants of bed use

The individual related factors which are known to increase the use of hospital beds are outlined in Table 2. Those with Severe Mental Illness (SMI) are most likely to have the greatest use of hospital beds. Therefore it is crucial for strategic service planning that they are identified and their needs given priority if the use of hospital beds is to be appropriate and efficient and if a redeployment of resources is to become a reality.

Table 2: *Individual factors which influence bed usage*

Patient factors which increase psychiatric hospital bed usage

Socio-demographic factors:	Young Male sex Lower socio-economic class Black Live alone or in unsupported accommodation Have no carer
Clinical factors:	SMI including schizophrenia, manic-depressive psychosis and other psychoses Vulnerability to suicidal or forensic behaviours Concomitant physical morbidity Dual diagnoses—concurrent alcohol or drug abuse
Previous pattern of service use:	Recently discharge from psychiatric hospitals/institutions Multiple previous admissions Minimal insight or control over their illness Poor collaboration with medication and other treatment strategies No trusting relationship with carers or professionals Previous detention under the Mental Health Act

Service component which influence bed use

The Health of the Nation Key Area Handbook (1995) sets out a consensus of the components of a comprehensive mental health service (Table 3). This section summarises briefly how a number of them may impact on bed use.

Table 3: *Components of a mental health service which influence bed use*

Service components which influence bed use
Case identification, CPA register & needs assessment
Crisis response services
Hospital and community places
Assertive outreach and care management services
Day care
Assessment and consultation services
Carer and community education and support
Primary care liaison
User advocacy and community alliances

Case registers and needs assessment services

A significant proportion of the severely mentally ill who are most likely to use hospital beds are not in contact with the secondary mental health services. The South Camden Schizophrenia study undertaken by Pantellis *et al.* (1992) and the long-term follow-up of people with severe depression (Lee & Murray, 1991) indicate that the percentage who have either fallen from all care or are only in contact with social, housing, primary care or voluntary agencies may be as much as 45%. This figure reduces where community services are accessible and well established. It is important to note for planning purposes that in the early stages of increased accessibility of newly established community services, the number of individuals identified as needing the services can rise by as much as 30%. This frequently occurs when services are reducing hospital beds while concurrently developing community services.

Rational planning of bed numbers is likely to be more effective where the majority of those with severe and long-term difficulties are known and have had their needs assessed. This includes their housing and monetary needs. Although some of the severely mentally ill lead transient lives, this is often as a consequence of their inappropriate housing and support, rather than a preference for a nomadic existence. Giving priority to identifying the SMI allows the establishment of case registers which in many areas are composed of the Care Programme Approach registers. Without a detailed knowledge of the numbers and needs of the SMI in any area it is impossible to accurately predict bed use and therefore to plan and develop an adequate number of beds.

Crisis intervention services

When available on a 24 hour day, 7 day basis, crisis intervention services can prevent inappropriate hospital admission. The model of crisis team operating in this is a long established feature in Australian community mental health (Houltway & Reynolds, 1984) and is a growing development in the UK (Tyrer, 1994). However, currently the majority of crisis services provided nationally are in accident and emergency departments and largely by staff inexperienced in assessing and treating mental health problems (Johnson & Thornicroft, 1995). In order to be effective crisis services need to be available on a 24 hour, 7 days a week basis. There is universal agreement between users, carers and GPs about the qualities which denote an effective crisis services. This includes: a single rapid access point of contact, a rapid response within 24 - 48 hours, rapid access to social services for assessment under the Mental Health Act, assessment and treatment by experienced workers, preferably who already know the client, are trained in effective interventions, can undertake home based treatments and provide follow-up for those who have made para-suicide attempts.

Assertive outreach and care management services in community mental health teams

National studies indicate that British Community Mental Health Centres and community teams have replicated the American experience of failing to prioritise the SMI and drifting to treating the less severely ill. This, in effect means that the most vulnerable people must become self-sufficient in terms of obtaining and co-ordinating their own care. One of the consequences of mental illness in those who suffer the most severe forms is that they can find it difficult to lead organised and 'timetabled' lives, and in addition are reluctant to access traditional services. This occurs both as a result of cognitive impairment and is not helped by the very negative experiences and perceptions often held by those who have experienced frequent hospitalisation. The result is that many mental health service users fail to obtain the co-ordinated package of health and social treatments they need. A response to such problems has been to develop assertive outreach and case management teams. These specialist teams have provided each user with a named worker who co-ordinates the total package of care. Attention is paid to the process of engagement of the user into the service. The Assertive outreach function means that the teams do not necessarily expect reluctant users to come to them and will make real efforts to find them out wherever they are. Research indicates that for a minority of the most severely ill assertive outreach care plans are essential if they are not to fall from the safety 'net' of care. If these methods are to be applied on an extensive level nationally, however there is a major training agenda for Community Mental Health Teams.

Day care and assessment services

Day hospitals and centres form an important role in preventing unnecessary hospital admission (Holloway, 1988). Likewise, moving out-patient clinics into GP surgeries, has, in some areas had an impact on hospital admission rates, both in decreasing admission rates and length of stay. Primary care clinics can attract back into care the homeless, women and young men with paranoid symptoms who fall out of traditional hospital care (Tyrer, 1984). Improving liaison with primary care teams can facilitate early intervention and relapse prevention. The non attendance rates for psychiatric out-patient appointments has been reported as up to 45%. Unless there is assertive follow up of patients who fail to attend arranged appointments with clear guidelines for crisis management and discharge planning patients become lost to the mental health services. The history of Christopher Clunis (Ritchie Report, 1994) is an illustration of this.

Interventions which prevent relapse

The range of effective and evidence based interventions which affect relapse rates and therefore use of beds include psychoeducational care packages as a routine when medication is prescribed, family problem-solving therapies, provision of adequate housing and welfare benefits, behavioural-cognitive therapies, relapse prevention interventions. However, very few staff are trained in such techniques and there is evidence that many patients receive only medication in inadequate treatment regimes (Thompson *et al*, 1995). Likewise, despite the evidence, few services engage adequately with carers who can play a vital role in relapse prevention and decrease hospital admission.

Staffing levels and configuration

The provision of an adequate staffing structure is equally important. In order for a community mental health team to function effectively, consideration has to be paid to issues of skill mix and caseload/casemix. The balance of trained staff and well supervised support workers is crucial if safe, appropriate care is to be provided. Stein and Test, two proponents of community care, consider that an adequate level of staffing should be:

1:10   For individuals who are very disorganised, frequently relapse, seldom come to mental health provisions, have poor understanding of their illnesses and who need frequent assertive outreach.

1:15   For individuals who will occasionally come to services, work in a collaborative way with treatment regimes but still have frequent relapses.

1:40   For individuals who have been involved in psychoeducational initiatives, can predict and control relapses on occasions, have a trusting relationship with carer or professional and will seek help when appropriate.

1:200   For individuals who require infrequent contact, often with only intermittent outpatient care, who are in work and have control over their illness.

Towards a system of planning bed use

In determining the nature and volume of beds required in the mental health system, it is helpful to define the role which 'beds' must fulfil. The functions range from: a home for life, respite from a stressful home or environmental situation, assessment of a new or recurring problem, treatment in an acute episode where there is a high risk of either self-harm or harm to others, rehabilitation, short, medium or long-term management of challenging behaviour. The older style asylums often accommodated many of these functions on one site. In current community-orientated services, there is a need to develop a range of facilities which serve these multiple and necessary functions in an efficient and cost-effective manner. In any local area developing an appropriate configuration of modern day 'beds', the level of provision depends on the severity of the problems, the degree of risk, the availability of alternatives and the level of management and organisation of the mental health service system.

Table 4: *Estimated numbers of places required in residential settings for "ideal" mental health service for population of 250,000*

Type of Provision	Range of Places
24 hour staffed residences	40–150
Day staffed residences	30–120
Acute psychiatric care	50–125
Unstaffed group homes	48–80
Adult placement schemes	0–15
Local secure places	5–10
Respite facilities	0–5
Regional secure unit	1–10

Table 4 indicates the number of beds required in any mental health service. (Wing, 1992; Strathdee & Thornicroft, 1992). As can be seen the variation is large and can be partly explained by the significant differences in morbidity across districts. The OPCS National Psychiatric Morbidity Survey (1995) has demonstrated four fold variation in levels of morbidity between rural and urban inner city areas. There are many reasons for this which include: the relationship to levels of deprivation, degree of homelessness and mobility of population, crime rates with drug abuse.

There are numerous problems with calculating necessary bed numbers: firstly, the lack of an agreed definition of levels of support, lack of agreement about models, for example should they be hospital based, community sited or in DGHs. Decisions about acute bed numbers have most often been made in the past based on Jarman indicators in a local community (Jarman, 1983; Jarman & Hirsch, 1992). However these indicators are merely based on the average utilisation figures for communities with equivalent socio-demographic characteristics. Table 5 presents a framework for analysis of the levels of support

155

and the continuum of residential places necessary in the community if acute bed use is to be optimal.

Table 5: *The continuum of supported accommodation needed for people with mental health disorders*

Level	Accommodation type
1	Permanent LA or private housing with support
2	Housing with support to prevent eviction, assist payment of rent
3	Housing with day-time domiciliary supervision
4	Group homes with supervision (non-professional)
5	As 4 with support from visiting professional staff
6	Sheltered boarding and lodging out schemes
7	Supervised hostels with residential staff
8	As 7 with duty nursing staff
9	Intensive supervision hostel or hostel-ward
10	Basic nursing unit

Classification of types of supported accommodation drawn from (Wing & Furlong, 1986; Thompson, 1995).

This draws on the original work of Wing & Furlong (1986) but takes into account detailed analysis of surveys of provision across several agencies (Thompson *et al*, 1995; Lelliott *et al*, 1995; Faulkner *et al*. 1994). Defining support levels requires analysis of the number of places in the residence, the staff : client ratio; the percentage of trained to untrained staff; percentage of qualified nursing staff, level of cover from staff who are awake at night and availability of staff on call and present on a 24 hour, 7 day basis. Provision at the lower levels of support is much more common.

Analysing acute bed use

Bebbington *et al*. (1994) developed a helpful bed audit technique in analysing the reasons for bed use in an acute hospital setting. They undertook a one-day census of all patients in acute beds in an inner London unit. In order to determine the reasons for the admission and to consider its appropriateness they collected information in ten categories which they felt would have influenced admission. This was done by analysing information from the case notes and by interviewing the keyworker. Their findings, for the very deprived inner city are where they worked were that: almost all admissions had been for a relapse of a schizophrenic or manic depressive episode, one third had been in-patients in the previous month, 57% lived alone while a further 27% lived with relatives, only 7% of the admissions were planned and almost one quarter were compulsory admissions. Similarly, one of the most consistent findings of the Mental Health Taskforce London study (1995) was that between 30 - 70% of acute in-patients are 'revolving door regulars'. In Bebbington *et al*'s study keyworkers considered that 65% of the patients would have been more appropriately managed in 'a high supervision hostel with good staffing levels, able to cope with acute disturbances day or night. In their national audit of new long-stay patients, Lellitt and Wing (1994) found similar figures.

Acute bed blocking and service gaps

As indicated above, acute beds are only one part of a total service system. Hospital beds are often occupied by individuals who no longer need 24 hour, 7 day nursing care but still need specialist input. Perhaps one of the most important gaps in the majority of British services are those for what has been termed the 'new long stay'. They can be defined as those aged 16 - 64 years, with chronic and severe mental health disorders who require: daily monitoring of their mental state due to chronic psychosis, frequent monitoring of risk of violence either towards self or others, storage, administration and supervision of medication on daily basis, skilled management of challenging behaviour, provision of crisis intervention at night if required, assistance with self care and daily living skills, supervision to attend day care and rehabilitation activities, integrated working with multi-disciplinary and multi-agency teams.

Analysis of bed blocking

Analysis of many community services (Audit Commission 1994; and Mental Health Taskforce London, 1994) indicate that many individuals currently occupying acute beds could be more appropriately located in 24 hour nursed staffed facilities. Table 6 suggests a method of analysis for such a group.

Table 6: *Analysis of categories of acute 'bed blockers' to inform the planning of appropriate alternatives*

Category of individual requiring 24 hour nurse care	Expected length of stay in such facilities	Current location
Admission diversion those with acute psychosis who are not sufficiently at risk either to themselves or others to need admission to hospital beds but who require monitoring and supervision by staff with a trained nurse available on a 24 hour basis	1–6 weeks	Acute beds or unsafe at home
Planned respite those who have relapses on a regular basis and for whom planned respite from environmental stresses will prevent relapse	1–8 weeks	Acute beds or unsafe at home
Improved after acute relapse those currently blocking acute beds who have recovered to the extent that they no longer require the full range of medical and nurse services but who are still sufficiently unwell to need 24 hour care. Their length of stay can be between 1 - 6 months (in the acute unit)	1–8 weeks	
New long stay the new long-stay who have been in an acute hospital bed for more than six months and less than five years	6–24 months	Acute beds or in unsafe and inadequate accommodation in the community
Challenging behaviour those with a history of violence and challenging behaviours who are rejected by the majority of housing associations. This may include those on a section 37/41.	6–24 months	Acute beds, prison MSUs, private sector ECRs
Half-way rehabilitation setting those who require a rehabilitative environment which includes the need for supervised medication and mental state and risk assessment out of a hospital setting.	6–18 months	acute beds

Community alternatives to hospital beds

Community alternatives which complement hospital beds include admission diversion facilities, facilities which increase throughput, longer term rehabilitation and halfway hostels, and community accommodation for mentally disordered offenders. Table 7 indicates some of the national and international models used. Additional examples of alternative provision in the UK include: the unstaffed crisis flat at Bassetlaw; the Nunhead crisis and respite houses and Lyme Brook community mental health centre beds.

Table 7: *Alternatives to hospital beds*

Non-hospital based residential alternatives

Name	Description
Psychiatric Health Facility	Described in the USA; small 9- 40 bedded units established in a non-hospital setting for acute short-term treatment; 24 hour staffing which is usually less trained than in a psychiatric hospital; Variable length of time for admission; as an alternative to admission to the psychiatric hospital; no difference in clinical outcomes at 60% of the cost of an equivalent hospital admission.
Rehabilitation Hospital Hostel	Established in the UK, as units separate but within hospital grounds for the new long stay patients; provide intensive rehabilitation by 24 hour highly motivated staffing; higher proportion of 'unskilled' and nursing staff to other staff; 50% of residents usually can be discharged after long admissions to group homes; no cost evaluation reported.
'Crossing Place'	USA; unit outside the hospital setting with 6 - 32 beds as an alternative to hospital admission for crisis management and rehabilitation; 24 hour staff share tasks with residents who are encouraged through rehabilitation and psycho-education to increase their own coping mechanisms and community support links; decreased re-hospitalisation at 35% of the cost compared to hospitalisation.
Respite Care Facility	Described in the USA; 30-bedded unit or planned admissions every six to eight weeks for patients with severe mental illness who live with their families for period of respite; 24 hour staff also provide contact between admission; patients cared for under case management lines; leads to improved contact between carers and the health professionals involved; positive outcomes on carer burden and expressed emotion within the family household; patients who have previously been shown to fall out of contact with services have maintained contact with decreased hospital readmission rates; no cost evaluation reported.

continued

Non-hospital based residential alternatives	
Name	Description
Halfway House	Described in the USA and UK. 4–8 bedded 'normal' houses in the community which are used for medium to long-term placement for graded discharge and rehabilitation; 24 hour staffing most of which is 'untrained' but with some nursing staff; similar to hospital hostels but are outside the hospital grounds and provide for more integration in community living.
Quarterway House	Described in the USA; for patients who are not ready for a halfway house; used for patients who are described as impossible to place' psychotic patients; houses usually small and have 24 hour nursing; decreased costs compared to hospital control group; but no reporting of discharge or readmission rates.

Bed management techniques which lead to effective bed use

Wherever the beds, research indicates that there a range of techniques which can be employed to maximise effective use. These include:

Organisation of service: Sectorisation of psychiatric services allows continuity of care (Strathdee & Thornicroft, 1992).

Integrated hospital and community services: Research has demonstrated that without an integrated approach where community teams have control over their own hospital beds, both bed use and length of stay are significantly increased and continuity of care is decreased. A worrying trend identified in a recent survey was where purchasers regarded beds as a separate entity to the rest of the service system. Hard pressed clinicians and provider managers, through effective management techniques in some areas is where, when through good practice bed use is effective, the unused beds are sold off as ECRs with local clinicians attempting to provide and establish a good local services while caring for distant 'cuckoos' (Muijen *et al* 1992; MHTF: London, 1994).

Site of assessment: Initial assessment being undertaken at home. Where senior clinicians see patients for the first 'outpatient' assessment at home instead of the hospital clinics admissions may be reduced. Where assessments take place at the site of the acute beds, the likelihood of inappropriate admission is increased.

Senior gate-keeping: Where senior doctors or nurses are constantly involved in any decision to admit a patient, their ability to make a more informed decision and to take risks more appropriately decreases hospital admissions.

Bed manager: In services where an experienced nurse provides a triage function bed use is likely to be decreased.

Discharge planning: In the event of a homeless person being admitted, if priority is placed on immediate referral to housing services, inappropriate and extended use of beds can be prevented.

Continuity of care: The most likely time of re-admission and suicide attempts is in the first 4 - 6 weeks after discharge. Outpatient appointments may be appropriately given within this timescale rather than at a later stage. Any follow-up by keyworkers, case managers, caremanagers, CPNs or others is more likely to be successful if it is intense in this vulnerable period.

Urgent out-patient services: Where urgent out-patient appointments can be offered as part of a comprehensive service, this reduces the need for inpatient admissions.

In conclusion, there are no easy answers. Fig 2, which indicates the evaluation of a bed strategy in one sector services (45,000) population in South London is in no sense an illustration of a 'perfect approach' and is described in detail elsewhere (Mental Health Foundation, 1994). It is included to demonstrate the need for a strategic approach, an understanding that change is incremental and takes time. The development of a range of hospital and community beds in any area will depend on local need, local resources in terms of money but also the skills, creativity and safe risk taking of the local clinicians and managers.

A checklist for purchasers, clinicians and managers in planning and organising bed numbers and use

A   Organisational level

1	Is there accurate current data on the socio-demographic composition of the area?
2	Has an epidemiological analysis to identify the level and nature of psychiatric morbidity in the area been undertaken?
3	Is there local inter-agency agreement on a definition of SMI, and agreement that they are the priority group for the use of resources?
4	Are there formal mechanisms of inter-agency liaison between health, housing and social service agencies?
5	Is there a local understanding that as services move into the community, there may be up to a 30% increase in the number of people with SMI identified and engaged?
6	Do the CMHTs control admission and length of stay to their own beds?

B   Care Programme Approach and care management registers

1	Are Section 117 procedures operating in the providers?
2	Is there a well established Care Programme Approach?
3	Are all the identified SMI on the CPA or are there plans to conduct the assessment and develop CPA over time?
4	Is the CPA integrated with Care Management?
5	Are there joint registers of the SMI established with local general practices?

C   Service components

1	Is there a continuing care service for the SMI in each provider until?
2	Is there a case management team for the SMI?
3	Are there mechanisms for identifying patients who lose contact with care through assertive outreach techniques?
4	How many of the patients on your CPNs caseload have a severe mental illness?
5	Do the CMHTs have an operational policy which defines and priorities the SMI and mechanisms for caseload review and monitoring?
6	Are there regular audits of bed use by the clinicians with feedback mechanisms to allow priorities to be influenced?

D   Alternatives to inpatient admission

1	Are there community alternatives to hospital beds such as crisis flats/crisis houses?
2	Are there single access points of contact for 24 hour, 7 day crisis intervention service in the providers?
3	Is there a facility for planned respite care?
4	What is the level of high support accommodation in the community, for example community hostel staffed by experienced workers 24 hours a day, for the most vulnerable patients?

E   Assessment services

1	Do you have established clinics or other forms of liaison with the GPs in your sector?
2	Do you have initial assessment of patients in their own homes?
3	Do you have initial assessments of patients by senior professionals?

F   Bed Management strategies

1	Is there gate-keeping to beds by senior experienced clinicians?
2	Is there a dedicated bed manager?
3	Are outcome and thus planned discharge dates set as soon as possible after admission?
4	Are there arrangements for the homeless to be referred to housing services as soon as possible after admission?
5	Can the local housing department hold surgeries for the homeless?

References

Bebbington, P. *et al* (1994) Inner London collaborative audit of admissions in two health districts. *British Journal of Psychiatry,* **165**, 743–749.

Craig, T. *et al* (1994) *The Homeless Mentally Ill Initiative. An Evaluation.* London: HMSO.

Davidge, M., Elias S., Jayes B. & Yates J. (1993) *Survey of English Mental Illness Hospitals March 1993. Inter-Authority Consultancy and Comparisons,* University of Birmingham, Birmingham.

Department of Health (1994). *The Health of the Nation. Key Area Handbook. Mental Illness.* HMSO, London. (2nd edition).

Faulkner, A., Field V. & Muijen M., (1994) *A survey of Adult Mental Health Services.* The Sainsbury Centre for Mental Health.

Goldberg, D., Bridges K., Cooper W., Hyde C., Sterling C. & Watt R. (1985). Douglas House: a new type of hostel ward for chronic psychotic patients. *British Journal of Psychiatry* **147**, 383–388.

Goldman, H. (1981). Defining and counting the chronically mentally ill. *Hospital and Community Psychiatry* **32**, 21–27.

Holloway, F. (1988). Day care and community support in Lavenders A. & Holloway F. (eds). *Community Care in Practice*, Chichester: Wiley.

Hoult, J., & Reynolds, I. (1984). Schizophrenia: a comparative trial of community oriented and hospital oriented psychiatric care. *Acta Pschiatrica Scandinavica* **69**, 359–372.

Jarman, B. (1983). Identification of underprivileged areas. *British Medical Journal*, **286**, 1705–1709.

Jarman, B., Hirsch (1992) *Statistical models to predict district psychiatric morbidity. In Measuring Mental Health Needs.* (Thornicroft, G., Brewin, C. & Wing, J. K. eds). Royal College of Psychiatrists, Gaskell Press, Chapter 4.

Johnson, S. & Thornicroft, G. (1995). Emergency psychiatric services in England and Wales. *British Medical Journal*, **311**, 287–288.

King, M., Coker, E., Leavey, G., Hoare, A., Johnson-Sabine, E. 1994 Incidence of psychotic illness in London: comparison of ethnic groups. *British Medical Journal* **309**: 115–119.

Lee, A. S. & Murray, R. M. (1988). The long-term of outcome Maudsley depressives. *British Journal of Psychiatry* **153**: 741–751.

Lelliott, P. & Wing, J., (1994) National audit of new long-stay psychiatric patients. 2: Impact on services. British Journal of Psychiatry, **165**: 160-169.

Lelliott, P., Audini, B., Darroch, N., (1995) Resolving London's Bed crisis: there might be a way, is there the will? *Psychiatric Bulletin*, **19**, 273–275.

Mental Health Foundation (1994) *Creating Community Care.* London: MHF

Mental Health in London. Priorities for Action. (1994). Department of Health, Mental Health Task Force. London.

Pantellis, C., Taylor, J. & Campbell, P. (1988). The South Camden schizophrenia survey. *Psychiatric Bulletin*, **12**, 98–101.

Ritchie Report J. (1994) *Report of the Inquiry into the Care and Treatment of Christopher Clunis.* London: HMSO.

OPCS (1995) *The National Psychiatric Morbidity Survey: Household Survey.* HMSO, London.

North East Thames and South East Thames Regional Health Authorities. (1994) *Report into the Inquiry into the Care and Treatment of Christopher Clunis.* HMSO, London.

Strathdee, G. & Thornicroft G. (1992) Community Sectors of needs-led mental health services. In Thornicroft, G., Brewin, C. & Wing J. (eds). *Measuring Mental Health Needs.* Gaskell, London.

Thompson, K., Phelan, M., Strathdee, G. & Shiress, D. & (1995) *Mental Health Care: a giude for housing workers*. London: MHF.

Thornicroft, G. & Bebbington, P. (1989). Deinstitutionalisation: from hospital closure to service development. *British Journal of Psychiatry,* **155**: 739–753.

Tyrer, P. (1984). Psychiatric clinics in general practice: an extension of community care. *British Journal of Psychiatry* **145**: 9¬14.

Wing, J., & Furlong, R. (1986). A haven for the severely disabled within the context of a comprehensive psychiatric community service. *British Journal of Psychiatry* **149**, 449–457.

Wing, J. (1992). *Epidemiologically based needs assessment: mental illness.* NHS Management Executive, London.

5 Independent Sector Providers

MARGARET CUDMORE

Provision

Psychiatric services in the UK's independent sector have grown rapidly in recent years and, as such, its establishments have increased from 37 in 1987 to 68 in 1994. Similarly, the number of beds have grown from 1,880 to 2,863 during the same period. Today, independent sector services account for a much higher percentage of activity than the 6% of the total UK in patient provision—or beds—that they represent and all the signs are that the sector will continue to grow irrespective of who is in government.

Taking the independent sector as a whole, including psychiatry, few can deny that the UK has been operating a mixed economy of health and social care provision for many years. Indeed, given traditional British regard for such principles as mutuality and communication self-help it is legitimate to argue that the sector and its involvement in mainstream UK healthcare can be traced back to the 17th, 18th and 19th centuries.

With its long and established traditions of high quality value for money services, today's independent sector provides some 20 per cent of all UK elective surgery including, for example, 20 per cent of all coronary heart by pass operations and 30 per cent of all hip replacements. It also accounts for 74 per cent of all long term nursing and residential care provided by some 16,010 homes and centres.

The sector's diversity means that it embraces a wide range of client groups which in addition to medicine and surgery include the elderly, the mentally ill, the elderly mentally ill, the physically disabled, and children and adults with learning disabilities. Independent psychiatric hospitals and homes also offer specialist care in acute psychiatric conditions, in the field of head injury rehabilitation, child and adolescent care and for patients with challenging behaviour. Its services are not only residential but often include other important elements such as domiciliary, day and respite treatment and care.

Since 1980 there has been a six fold increase in the independent sector's acute psychiatric and long stay provision. This has been encouraged by recent government reforms: not least the requirements of the NHS and Community Care Act which stipulated 85 per cent of all public community care expenditure should be spent in the private sector on either residential or domiciliary care.

Size of total sector	Total	Bed Numbers
Acute Hospitals	227	11,681
Psychiatric and substance abuse units	68	2,863
Nursing homes –voluntary	351	15,000
–private	4,660	168,200
Residential Homes –voluntary	1,782	51,000
–private	9,217	165,400
TOTALS	16,305	414,144

Sources: Independent Healthcare associations Acute Hospital Survey
1995; Laing's Review of Private Healthcare 1994.

Value

Medical care in the independent sector, as in the NHS, has to be paid for and
the majority is presumed to be funded through private medical insurance. It is
clear, however, that taking out insurance against medical costs is not the only
way in which these services are funded. Many of the psychiatric services
available currently fall outside of the remit of insurance cover and consequently
this only accounts for about 10 per cent of the total expenditure on independent
provision.

Nevertheless, around seven million people do have medical insurance;
including a million public employees. A further three million people have health
insurance which pays out cash benefits when they are ill and in need of
treatment. Together, some 10 million people have one form of medical or health
insurance or another, which is again more people than currently belong to
trade unions or attend church on a regular basis. There are yet more people
who simply pay for care as and when they require it.

In terms of total expenditure, today's independent health and social care sector
is comparable to all consumer spending on air travel or DIY.

Value of independent sector supply of health and social care: major markets, UK 1993	£ million
Acute sector	1,868
Long term care of the elderly and physically disable	5,256
Homecare	449
Mental illness or learning disabilities	126
Pharmaceutical products	3,960
	11,659

Source: Laing's Review of Private Health Care.

The proportion of Gross Domestic Produce (GDP) spent on health care in the UK is frequently quoted as being lower in comparable European Union and OECD countries. While this may be true, what is not often mentioned is that the difference is not caused by low public spending but instead by the relatively low level of private spending in the UK.

International comparisons	UK	EEC	OECD	USA
GDP on independent health care	1.1%	2.0%	3.6%	7.5%
GDP on public health care	6.0%	6.3%	6.1%	6.3%
Total GDP on health care	7.1%	8.3%	9.9%	13.8%

Source: (OECD, 1992)

The above figures clearly demonstrate peoples willingness to spend their own money on their health and, as such, any system which discourages them from doing so will merely place a greater burden on the NHS. Given government now has only limited scope for increasing public expenditure it follows that any future administration committed to increasing health and social care budgets will have to look seriously at increasing non-governmental forms of expenditure.

Indeed, it would already require three or four pence on the basic rate of income tax simply to replace current private spending on treatment and care by additional NHS and local authority services. This, however, understates the true cost, as it does not take into account the Corporation Tax, VAT and other taxes paid by health and social care organisations which would be lost to the Exchequer. Realistically, an increase of the order of five pence on the basic rate of income tax would be required to replace independent health and social care by government spending.

Employment

As well as being a major provider and significant contributor to the national economy, the independent sector provides employment for 449,000 people: 75 per cent of whom are women. For every two people who now work in the NHS, one is employed in the independent sector. In terms of the total number of people employed, this is comparable to agriculture, the postal and telecommunications sector, or the non-military civil service. Not only does the UK's independent sector employ a third of all nurses, but, today 80 per cent of medical consultants have some sort of private practise and 28 per cent of consultant psychiatrists admit patients to independent sector facilities.

THE PROVIDERS

There are currently 68 hospitals and clinics in the UK's independent psychiatric sector: most of whom are located in South East of England as shown on the map. They range in size from less than 16 beds to over 400 beds; with the majority at the lower end of the spectrum averaging between 15–50. Three large groups own the majority of the establishments although there remains a considerable number of one off, or 'stand alone', operators. The prices charged vary considerably with the type of work undertaken and the local cost base, but prices average around £200–£250 per bed day for acute care.

While there are a number of commonly held assumptions about the sector which are not always accurate, several key points need to be covered, which include:

- **Services are aimed at wealthy middle class patients**

  With the arrival of the mixed economy in UK healthcare independent provision is increasingly being accessed by an ever wider range of people, many of whom are sponsored by the state. Independent provision is no longer the preserve of a wealthy middle class, instead, it is a resource which is benefiting our society and its members as a whole.

- **Queue jumping eradicated**

  The introduction of more sophisticated purchasing mechanisms by both the National Health Service and Private Medical Insurers, together with provider policing has virtually eradicated any possibility or opportunity for queue jumping. Increasingly, patients are unable to hop from one payer to another unless there is sound justification, both clinically and financially, and is agreed between all parties. Some authorities and providers already have protocols for these situations.

- **Patients cannot be kept in to maximise income**

  Ten years ago this may not have been true but in today's economic climate such malpractice has been virtually eradicated. A variety of safeguards are in place to protect against unnecessary inpatient treatment. Both National Health Service and Private Medical Insurers have their own ways of reviewing length of stay. Throughout the industry the length of stay has dropped to an average of about 23 days for acute general psychiatry compared to between 28–32 days five years ago. There are many reasons for this, but most important is that providers are now motivated by the need to develop long term relationships with purchasers, rather than seek short term returns. This new relationship has resulted in a number of operators going out of business.

- **Unnecessarily high salary costs are paid to attract staff away from the NHS**

  There is no evidence to substantiate this claim. Many independent sector operators structure their pay policies to avoid some of the more onerous terms and conditions set out by the former Whitley Council arrangements in relation to sick pay, pension benefits, study leave, etc. Salaries are often related to productivity and a true comparison is unlikely to confirm that high remuneration packages are in place.

- **Returns for hard work**

  About 20 per cent of acute psychiatric admissions to the sector are for detained patients. This reflects the high level of dependency amongst patients admitted to the sector. Work is categorised as approximately 75 per cent acute, 15 per cent dependencies, 10 per cent behavioural, brain injury, eating disorders, adolescents, non acute care, etc. The majority of services operate 24 hours a day, 365 days a year, and most patients are admitted on an emergency basis. During the 1994–95 period, an increasing number of providers were called upon to offer emergency cover for NHS providers. It is unlikely that any great distinction would be found when comparing the patients in similar public and private hospitals.

Strong traditions

As was mentioned at the beginning, the roots of the UK's independent sector date back to the 17th and 18th century and, as such, a number of its hospitals have been working continually in the healthcare market for 200–300 years. Given this proud record of service it is important to point out that most, if not all, dependent operators tend to take a long term view of health policy and in this context have found the last 10–15 years a time of turbulent change and opportunity.

Encouragingly, it would appear that despite flaws in the current health care system, purchasers and providers of psychiatric care are slowly beginning to establish common ground and work together for the future. There is without doubt a clear and shared desire to improve services for the mentally ill and those in need.

PURCHASING

Today, the reality for mental health services is that increasingly the state is reacting to the under-resourcing of mental health provision by purchasing services on an ECR basis from the independent sector. Although it would be easy to slip into the rhetoric of competition, and to highlight the statutory requirements on purchasers to consider long term relationships with independent sector providers, the reality is that such relationships will only be borne from the establishment of trust and confidence between individual purchasers and providers and not as a result of adherence to political edicts such as the private finance initiative, market testing or tendering processes. ECR purchasing buys time to consider contractual confidence. It is not surprising therefore that in these early days of the purchaser provider split the vast majority of purchasing of independent sector provision during 1994 was on an ECR basis.

The use of ECR purchasing in this way effectively buys purchasers and planners time to transfer longer term investment to alternative treatment options. The use of the independent sector effectively bridges the gap whilst emphasis can be switched from institutional care to community care. Emergent community services are taking their time to impact on the need for in patient treatment, hence the apparently unplanned and widespread use of independent facilities. While this demand continues to escalate, it can be expected that this phenomena will be relatively short lived: perhaps 3–5 years. Only 5% of activity in 1994 was on the basis of block contracts. Purchasing of this sought bears witness to the benefit of real collaboration.

Collaboration has already proven itself as a better way forward and has produced some outstanding results. It works best when the purchaser enters into a dialogue with the potential providers *before* drafting the tender document.

The benefits of dialogue between purchasers and providers

- New ideas can by explored
- The best and most achievable approach can be defined
- Realistic outcome measures can be established
- The experience of the provider can be drawn into the dialogue
- Cost saving approaches can be identified
- The most effective documentation procedures can be defined
- Admittance criteria can be examined
- Reporting mechanisms are defined
- The mental health needs of the particular population are addressed

The result of such a dialogue as evidenced by the West Kent Health Authority's approach to child mental health services is the production of a meaningful long term (5 year) purchasing strategy. It does of course mean that each proposal is tailor made around the best arrangement that each of the providers collectively can offer. This makes work for the purchaser but without question achieves the best results for the patient.

PRICING

Most independent sector providers base their prices on cost, plus a margin to reflect their investment needs in respect of borrowing from investors or to service developments and maintenance of assets. In many ways, this makes them no different from the NHS Trusts. In the past, prices have been loosely set through negotiation with British United Provident Association (BUPA) and Private Patients' Plan (PPP)—as the largest of the Private Medical Insurers (PMI's). however, in recent years the contractual relationship between PMI's and independent sector providers has been changing. In 1991 the process of pre-authorisation was introduced for all PMI admissions to independent psychiatric beds. Unlike the initial arrangements, this process did not focus on price, which was the subject of separate annual negotiations, but on the clinical suitability of a patient for in-patient treatment and the suitability of the treatment being proposed. The process made it incumbent upon the admitting consultant that he or she describe the symptoms warranting in-patient treatment, whilst simultaneously describing the treatment being proposed to address them, together with the anticipated length of stay. It ceased to be sufficient for a consultant or a GP to indicate that in-patient treatment was warranted, further evidence to this effect was to be provided. Latterly, it also became necessary to describe the measures that had been taken prior to the consideration of in-patient treatment. Admission criteria was adopted by the insurance companies against which the pre-authorisation process was applied. The system effectively began to gate-keep the use of in-patient facilities for insured patients and resulted initially in significant reductions in cost as the length of stay within the industry reduced. A copy of the pre-authorisation criteria adopted by one insurer is described below.

Pre-authorisation criteria used prior to admission

Suicidal Risk

The patient is considered to pose a serious risk of suicide or self-harm.

Aggressive behaviour

The patient is behaving in an aggressive manner due to psychiatric illness and the aggression leads others to fear injury from the patient.

Self-neglect

There is functional impairment to the extent that the patient is unable to look after himself adequately and/or there is insufficient support from family and friends.

Nutritional deficiency

There is inadequate food or fluid intake. This may occur in anorexia nervosa or stupor and requires specialist treatment to restore body weight, hydration and general nutritional status.

Diagnostic assessment

The patient is believed to be suffering from a major psychiatric disorder but the diagnosis cannot be established at out-patient consultation and closer observation is required.

Failed out-patient treatment

The patient has not responded to out-patient and/or day-patient treatment.

Specific treatments

The patient requires treatment which can usually only be given as an in-patient:

ECT (although this may be given on an out-patient/day case basis in certain circumstances)

continued

continued

Intravenous therapy
Detoxification from drugs and alcohol
Intensive behaviour therapy
Pharmacotherapy requiring close clinical and laboratory monitoring.

The process has now been extended to cover both outpatient and day treatment as well. This level of clinical scrutiny has become common place within independent sector hospitals. Some PMI's are now going one stage further. BUPA has commissioned and published clinical protocols for a number of psychiatric conditions which are being proffered as a guide to good practice. These guidelines have not, as yet, been introduced into the pre-authorisation process and will pose some interesting ethical and legal issues if and when they are introduced. Just what clinicians make of such guidelines is another debate but the BUPA document does offer lessons for purchasers in defining services. Price is now being negotiated, not on the price per bed day, but on the price for the completed episode of treatment. This is a further mechanism for controlling cost and restricting the supply of services quite understandably to that which is considered by the purchasing agent to be affordable. As the relationship between the public and independent sector develops, purchasers should seek to explore the price advantages that could be negotiated from independent sector providers, by offering payment at an earlier stage that recognises the benefit to providers of cash flow easement.

Foreword

Experience has shown that purchasing any health care service is an inherently complex process. Certain features of psychiatry exacerbate this, for either the individual purchaser, the private medical insurer or the public sector purchaser.

- The patient is not always in agreement with the transaction at the time it occurs.

- Sometimes diagnosis is a matter of judgement not fact.

- Treatment methods can vary between practitioners.

- There are few objective measures of outcome.

In the absence of reliable clinical or financial comparisons purchasing is being based upon price and activity.

Until contracts can be based upon meaningful outcome measures which help to define value for money, purchasing will remain an inherently lopsided process. Most contracts for mental health services appear to specify price and activity levels in considerable detail but make only cursory reference to outcome. As yet there are no universally applied measurement tools in mental health even though much good work is being done in some quarters to establish some. Those that are in use tend to be either based in clinical academia or more pragmatic in origin. Even when such measures are available of either persuasion there is little to compare them to and hence they become devalued by the lack of a frame of reference.

Most patients tend to take a very subjective and practical view about value for money. For example, a head injured patient wants to know: "Will I be able to live with my wife and kids when I leave here?" "Will my wife leave me? Will I ever be able to work again?".

Being able to answer some of these questions is far more important than tabulating activity levels.

Accommodation Status	Before Injury	Before Admission	On Discharge
At Home	61	29	41
Other Residential care	1	6	15
Hospital	0	27	6
	62	62	62

Source: Ticehurst House Hospital Activity Data 1989–1992.

In the psychiatric service, the main indicator is whether or not a person's quality of life has improved. It can be argued that this is also the best measure of outcome for all medical and surgical episodes. Further work must be undertaken to enable effective value for money decisions to be made and it is incumbent upon every provider to assist in this process.

Putting aside some of the suspicions and prejudices that still lurk, independent providers will only be able to satisfy the needs of the NHS **if they are able to offer a service that can be provided for, at a price that is less than the *real* cost that would be incurred by the NHS.** Here, we are talking about a comparable or better service—bearing in mind the cost of resources for providing specialist services that would need to be borne by the NHS in the absence of an independent provider. So far, however, there is little evidence that such comparisons will ever be able to be drawn. It is an irony that both public sector and independent providers feel disadvantaged by the lack of a mythical "level playing field". Each feels that the other has been accorded some competitive advantage in the order of things. This situation is exacerbated by the lack of any meaningful data emerging from either the NHS Trusts, the Department of Health or the Audit Commission about costing within the public sector. Once again, the absence of research in this arena is clouding the evaluation process and inhibiting the cost most effective purchasing of services.

For the independent provider the attraction of publicly funded work is threefold:

- Credit worthiness
- Regular payments
- Regular flow of patients.

In conclusion, the current climate is very volatile with economic, political and legislative uncertainty. Pragmatism seems the most effective way forward for the present. Many public sector purchasers and providers have already put aside the legacy of the past as they develop exciting and innovative alliances with the independent sector. As we look to the future, and given the general trend towards consumer choice, higher living standards and the demographic changes facing the UK, there can be little doubt that the independent sector will have a major role to play in the future development of high quality services for an ever increasing range of people. However the future shapes up, it is certain that there will be a significant role for the UK's independent providers of care. As we move towards a new consensual era which accepts the mixed economy, we can expect that more and more people will come to accept the view that what really matters in healthcare is not whether a service is delivered in a privately or a publicly owned hospital or unit, but the level and quality of the service offered. It is for all our futures that the mixed economy is developed and strengthened further over time.

6 Housing Component of Mental Health Services

CLIFF PRIOR

The importance of housing

Housing is the foundation of community care. Commonly placed high in the priorities expressed by people with mental illness themselves[1], appropriate housing has been highlighted as a crucial component of community care in a series of recent studies and inquiries[2,3,4,5]. Like everyone else, people with a mental illness need an appropriate place to live, somewhere they can feel at home and secure. A home should offer privacy and seclusion, but it should also be capable of being a base where people can receive the care and support they need and from which people can develop an active social life and participate in the wider community.

Housing problems are common among people with severe mental illness, with 11% of people diagnosed with schizophrenia being homeless, or in a hostels or nightshelters for the homeless, compared to 15% in hospital as inpatients and 15% in specialist accommodation[6]. Yet a below average of level of resources is devoted to those who are homeless[6].

Homelessness damages peoples health—including their mental health[7]. Mental health and housing problems often become deeply intertwined, with mental illness precipitating loss of housing, and homelessness frustrating the effective provision of care. Homeless people with mental illness present particular risks, primarily to themselves, and were recommended as one of four categories of people needing special supervision by the Ritchie Inquiry[3]. Tackling housing problems and mental health problems in a coordinated way is a far more effective response to the problems faced by homeless mentally ill people than responding to either one or the other alone[8]. Yet housing and mental health services are still mainly developed in isolation from each other, with links between community care and housing assessment procedures rare[9]. Coordination is vital.

Interagency working

The starting point for an effective housing and mental illness strategy is the recognition that it must be an interagency task: health, social services and housing as well as the service users themselves are all vital players. No one agency will have the skills, resources, understanding or even awareness of all the needs.

Three way interagency working is no easy task, particularly as these agencies have very different working cultures, work to different priorities, each have their own problems and constraints, and will in most cases have different boundaries and be in the process of restructuring driven by different policies of separate central government departments. Progress will depend on mutual recognition of these difficulties. Work by a single agency would almost always be quicker and is very tempting, but has proved much less successful and indeed dangerous in the longer run.

The areas which have made good progress on an interagency basis offer some hints:

- identify the key people in each agency—you will need both energetic 'champions of the cause' and the people with formal decision making power in each agency; form a regular coordinating group

- devote time to hearing about each other's priorities, problems, operating methods and structures; extend this through each organisation, providing training across the agency divides so that staff at all levels improve mutual understanding

- make your case—demonstrate the need for housing for people with mental health problems with facts and figures

- identify a common agenda which is relevant to *all* the agencies involved and helps meet problems faced by each agency, eg meeting the needs:
  - of health providers for access to an appropriate range of housing with support
  - of social services purchasers for realistic management of their community care budget
  - of housing managers for access to mental health professionals when tenants became ill
- appoint at least one lead person in at least one of the agencies—an officer whose job is to coordinate work across the housing/ health/social care spectrum; because of their community care responsibilities, this person may often be best based in social services
- work out a long term strategy for progress, recognising that 3 to 5 years is the shortest realistic timetable for developing anything approaching a comprehensive solution.

Interagency working is necessary but laborious. Effort should be focused on the issues most needing joint approach:

- overall assessment of the needs of the local population
- strategic planning and commissioning the broad range of services
- setting quality standards and establishing monitoring arrangements to deal with all aspects of the service and all areas of risk—housing, social and medical care
- joint purchasing of medical services
- assessing and responding to individual needs: care planning and management
- service provision to individuals needing the skills of more than one agency.

A second list of priorities emerges from looking at the points in the life of someone with a serious mental illness where it is most likely that housing and mental health services will be needed together:

- support to people who have a mental illness to sustain their housing (36% of Homeless Mentally Ill Initiative clients had lost a council or housing association tenancy[8])
- urgent response to breakdown of existing housing
- outreach to homeless people and those in hostels and shelters
- discharge from hospital
- discharge from care or reduction in care when someone is felt to have improved sufficiently
- management and professional medical and social support to specialist housing schemes.

Understanding the housing field

Housing development and management are skilled areas of work which should be undertaken by specialist agencies. Health services are generally poor managers of housing just as housing managers would make poor psychiatrists. However, it will be important for health managers and professionals to have a basic understanding of how the housing field operates.

Three key aspects are the agencies involved, the roles of the principal groups of staff, and the main current concerns of housing staff. These are outlined in boxes below.

Who's who in housing

Department of Environment:	DoE is the central government department responsible.
Housing Corporation:	quango appointed by DoE and responsible for funding and regulating housing associations.
Local authorities:	district and borough councils are the housing authorities; they are still the largest providers of rented housing but are increasingly moving to the 'enabling' role of planning, assessing need, and prioritising and funding development.
Housing associations:	main developers of new social housing; housing associations are charities or not for profit companies regulated by the Housing Corporation.
Voluntary agencies:	much specialist housing with support for people with mental health problems is run by charitable or voluntary agencies; these may be large national agencies or smaller local providers.

Housing people

Allocations staff:	o	deal with assessment of applicants and offers of accommodation.
	o	aka lettings officers, waiting list section.
Homelessness team:	o	deal with applications for housing from homeless people, finding emergency accommodation and longer term housing.
	o	aka homeless families team, housing emergency office.
Development teams:	o	deal with development of new housing, usually working to a brief from housing managers.

continued

---

continued

	O	aka technical services team, programme managers, project officers.
Housing managers:	O	deal with lettings to new tenants, rent collection and arrears, transfer requests and tenancy problems.
	O	aka housing officers or assistants, estate managers.
Maintenance:	O	deal with repairs.
	O	sometimes part of technical services teams, sometimes part of housing management.
Supported housing manager:	O	in housing associations, responsible for specialist care or support.
	O	aka special projects team, housing with care team.

Key current concerns in the housing field

Rents and affordability

Council housing rents have risen faster than inflation. Housing association rents have also leapt up following cuts in capital subsidy. Rents are now at levels where few tenants can escape the poverty trap of dependence on housing benefit.

Cuts in new development

Councils are scarcely able to build any new homes. Even housing associations are now severely restricted by cuts in funding for development. This affects funding for both specialist schemes and general housing.

Homelessness

A high proportion of lettings are now devoted to housing for people who are regarded as priority homeless, leaving fewer homes for other people on waiting lists.

Social balance

As richer tenants have exercised the right to buy and new lettings have been limited to those in greater need, social housing has lost its broader social mix. Estates may now have a high proportion of tenants with multiple problems and extreme poverty.

Stock transfers

Many local authorities are transferring their housing stock to housing associations. Councils are moving to an enabling rather than providing role. While retaining the responsibilities for waiting lists and housing the homeless, they now fulfil these through nominations for housing association lettings.

continued

continued

Compulsory competitive tending
CCT is scheduled to be introduced to housing management and maintenance in local authorities. There are fears this will result in a narrower definition of housing management, excluding welfare and support functions.

Local government boundary review
Many local housing authorities are affected by planned or possible boundary reorganisation. In some areas the uncertainty can have a paralysing effect on planning.

Special needs housing review
The revenue funding of housing with care and support through the Housing Corporation has been under review for several years. The last change in 1995 introduced a cash limited budget, competitive bidding for new grants and reviews of each existing scheme every 3 years.

Types of housing

Housing options for people with mental illness are commonly stereotyped into categories such as registered care, group homes and ordinary housing. While these are the most common types of provision, they lump together several factors. Unpicking the factors helps to promote clearer planning to meet actual needs which may not fit into the usual boxes. For example, people needing high levels of support are often referred to shared house schemes. Yet for people with personality disorders, shared housing can be highly inappropriate and create management problems which could be avoided by, for example, housing in a scheme of self contained small flats grouped in a block with a staff presence.

The main dimensions can be analysed into 5 headings: the built form, staff levels, staff types, legal status, and intended client groups. The options under each heading are outlined in the box below.

Types of housing: 5 dimensions

Dimension	*Options*
Built form:	o ordinary flats and houses
	o flats dotted around an estate or small area
	o flats grouped into single block
	o shared flats and small group homes
	o larger group homes/small hostels
	o hostels and care homes
Staff levels:	o support staff on call or based at an office which tenants can visit
	o visiting staff—peripatetic support
	o staff in the premises for part of the day

continued

continued

           o   staff in the premises most of the day, perhaps with
                          on call service at other times
           o   24 hour presence, sleeping at night
           o   24 hour working cover
           o   double cover or higher

Staff levels can be increased or reduced to respond to changing needs.

Staff types: o   untrained helpers
               o   trained but unqualified staff
               o   social care qualified staff (CSS, NVQ)
               o   qualified social workers (CQSW, Dip SW)
               o   nursing assistants
               o   nurses
               o   psychiatric nurses

It is important to be clear about the extent to which staff are provided to offer care and the extent to which they are there to supervise or exercise control.

Legal   o   ordinary flats and houses
status: o   shared flats and houses
               o   hostels and 'houses in multiple occupation'
               o   registered care homes
               o   registered nursing homes

The more specialist forms of housing are subject to increasing regulation from several authorities, including planning, environmental health, fire safety, and registration.

Client   o   intended level and types of need
groups: o   specialist needs (eg alcohol, drugs, offending)
               o   gender
               o   age
               o   ethnic groups
               o   excluded groups

Specialist projects will generally have both a target client group and lists of exclusions, e.g. people with histories of violence.

Most areas will be starting off with a range of existing provision set up by different agencies to different agendas. There may be gaps, overprovision of some types of schemes, or schemes meeting a need which is no longer a priority. Projects may not be coordinated, so that the option of transfer from one project to another more suitable one is missed, and people are left in inappropriate settings. Misunderstandings may exist about the role of each project, leading to inappropriate referrals and support arrangements. Projects may have exclusion categories which overlap so that there is nothing available at all in the area for some of the most at—risk patients, eg those with histories of violence of substance abuse.

Simply mapping all the existing provision, using the 5 dimensions outlined above, can be an invaluable exercise. As well as forming the starting benchmark for planning, it may help each project to understand its own operation and how it fits in. When mapping the sector,

o   ask how people get access to each project

o   ask who has *actually* been housed recently (often different to what it says on paper)

o   ask who is excluded

o   look at non specialist provision eg ordinary council and association housing, and hostels for homeless people, as well as the specialists.

Whatever your starting point, you will need to move to having a range of provision to meet the range of needs. There will never be one single solution. As the Audit Commission have highlighted[13], far more people can be helped effectively if available resources are deployed across a range of services, tailored to meet the range of needs. The range will almost certainly include:

- very high care NHS provision

- registered homes offering high but not medical level of care

- group homes and shared flats

- supported self contained housing

- support teams flexibly deployed to support people in ordinary housing

- back up support to non-specialist projects which may house some people with mental illness, eg hostels for the homeless, offenders, drug/alcohol services, womens refuges

- specialist provision for specialist needs

- emergency provision for people in a crisis.

Funding and resources

Funding of housing particularly housing with care is extremely complex and constantly changing. The current position is set out in the box below. Fortunately there are specialists on this issue in many housing associations—usually called special project managers or supported housing managers. Community care purchasers in social services will also be able to contribute expertise.

Components of funding

Source	Type	Value	Restriction
Housing Corporation	HAG: Housing Association Grant—capital funding for new homes	Usually 40–80% of cost, but up to 100% for some specialist schemes·	Only available to registered housing associations (this may change in 1996)
	SNMA: Special Needs Management Allowance—revenue funding for housing with support	c£1000–3000 per resident per year	Tight cash limits and cuts over the last couple of years with frequent rule changes
			Need local authority backing for new schemes
			Hospital reprovision schemes, nursing homes and respite care specifically banned
Local housing authorities	LA HAG: Local authority capital grant to housing associations for new homes	As for HAG above	As for HAG above. Not all authorities have programmes
	Revenue support: authorities can grant aid under several powers; revenue for services to vulnerable homeless people is a common priority area	Highly variable, but rarely more than a few thousand per person per year	Varies with the legal power being used
Social services authorities	STG: special transitional grant—the funds being transferred to social services from the benefits budget to pay for community care, including residential care	Typically around £10,000 per person pa, less contributions from personal benefits, for residential care	Must spend 85% in 'independent sector' (ie private and voluntary) Huge demand from people expecting residential care and those wanting care in their own home
	MISG: Mental Illness specific grant—introduced over the last few years as ringfenced money for services to people with mental health problems	Highly variable. Increasing but still small scale compared to health budgets	For new services

continued

Source	Type	Value	Restriction
	Capital: rarely given except to improve or reprovide existing facilities Revenue: social services can fund services from their main budget, as well as from STG or MISG		
NHS	Capital: whether from hospital closures or investment in new provision Revenue: the NHS is by far the largest revenue budget holder for people with mental health problems		NHS funding for housing is probably best focused on high care housing, including 24 hour staffed facilities, schemes with nursing staff, and respite care
Benefits	Housing benefits: for people in rented housing	local limits vary widely, but most areas would accept charges of £80–100 pw for housing with support	Not for residential care Means tested Will not cover 'personal services' such as food, nor charges for care beyond a basic level
	Residential care allowance: for people in registered care homes	around £50pw	Only for people in residential care
	Income support: for personal needs, plus premiums for those with long term illness or disability		Means tested
	Incapacity benefits: for those with long term illness or disability		Medical assessment

Existing resources: This table only shows funding opportunities, but making better use of existing resources is equally if not more important. Use of ordinary housing, change of use for specialist housing, redevelopment of social services and NHS facilities, all offer opportunities for service improvement.

1995 Housing White Paper: 'Our Future Homes'[12]

The Government published a White Paper in 1995 setting out a series of proposals for reform of housing law and finance. The key points are:

- opening up Housing Corporation funding to competitive bids from private companies

- revised eviction powers for private landlords

- new limits on housing benefit—but voluntary sector supported housing will be exempted

- 12 month probationary council tenancies and other measures to make it easier to evict anti-social tenants

- homelessness legislation changed so that homeless people only get short term help with a review every one or two years

- all council lettings and nominations to housing associations to be made from a council housing register.

The measures are likely to become law in 1996. The last two points will particularly affect people with severe mental illness, who are often housed under homelessness arrangements or through special quotas. Health and social services should renegotiate with housing authorities to ensure effective provision is made in the criteria and procedures for the new housing registers.

Agreeing a joint strategy

Absolutely critical to the success of your joint strategy will be agreement rather than argument about who pays for what. There is no easy answer to this and it may be unproductive to raise it until all parties have agreed on their respective priorities and areas of common ground. However, there are some starting points:–

- health will have to pay for the very high care provision with nursing or medical care: no one else can; an NHS Executive report published in February 1996 outlines the need for NHS funded 24 hour staffed accommodation and describes implementation strategies. [17]

- registered homes and other projects funded by social services will probably have to be part of the community care assessment and budget systems

- health and/or social services will have to fund any respite provision, as this is excluded from most housing funding systems

- housing capital and revenue for supported housing is useful but very restricted and can only make a contribution

- a mixed package of funding for a project will often be necessary and have the advantage of signing up all agencies to the scheme's success

- access to the general housing stock is very important, and housing providers are likely to be much more willing if care providers can guarantee appropriate support

- a little imagination can turn up surprising resources, through reuse of existing buildings or land in each agency—it is worth identifying an entrepreneurial member of staff and giving them some headroom to turn up options (but make sure their ideas are thoroughly checked!)

- consult widely when planning—other agencies may have excellent suggestions or useful contributions to make.

The development of new housing takes time—usually 2 to 4 years from conception to management. It is fraught with pitfalls. NIMBY responses from neighbours are a particular problem, as are changes in central government policy and funding rules. Be prepared for some false starts, and wherever possible work in a partnership with a housing organisation experienced in the development of specialist housing. But despite the problems, setting out a funding and development strategy and publishing it widely will give providers the chance and encouragement to develop and propose better quality projects.

Assessing needs

Once joint working arrangements are in place, you are clear where you are starting from, and you have developed an understanding of the field and how it is funded, assessment of local needs becomes the next vital step. A comprehensive overview of needs will require the input of a wide range of agencies: it is important to recognise that many people with severe mental illness will not present to mental health services, but to other agencies they regard as more accessible, eg

o	projects for homeless people
o	specific ethnic minority and refugee groups
o	womens refuges and other services for women who have been abused
o	agencies for people with drug or alcohol problems
o	probation, police, and other criminal justice agencies.

Joint needs for housing and mental health care may emerge from

o	people leaving hospital, prison or other institutions
o	people already in specialist provision which is no longer appropriate to their needs
o	people living with family or in their own home who need support to stay there or move elsewhere
o	homeless people identified as having mental health problems.

All these aspects must be included in the overall assessment, as well as direct consultations with user groups to establish their first hand views of the gaps. Some areas have developed protocols for needs assessment, and the University of Southampton are publishing the results of piloting one model in 14 local areas[13].

Comparison of the overall needs assessment with the map of existing provision will enable priorities to be set for commissioning new services and setting an agenda for change in existing ones.

Individual needs assessment

The second level of assessment will be of individual needs. Currently few areas make effective links between assessment of mental health by health professionals, of community care needs by social services, and of housing needs by housing services. Even at the most extreme end of the spectrum, homeless people assessed as a priority by housing officers because of mental illness are rarely referred for community care assessment, and in fact rarely get access to a social services assessment unless leaving a hospital[2,9]. So even if housing needs are met, care provision may be dangerously inappropriate. Housing officers are not qualified to assess the adequacy of care provision, nor do they have the time to try.

Joint assessment by housing, social services and health staff is essential for people who are homeless. Emergency housing or homeless persons officers may not be familiar with this area of need nor know the range of options available, but they will only develop this expertise if exposed to the needs— and they remain the key gatekeeper to permanent social housing. Some areas have set up procedures for automatic cross referral to the other agencies, and have established multi agency panels to review the needs of those with complex needs.

For people who are not homeless but need alternative housing and/or care, joint assessment will still be important but could be tackled in a different way. From the housing side, it would be lettings, allocations or referrals staff from housing management departments rather than homeless persons officers who would be involved. If a housing and mental health coordinator has been appointed in one of the agencies, they can play a vital role in contributing ideas about the availability of appropriate services.

Individual needs do not stay still once one assessment has been done. Review dates must be built in, and keyworkers must have the authority and opportunity to raise the needs of clients if things do not work out or needs have changed.

Whatever the structures are put in place for needs assessment, there are some golden rules worth bearing in mind:

- seek the views of the service user
- ensure the service user is informed of the options
- if people are moving out of your area, make sure there is a full handover to the new area's services
- do not regard private sector bedsits or B&B as an acceptable housing solution for anyone with a severe mental illness unless they strongly prefer it themselves and frequent contact with care staff is arranged

- monitor assessment and referral to make sure that if 'difficult to place' groups of clients are emerging, priority is given to filling that gap with appropriate services

- recognise the importance of the contributions of housing managers, care managers and health professionals—the picture will be incomplete without any one of these

- mental illness may not be the only problem facing the individual—work on all their needs with a coordinated response

- beware of a complacement acceptance of low standards: homeless mentally ill people have received so little for so long that there is a dangerous tendency to view anything as better than nothing.

Specialist needs

It may be possible to design a mainstream service to meet most people's needs, but some critically important areas of need will need specialist attention. Some of the most significant are listed below.

Housing and mental illness: specialist areas of work

- outreach to the homeless people[8,15]

- co-morbidity with substance abuse

- services for people with 'personality disorders'

- work with young and challenging clients

- older people who are frail or suffering from dementia

- specific services for people from ethnic minorities

- gender specific services, eg for survivors of sexual abuse

- services for refugee communities

- mentally disordered offenders: different access routes for most, but different services may be needed for a smaller number

- overlap with services for people with learning disabilities—for those who also have a mental illness.

A comprehensive local strategy will recognise all populations with mental illness, and take the services—or at least the routes of access to services—to them. If the number of people with some of these needs are very small, it may be better to cooperate with neighbouring areas and produce a regional solution. Some of the needs will involve other agencies, eg probation and forensic services for mentally disordered offenders, refugee organisations for refugees, etc.

Managing the sector

This article has dealt with the setting up of a coordinated response to housing and mental health illness. But even after this initial work, the sector will need continuing attention to sustain the progress made; it will not look after itself, as the natural tendency of staff to work within their own agency, profession and culture will always be pulling coordination apart.

The cultural aspects of joint working are particularly important. Staff in hostels and day centres for homeless people report that clients are not helped if their needs do not fit the medical categories (a particular problem for people with 'personality disorders'), and that clients will not trust nor disclose their needs to the staff 'flown in' to make assessments.

There is still a strong current of anti-psychiatry in many social care agencies, and still a strong tendency among some medical teams to disparage and underrate the importance of social care and housing provision. Multiagency arrangements will fail unless these cultural factors and prejudices are recognised, tackled, and managed firmly.

Improving trust and mutual understanding takes time and energy. Useful options include:

O	training/briefing across agencies
O	interagency visits
O	longer job swaps, placements and secondments
O	published material about aims, working methods and structures
O	regular refreshers in recognition of staff turnover
O	opportunities to identify and deal with mutual problems and complaints
O	joint assessment and review of individual needs
O	attention to making the links at each level in each agency's hierarchy.

Finally, service and staff standards are an area to give particular attention. Skill mixes are changing rapidly in housing and care services, and there is frequently suspicion that jobs are downgraded for purely financial reasons. A realistic match must be made between client needs, job roles and training/qualification levels[16]. The availability of appropriate training, qualifications, and funding to pursue them, is still very limited in the supported housing field. Local arrangements and continuing advice and support from mental health professionals are therefore vital. As needs change, services often drift away from their original remit without adequate attention to the implications. Clear, published aims, objectives, working methods and service standards, linked to clear training and job roles for staff, will help managers and commissioners to identify emerging gaps before they become critical.

References

1 Sheppard, G. *et al* (1994) *Relative Values*. Sainsbury Centre for Mental Health: London.
2 Mental Health Foundation (1994) *Creating Community Care*. Mental Health Foundation: London.
3 (1994) *The Report of the Inquiry into the Care and Treatment of Christopher Clunis*. HMSO: London.
4 House of Commons Select Committee (1994) Better off in the Community? *The care of people who are seriously mentally ill*. HMSO: London.
5 Mental Health Taskforce (1994). Mental Health in London: *Priorites for Action*. HMSO: London.
6 Kavanagh, S. (1994). The costs of schizophrenia. *Mental Health Research Review 1*. PSSRU: University of Kent.
7 Royal College of Physicians (1995). *Homelessness and Health*.
8 Craig, T. *et al* (1995). *The Homeless Mentally Ill Initiave*. HMSO: London.
9 Department of Health (1994). Implementing caring for people: *housing and homelessness, report of the community care monitoring special study*. Department of Health.
10 Quoted in Hill (1994). *Housing for those with Mental Health Problems*: some background statistics prepared for the MHF Inquiry. Mental Health Foundation: London.
11 Office for Public Management (1992). *Assessment of the Housing Requirements of People with Special Needs over the Next Decade*: a report for the National Federation of Housing Associations. NFHA: London.
12 Our Future Homes: *The Government's Housing Policies for England and Wales* (1995). HMSO.
13 Watson, L. *et al* (due in 1995). *Community Care Planning:* an Analysis of Housing Needs; a series of 14 reports on separate studies in different local authorities. University of Southampton.
14 Audit Commission (1994). *Finding a Place:* A Review of Mental Health Services for Adults. HMSO: London.
15 Chris Leigh (1994). *Everybody's Baby:* Implementing Community Care for Single Homeless People. CHAR: London.
16 *Report of the Inquiry into the circumstances leading to the death of Jonathan Newby (1995)*. DHA: Oxford.
17 *24 hour nursed care for people with severe and enduring mental illness*. (1996) NHS Executive: Leeds.

7 Implementing the Core Service Components—Commissioning and Contracting

SUE GALLAGHER

Commissioners: animal, vegetable or mineral?

It is a privilege to be a purchaser, or, if we use our preferred and more accurate terminology, a commissioner. It is a bruising and humbling experience at worst and a motivating, inspiring experience at best. Expectations of commissioners are very challenging and the pressure of work is immense and constant. We have power because we have money and because our decisions are important for people and services—but power is a relative term when it is based on negotiation and influence—we rarely feel powerful. We are expected to have expert knowledge to inform these decisions but we hope we earn respect if we acknowledge our need to learn. On bad days, pressures, numerous priorities, conflicting policies, or the many obstacles to progress achievement of 'health gain' seem very slow. On good days, the privilege of commissioning an extraordinarily committed service of carers to achieve of its best for our population, helps us over the hurdles. When some of us became commissioners, we were lucky to have the 'map' of game keeper turned poacher, for we had been providers. We had to find quickly the map that guided us to what 'health gain' meant, the process for achieving it and some success criteria.

A simple view of health gain

Mission

- Improve health
- Reduce suffering/disability
- Add life to years and years to life

Process

- Needs assessment
- Service development/strategy
- Financial strategy
- Purchasing/contracting

continued

> *continued*
>
> - Mobilising support
> - Quality assurance and accountability
>
> **Success**
>
> - Tangible, demonstrable improvements to health and health service
> - Improvements that reflect priority needs and stakeholder views

When we had struggled for a while in the purchasing/contracting world, we could summarise some reasons about 'how to do it'.

> - It is what we do, not what we say—preserve the forests, if not planting the saplings
> - Invest time in understanding the business of professionals: this is the key to understanding what we purchase and to getting a shared and agreed way forward, between clinicians, provider managers and commissioners; and it is motivating for everybody
> - Distinguishing 'need' from 'demand' and 'supply' is important by talking to users, by looking at needs as perceived by other stakeholders, by understanding local and national data.
> - Give clarity about priorities and put our money where our mouth is—this is crucial to resilience in the face of numerous pressures and to building strategic partnerships with other agencies and with providers.
> - We can use the incentives of health gain funds to improve the specificity of what we are purchasing (why, what, how for what gain?); explore effectiveness; and put money where it might have rarely gone before, where the voices were not the loudest.

Need—who, where, what, why?

Commissioning health services for people with severe and enduring mental illness starts with a quiz, with some quite difficult to answer questions.

- On whom is the money spent?

- On what is it spent? Where is it spent?

- Is this what we would expect, given a national/external perspective on need?

- What is the quality of life of who we spend money on?

- How effective are we in improving health and life?

- Do we comply with our statutory responsibilities?

- What is the perceived quality of the service—by users, carers, primary care practitioners, secondary care professional, other agencies?

- What are the constraints to better meeting needs? The opportunities for improvements?

We may seek the answers to these questions through a variety of means. Mapping or tabulating how the money relates to activity and to individuals' contact with the service, can be a very powerful highlighter of the need for change; listening to the many stakeholders and sampling care plans and care management, and pulling out the common threads of concern; can be illuminating, looking at 'what if' scenarios opens doors to opportunities, and analysing source and post codes of referrals is essential.

We are likely to find that 'revolving door' patients who are seriously mentally ill are very significant in how we spend our money but that many people believe that the quality of their care plans and support could be much improved with more targeted resources. We will hear GPs telling us of the pressures that they have in their surgeries and how necessary it is to attend to the less severely mentally ill and we will recognise poor communication between primary and secondary care. The priority clients of the Local Authority, the Police and the Probation Service are likely to be people familiar to the community mental health services. The need for 24 hour supported accommodation and better access to out-of-hours services will be emphasised time and time again. It will be clear that placing the priority on people with severe and enduring mental illness is an undeniable pre-requisite of commissioning good mental health services.

Service development to give priority to people with serious and enduring mental health problems

What is good practice locally and nationally? What are the strengths that can be built upon? Are we clear about who is within our priority client group and where they are within the services we purchase? A partnership of commissioners working with providers and key people from the Local Authority and other interested agencies, is critical to achieving good service design and service development. Commissioners need others' expertise and 'champions' of the cause within provider organisations and other agencies. Given that demand exceeds available resources and concentrating on people with serious and enduring mental health problems will expose significant inadequately met need, it is fundamentally important that commissioners do not discuss any service changes which they are not prepared to help fund or take an active role in achieving. Experience would suggest the following priorities for early attention and action:

- Establishing a long term case register to identify who is the priority focus, and their living circumstances and experience with mental health services, at least on an annual basis.

- Recognising the need for a range of supported and 24 hour staffed housing and working with the Local Authority and housing associations to achieve this, using a mixed funding approach.

- Listening to the experience of fragmented care and disparate professionals attempting to achieve co-ordinated care, and developing community mental health teams, with a team base, administrative support, centralised referral systems, and unambiguity about their priority client group.

- Establishing a fund of 'seed corn service development money' to use to be able to respond positively to the many good ideas for improving services, many of which will require very small investment for clear health gain or to boost morale and keep users and professionals involved and motivated.

- Clarifying responsibilities for people of no fixed abode and for people who are frequently moving across service boundaries.

- Resourcing a stronger user voice.

- Focusing on the practical realities of good needs assessment and adherence to the Care Programme Approach from the point of initial contact.

- Working hard to achieve integrated health and social service CMHTs and joint agency decisions on priorities, operational policies, CPA management etc.

- Focusing on how to improve responses to those who are frequently admitted, and those who are bed blockers.

It is a key responsibility of commissioners to balance the view of all the stakeholders and make decisions about priorities and how to help facilitate and fund them. This is a key joint commissioning responsibility between Health and Local Authorities having involved many others. Strategy formulation needs to be underpinned by clear milestones and review periods and not tablets of stone. Whilst the 'what' of the objective may be clear, the means of best achieving this may not be clear and an evolving process which builds in sufficient flexibility to learn from implementation and local and national good practice, is critically important.

How do we afford better services and mobilise external support to help achieve this?

Can we afford what we believe we need? Can commissioners share risks with providers within a robust strategic partnership? Can we share costs, appropriately, with other agencies? Is a joint strategy with the Local Authority and the FHSA feasible? Can we engage with the voluntary sector and housing associations on joint initiatives? Can we be credible and motivate mental health professionals, GPs and users to be involved and to stay involved? Can we address the public's concerns?

Developing joint Health and Local Authority strategies which are supported by providers, and the wider world and which motivate engagement and practical action, is not easy. The different agendas of the different stakeholders need to be understood and there will need to be a range of incentives. Assessing what different people would regard as the success criteria, against which the achievement of better services for the severely mentally ill should be measured, is an important starting point. In practice, this needs to be discussed, openly, with honesty about perceptions of strengths and weaknesses and with the lead agencies stressing, repeatedly, their need for feedback and reminders of the realities—the reality of the experience of users trying to survive in an unsympathetic world; the reality of professionals trying to plan and implement whole person care programmes and promote seamless care; the reality of the Police repeatedly returning the same people who have absconded from in-patient care; the reality of GPs with a practice surgery full of distressed and depressed people.

Creating maximum opportunities for joint working between interested and committed people from different organisations is, in itself, a good way of promoting improved practice, through more trusted and mutually supportive relationships, better knowledge of each other's roles, responsibilities and constraints, and why people act in the way they do. It is a commissioner's responsibility to help promote these opportunities for joint working. It is also a commissioner's responsibility to ensure that the simple ways of helping to improve the quality of service delivery that may emerge, can be acted upon and taken forward, so that people feel it is worthwhile to continue to invest their time, to continue to battle away at problem solving, to give incentives. A commissioner is an enabler, a broker, and commissioners need to be accountable for how they spend resources to target need, both in the distribution of the money but also in the time that is asked of practitioners that diverts them from direct patient care.

My priorities within the context of sustaining external support and involvement in commissioning improved mental health services would include:

- Strengthening the non-statutory sector provider role and giving this sector a strategic significance in using the expertise that it offers.

- Investing in the grey areas between health and social care that are so often of such importance in creating effective support for users.

- Focusing CMHTs on working with GP practice populations (with a geographical safety net catchment area) and improving communications with GPs, on a personal level.

- Identifying professionals in CMHTs to liaise with/offer support to, each independent sector facility/organisation offering a service to people with serious mental illness in their patch.

- Prioritising the joint agency resources to ensure housing support workers for people moving on to council estates and/or support workers working with CMHTs to provide a range of practical support and encouragement to users.

- Targeting resources to the more difficult to engage people and to the staff who are inspired to provide intensive rehabilitation and care management support to these people; and sharing their expertise and knowledge with others.

- Providing funds to help resource welfare rights advice, advocacy, legal advice, better information for users and carers, telephone help lines and lots of things which represent to the users meaningful occupation or somewhere friendly and warm to go.

- Looking closely at Mental Health Act use and Section 136 and 117 policies, with Social Services and the Police.

- Clarifying the crucial interfaces between general adult and specialist services, and expectations e.g. with respect to people with personality disorders, or substance misusers.

Creating alliances and partnerships helps to strengthen the force and capacity for change. It will also stimulate numerous good ideas and well substantiated arguments for more money to be invested in mental health services. The financial strategy to support the development of mental health services and to give credence to the achievement of the core service components must be a fundamental responsibility of the commissioners, working jointly with the Local Authority.

Having said this, the lion's share of the money spent on mental health services is within DHA budgets and, in my view, the DHA must be the principal authority prepared to take risks and carry risks financially, when developing strategies. This is not only because the maximum potential for redeploying resources is within the NHS but because without this overt leadership role, it will be very difficult to inspire the support of other agencies. In the old days, it used to be possible to 'bank' money for bridging purposes and to pump prime new initiatives. Regional Health Authorities used to be very helpful in facilitating this. With the cessation of Regional Health Authorities as we used to know them and the Treasury's concern to control more closely the flow of money, the rules within which DHAs must develop financial strategies are changing. There have always been numerous bureaucratic hoops through which managers have had to jump to secure and sustain the necessary finance for strategic development but it seems even more important, now, that we are all saying the same thing about strategic change—that is, that it will take 5 years at least and have a multiplicity of inter-related parts, including key major developments, and an underlying and constant need for revenue for double running periods, whilst new services are developed and before the older ones disappear; and financial planning needs to give some security that key developments that may take four years to materialise can be achieved. The requirement to produce business cases for key strategic changes is understandable in an accountable public service but we must strive to ensure that the context within which one business case is presented is clearly understood by those receiving it and that the whole programme of changes, which may require a number of inter-related business cases, is supported with a recognition of the crucial inter-relationships of each element of the expenditure programme.

Local Authorities and other agencies require some security around joint development initiatives from the DHA. Similarly, providers require some longer term commitment from the DHA before embarking on a series of service changes, all of which have inherent risks to them and their futures. In this context, DHAs need to invest considerable time and energy in developing affordable financial strategies with proper sources and applications of fund statements, and in reviewing these on an annual basis to sustain development at the pace that is necessary to achieve substantial and enduring improvements. Being realistic but challenging about the pace of change and the milestones of achievement and the resource decisions that must support these, is fundamentally important in achieving robust strategic partnerships. This does not mean creating tablets of marble and rigidly inflexible strategies—indeed, quite the opposite, as a constant underpinning of the financial framework must be the seeking of more cost effective ways of achieving improvements and multiple sources of income to help do this. Being opportunistic and pragmatic within a framework in which the DHA carries the principal responsibility for negotiating effective risk management strategies, is essential.

Some of the key components of a robust financial strategy to underpin the achievement of significant improvements in services for seriously mentally ill people, include:

- Ring-fencing/protecting Health Authority expenditure on mental health and explicitly accounting for this on an annual basis—as a key to engaging other agencies.

- Using efficiency and retraction savings from mental health contracts as a bank for pumping priming new local service developments; and finding ways of protecting this money across the financial years.

- Explicitly agreeing the prime funding responsibilities of each statutory authority and of the providers.

- Creating health gain incentive monies to experiment within a framework of monitoring and evaluation but underpinning these with a recurring revenue commitment to be able to sustain them if they prove successful following the evaluation.

- Clarifying the bottom line on future expenditure for mental health within the whole DHA portfolio of health expenditure.

- Being rigorous in identifying poorly used facilities, uneconomic services, vacant housing, questionable skill mix, and other ways of checking out value for money and cost effectiveness and then, engaging in constructive dialogue about how to use better the resources that are available.

- Creating a small reserve to respond to the pragmatic and simple suggestions that are so important to retaining involvement and motivation.

- Investing in needs assessment and recognising the urgency of substantially improved information systems that are operationally and strategically meaningful.

- Agreeing the key cornerstones to a strategy for service improvement and seeking all sources of funding to help build these, using an approach which strengthens the foundations and does not fragment into numerous projects.

To use all the opportunities that are potentially available for helping to finance a service development strategy requires significant investment of time, of manager, professionals, and finance advisors. Continuity of people in key positions who understand the background, who understand why decisions were made and the significance of these for the future, who have the knowledge that promotes resourcefulness and the confidence and ability to make quick judgements and justify these, is important. It may be necessary to invest in lead people to sustain their involvement and keep them. It will be necessary to spend time building the infrastructure of the financial frameworks so that they are intelligible to those people who are less closely involved but who are critical to keeping the priority on the development of the strategies. Stability of key people and the building of trusted relationships of key people within different agencies and across the provider/purchaser interface is worth investing in and may be overlooked with perilous consequences. There is nothing more disruptive than constant staff and organisational changes but if the commitment of key individuals can be maintained, the drive and the accountability can be maintained.

Getting the best out of contracting

How can we use the annual contracting process as a vehicle for commissioning changes in service? How can we make contracting more meaningful and constructive for clinicians? Can we create a contracting partnership which promotes mutual learning and personal/organisational development? How do we get the right balance between supporting a robust strategic partnership but retaining the rigour of independence in negotiation?

The annual contracting process is a key lever for delivering changes and critical to the accountability process for demonstrating to the public the value of resources invested. It is an arduous process and requires attention to detail to prevent misunderstandings about outputs, financial implications, and priorities. There need to be gains for both providers and purchasers in the contracting process and there is a wide consensus about the need to make it a more meaningful process for clinicians. It is their business that the contract is about and they need to own the currencies in which it is purchased and the measures against which its performance is monitored. Although the written documentation that supports contracts is important, it is now widely recognised that it is the face-to-face negotiation and agreements that ensure the delivery, and that whenever possible, these need to involve commissioners, provider managers and clinicians.

There is much that can be done within the contracting process to help establish the core components of service for people with severe and enduring mental illness. Some of the possibilities are noted below but a fundamental pre-requisite of each annual contracting round is to contract for more meaningful activity data and work towards more meaningful currencies of purchase. This must increasingly be based around the core community mental health team contribution; be based on individuals with the contacts and interactions of individual disciplines and the multi-disciplinary team being attributable back to individuals on the caseload. Increasingly, caseload information categorised in a way which separates out the different kinds of referrals and the different groups of users in contact with the service, and using the recommended tiered Care Programme Approach will become the norm. Building contract data from an identified caseload which is reported on the basis of general practice populations and geography and, thereby, can be related into a needs assessment framework for the population, is likely to be the most meaningful way forward. Looking at the key components of service delivery against this caseload, so that CMHT profiles of patients' activity outputs and outcomes are incrementally developed against costs, built up in the same way, will give a framework which promotes constructive dialogue between purchasers and provider managers and clinicians—a dialogue from which many opportunities for better utilisation of resources and improvement of service may be identifiable and mutually agreed.

It is important that commissioners and providers work together on new information systems that can help to achieve this and on the disaggregation of contract values to support this process. This presumes that a multi-disciplinary team is working together, has appropriate administrative support to help develop manual systems in the absence of computer systems to identify the team caseload, and is given information to review its use of other resources which it may not directly manage or control. Given the fundamental requirement to develop joint health and social care community mental health teams, it is also important that Social Services information is available to teams in a way that relates to their caseload. Commissioners can be helpful in facilitating these developments and in helping to negotiate the key components of a minimum data set which is meaningful to commissioners and to providers.

Some of the other ways in which contracting can be used to help lever change which is beneficial to service users and to professionals include:

> - Creating contract schedules which put CMHT work in the context of their use of day care and in-patient beds and other key resources for their population; and discussing contract outputs, targets and performance in a way that recognises that CMHTs are accountable for their use of these resources.
>
> - Devolving social care purchasing funds to CMHTs and creating a data set which helps describe how these are used on the basis of team caseloads.
>
> - Creating small flexible budgets for CMHTs to use, to stimulate creativity in the formulation of a care plans and enable the small things which make the difference for a user, realisable.
>
> - Monitoring the implementation of the CPA, Section 117, Supervision Register requirements by CMHT and putting energy into integrating these related policies and procedures so that they use the minimum amount of documentation and documentation that feeds computerised systems.
>
> - Making sure that some priorities for clinical audit support the main priorities for service development and quality improvement, but giving providers flexibility to pursue others.
>
> - Developing joint agency reviews of key performance areas and sharing information to help inform contract reviews and monitoring.
>
> - Giving providers the clear lead when this is critical to their organisational development.
>
> - Giving providers the money and responsibility for special contractual placements so that the best expertise is used in determining the most appropriate placements, within a framework of cost constraint and accountability to commissioners.
>
> *continued*

continued

- Sharing validation of data and data quality and undertaking in-depth studies to help the provider improve on this.

- Feeding back user experience and concerns in the contract discussions so that there can be discussion about these and agreed ways forward.

- Giving users funds to strengthen their participation and voice on quality issues and quality targets.

- Giving providers incentives to help manage demand, e.g. around acute admissions.

- Recognising that at times of great stress, when there is an excessive demand on available services, it is sometimes necessary to buy space, time and goodwill to focus on new methods of working.

- Building in dedicated time to get to know the services being purchased and see the reality of the constraints within which staff are working

- Identifying those problems which commissioners must take responsibility for resolving or helping to resolve and being prepared to account for relative progress in doing so within the contract discussions, e.g. the creation of alternative housing and move on accommodation to prevent bed blocking.

Constructive negotiation means give and take and recognition of each other's perspectives and constraints and opportunities. This can only be done effectively by involving as many of the key participants as possible, at appropriate stages in the process. It is useful to review after the three months of arduous work between January and March, how efficient and effective the process seemed to be, from the perspectives of purchasers and providers.

The 'wicked' problems

There are a number of 'wicked' problems which have bedevilled the development of improved services for people with severe and enduring mental illness, for many years. These problems have undermined progress despite priority being placed on mental health services and despite additional bursts of money or supportive policy thrusts, such as the inclusion of mental health in the Health of the Nation.

My list of 'wicked' problems include:

- The constant effort required to secure and retain the necessary funds to see through strategic change over a number of years, and how to ensure that change is driven through to a successful outcome, despite major uncertainties about resources and other key building bricks.

- Managing the lack of time to do things and the numerous priorities without jettisoning the involvement of key people.

- Creating non-firefighting time to reflect, build relationships, think creatively, whilst ensuring delivery against the key non-negotiable priorities within a corporate contract and the others which arrive unexpectedly during the year.

- Coping with feelings of scepticism, cynicism and powerlessness that can drown the commitment and resourcefulness of people in all parts of the service and users and carers.

- Poverty, poor housing, isolation, and the lack of meaningful activity for people with severe mental illness that undermines the resilience of workers and users, and the feasible achievements.

- Finding more and more unmet need, e.g. through court diversion schemes and through making services much more accessible and acceptable.

- The bad press and wrong messages that the media can give, that undermine the best of efforts and challenges morale.

Despite these and many other 'wicked' problems, many improvements are realised. Maintaining a belief that it is possible, the trust between key people and agencies, and the motivation of all the people who are committed to improving mental health services, are the ultimate sustainers of initiative, energy and resourcefulness. It is a commissioner's responsibility to help lead this and maintain positive progress. It is a commissioner's responsibility to use the power invested through money and decision making wisely, with ultimate and explicit accountability, overtly acknowledging that this role is executed on behalf of the residents of our population and in support of care workers in many agencies, without whose support and commitment nothing would be achieved.

8 Purchasing from a User Perspective

MARION BEEFORTH & HELEN WOOD

This chapter will describe the service system that is seen as needed, from the view point of the people who use them. The information has been obtained from two primary sources. Firstly, issues raised at the Mental Health Task Force User conferences held between end of 1993 and Nov. 1994. Ten conferences were held across Britain, with 100 users at each, totalling the views of over 1,000 service users/survivors. The second source is from a report on an extensive review of user literature (51 articles) commissioned by the Audit Commission in 1994 for their review of mental health services (Wood, 1994). The need for purchasers and providers to take account of service users views is well noted and acknowledged (Audit Commission 1994, Mental Health Foundation 1994, D.O.H. 1989, 1990), Beeforth *et al* 1990) *'User participation is important for making the service system effective in meeting individual need'* (Audit Commission 1994 pg 38).

Ten priorities

- Access to Information

- Presence of a Charter

- 24 hour, 7 day week availability

- Practical help

- Flexibility and Responsiveness to Individual Need

- User Run Services

- Advocacy

- Access to Specialist Help

- Something Meaningful to do during the day

- An Integrated System with Continuity of Care.

---

1 Access to information:

A wide range of information needs to be available, in a variety of formats (written, verbal, tape, video) using clear, simple language. It should be available in a range of languages and locations, easily accessible and preferably written by or with service users. Information may need to be given more than once, as at times of distress it can be very difficult to remember things or take it all in.

The most commonly described types of information requested include:

Information on

- **Rights:** Personal & Legal rights, rights for redress, how to make complaints and how those complaints will be addressed.

- **Medication:** including risks and benefits, side effects, expected duration of prescription, monitoring and review procedures.

- **Treatment:** Range of treatment options available, alternatives to medical treatment, talking therapies etc.

- **Care Plan:** A written copy of peoples care plan should be given to them.

- **Hospital Admission:** admission procedures, ward procedures and policies, length of stay, facilities, rules, status, visiting etc.

- **Services & Facilities:** What is available locally, both in hospital and in the community across all agencies, including self-help groups; how to access them and when they are open.

- **Staff:** What are the different roles, what can they offer, how to contact them, when they are available, what cover is available for when they are away.

- **Welfare & Benefits:** What are my entitlements, how do I apply, how does hospital admission affect my benefits, can I work etc.

- **Advocacy:** What independent services are available, what type of advocacy, what user forums are around and how to contact them.

---

2 Existence of a charter:

Many people who come in contact with services would find it extremely helpful to have access to a charter, this being a clear statement of intent outlining standards of what can be expected. It should include the following:

Statement of intent

- **Confidentiality about Information:** People need to feel that private and distressing information they pass on to professionals will be kept safe and not passed onto others without their express permission.

- **Safety:** People need to feel that when they come into hospital (or a community facility) that personal safety is held as a high priority, both from the point of view of violence as well as sexual harassment/assault. This is particularly the case for women, many of whom seek women only units. The importance of safety should also be extended to personal belongings. Provider units should make it explicit how they intend to keep people suffering distress safe. Safety also includes safe use of medication (not over prescribed).

- **Complaints Procedure:** People need to know that there are accessible means by which they can express their concerns about the treatment they are receiving, particularly to an independent source. The procedure should clearly state how to make a complaint and to who, how it is dealt with and how long it might take. A written and verbal response to complaints should be given.

- **Needs Led Service:** Service users want to know that the service they receive will reflect their specific needs, situation and be responsive to age, gender and cultural background. Flexibility and choice in treatment provision is essential, alongside their active involvement in determining the service they receive.

- **Involvement in Decision Making:** People want to know that they will have opportunities to be actively involved in determining decisions that affect their own lives.

- **Support:** People want to feel confident that they will receive the right level of support necessary to achieve a desirable standard of quality of life. They do not want to feel overpowered or ignored by services.

3   24 Hour, 7 day week availability:

Service users have for many years expressed the viewpoint that they cannot contain their crisis or distress to Mon–Fri, 9–5pm. Help needs to be available and accessible at the time it is needed. In many instances, this can prevent an escalation of the problem and reduce the demand for hospitalisation and crisis services. In addition to specialist health assistance, there needs to be provision of social supports in the form of evening and weekend activities. Social isolation is a frequent life experience of people in contact with mental health services. Service users need to know that there is somewhere they can go to meet people if they need support and or social opportunities.

Extended hours provision

- **Accessible Help in times of Crisis:** including alternatives to hospital admission e.g. crisis house; telephone help lines; 24 hour 7 day week response.

- **Focus on prevention and early intervention work:** helping people develop coping strategies; regular contact and monitoring of well-being.

- **Prompt Response:** short waiting times.

- **Access to Evening and Weekend activities and support.**

- **Extended availability of staff:** eg 8am–8pm seven day cover as a baseline for service provision.

4 Practical help:

One of the most strongly expressed needs is that of access to practical help. In many instances, neglect to attend to basic needs creates crisis situations and enhances feelings of not being able to cope. Services must attend to people's most basic needs first, if they are to make any impact on general emotional well being. This help should be imaginatively and flexibly offered, in many instances through multi-agency collaborative working practices.

Practical help:

- **Maximising Income:** Access to welfare and benefits advice to ensure people have a sustainable income to live on is essential.

- **Financial Assistance:** Assistance with keeping up to date with bills, rent and negotiating the housing and welfare system. Help with money management is also needed.

- **Help Finding Appropriate Housing.**

- **Activities of Daily Living:** Practical help with basic tasks at home eg cooking, home maintenance, shopping, personal care etc.

- **Help to build up self confidence:**

- **Social Contacts:** Support and introduction to social networks that individuals can develop.

- **Peer Support:** Creating opportunities for peer support through social clubs, user groups/forums, peer advocacy, self help groups etc.

5 Flexibility & responsiveness to individual needs:

It can be very difficult to objectively monitor a services ability to be flexible and responsive to needs. It is not a building, nor x number of professionals, frequently the indicators presented as the availability of a service. Purchasers and providers need to identify creative mechanisms for auditing service outcomes in relation to their ability to create appropriate and responsive service provision. Of course, the most candid measure is to ask service users. Flexible and responsive service features might include:

Flexible & responsive

- **Respect for individuality:**   Every individuals needs will differ according to age, culture, gender, personal background, social supports.

- **Choice:**   There should be opportunities for people to have choices over the type and style of treatment/service that might benefit them. This includes having alternatives and choice in location of service, alternatives to being admitted to hospital, choice of workers and treatment interventions including non-medical treatments.

- **Multi-disciplinary assessment**

- **People involved in decision making and views listened to**

- **Integrated system of health and social care**

- **Recording un-met need:**   for use in future planning.

---

6 User run services

Frequently people who have been in contact with mental health services have noted they would prefer services that are run by others who have had similar experiences. Service users as a group seek to have a more equal partnership with providers of services, being actively involved in determining, planning, providing and monitoring services. This may involve having control over their own resources or working in partnership with agencies, either as a purchasers or providers. The literature review for the Audit Commission report noted a preference for user run facilities and drop-ins as alternatives for the more traditional medical model of many statutory services. The Mental Health Task Force has produced national guidelines for a framework for local charters for user involvement. Real involvement is more than broad based consultation exercises. It also encompasses people active participation in decision making fora.

> **User involvement**
>
> - **Broader User Involvement:** Individual, unit, organisational and purchasing levels.
>
> - **Services run for and by other service users.**
>
> - **Support for Involvement:** Provision of resources, information, practical assistance, training, forums and structures, views listened to, financial reward for involvement.
>
> - **Support for workers.**
>
> - **Opportunities:** To be involved and for people to get together without professionals/service managers.
>
> - **Training:** for staff to allow users to be involved fully and for service users to acquire skills and confidence to do the job.

7 Advocacy:

Access to advocacy is having someone, independent from the service, who will assist the individual in obtaining the services they see they need, or in making a complaint. It could involve someone speaking on their behalf, or with that person, to ensure that their views are heard and individual rights are respected. It cannot be effectively done by a key worker other than in pursuing a negotiated care plan.

The right to seek an independent advocate (of their own choice) if desired, is seen as extremely important and necessary. This is particularly the case for people under the Mental Health Act. There should be accessible information on how to access an advocate and that this person is freely able to make contact with the individual concerned. Service users are very clear that a key worker can not fulfil this role as an independent voice.

> **Advocacy**
>
> - **Free.**
>
> - **Peer/Citizen/Legal Advocacy:** these are all different types of advocacy and it should be made clear which is on offer.
>
> - **Essential for people detained under Mental Health Act.**
>
> - **Training available.**
>
> - **Local charter for standards.**
>
> - **Support for independent projects.**

8   Access to specialist help:

Within the service system, their should be opportunities for people to gain access to specialist help, advice and treatment when and if desired. Involvement with specialist services should be negotiated. People in contact with the mental health service should also have equitable access to good physical care.

Specialist help

- **Benefits and Welfare Advice.**

- **Housing.**

- **Social Worker**

- **Health Professionals:**   Physical and mental health professionals

- **Education and Employment specialists.**

---

9   Meaningful activities:

People are looking for opportunities to participate in activities that help build skills, confidence and interests that are relevant to their lifestyles. Support needs to be available to help people use ordinary local resources to enhance feeling part of the local community and re-engage with community life away from specialist services. Help with employment is extremely important as well as availability of drop-ins and centres offering support in times of need.

Activities:

- **Valued, interesting and stimulating.**

- **Develop useful skills.**

- **Include:**   Work opportunities
             Social
             Leisure
             Educational
             Spiritual.

- **Reflect individuals life in terms of race, culture, gender, age and religion.**

- **Promote integration with their community.**

- **Available in Range Settings:**   naturally occurring community facilities, specialist facilities, people's homes.

- **Options to promote Choice:**   People may not want to do exactly the same thing every day.

- **Available Evenings and Weekends.**

---

10   Integrated services:

Purchasers need to establish an integrated network of services, promoting continuity and collaborative working. People often find it difficult to navigate their way around the range of different service agencies (inc. health and social services, primary care, housing, welfare etc.). Very often people feel like they fall between the cracks or end up in a position where two, or often three, agencies are working in opposition, with no one knowing what anyone else is doing. A very confusing and distressing position for the individual concerned to be in.

Integrated services

- **Joint Commissioning of Health and Social Care:**   Integrated system of Care Management and Care Programme Approach with joint needs assessment.

- **Better Collaboration with Community Agencies:**   Especially local 'Black' and ethnic minority community groups, voluntary organisations etc.

- **Integrated with Primary Care:**   including better communication between primary and secondary care agencies.

- **Good Communication Systems:**

- **People with Longer Term Support Needs:**   There should be a named individual (with holiday cover) responsible for co-ordination and liaison across agencies and between hospital and community services.

- **Evaluation:**   Mechanisms for evaluating effectiveness of service systems should be established and incorporate users as part of this process.

Monitoring user participation

The following are a sample of questions that can be asked in monitoring how both purchaser and provider units facilitate and support users in influencing service provision. They are not in any particular order of merit but can be used as a baseline for setting standards to ensure user participation.

Does your Trust have an independent advocacy service?
Who runs this service?

Do you support user groups/patients councils?
Do all units have user groups or patient councils?
Do you fund user groups?
Where do they meet?
Do you let them use your photocopiers?
Who pays their telephone bills?
Who funds them?

Do you have a users charter negotiated with local users?   Do you know the local charter? Are your services evaluated by users, so that services are accountable to users?

Do you have direct links with user groups?
    Is there a named person responsible for user involvement?
 	
Are users involved in interviewing new staff members?
    Do you provide training to enable users to do this?
    Are all people applying for jobs with your organisation sent information about your policy on user involvement?
 	
Are there arrangements for involving users in professional training?

Is there a particular service you are proud of? If so, can you describe it? Does your Trust have users on planning groups?   Are they democratically elected?
Are people able to discuss their preferences about treatment? Do people have a choice of worker, or can they change their Psychiatrist—for example, to have a woman worker?
Have there been changes resulting from consultation with users?   What evidence can you show for this?

Within the purchasing process, commissioners should ensure that users views are clearly taken account of, and that both the ideology and practical implementation of user involvement is made explicit in this process.

References

Audit Commission (1994) Finding a Place. *A Review of Mental Health Services for Adults.* London HMSO.

Mental Health Foundation (1994). Creating Community Care. *Report of the Mental Health Foundation Inquiry into Community Care for People with Severe Mental illness.* London, Mental Health Foundation.

HMSO (1989) Caring for People. *Community Care in the Next Decade and Beyond.*

HMSO (1990) *Community Care in the Next Decade and Beyond.*

Beeforth, M., Conlon, E., V., Hoser, B. Sayce, L. (Eds) (1990). Whose Service is it Anyway? *Users Views on Co-ordinating Community Care.* London Research and Development for Psychiatry (Sainsbury Centre for Mental Health).

Wood, H. (1994). What do Service Users Want from Mental Health Services. Report to the Audit Commission for *Finding a Place. A Review of Mental Health Services for Adults.*

Further Reading

Beeforth, M., Conlon, E., Graley, R. (1994). Have we got News for you. *User Evaluation of Case Management*, London, Sainsbury Centre for Mental Health.

Beresford, P. and Harding, T. (Eds) (1993). A Challenge to Change. *Practical Experiences of Building User Led Services*. National Institute of Social Work.

Brandon, A. and D. (1992). *Consumers as Colleagues*. London MIND.

Croft, S. and Beresford, P. (1993). Getting Involved. *A Practical Manual*. Open Services Project and Joseph Rowntree Foundation.

Hutchison, M., Linton, G., Lucas, J. (199?). User Involvement Information Pack. *From Policy to Practice*. MIND Southeast.

National Schizophrenia Fellowship (1992). How to Involve Users and Carers. *Guidelines on Involvement in Planning, Running and Monitoring Care Services*.

Rogers, A., Pilgrim, D., Lacey, R. (1993). Experiencing Psychiatry. *Users Views of Services*. London, MIND.

Smith, H. (1988). Collaboration for Change. *Partnership between Service Users, Planners and Managers for Mental Health Services*. London, Kings Fund Centre.

User Centred Services Group (1993). *Building Bridges between People who use services and people who provide services*. National Institute of Social Work.

9 Purchasing Mental Health Services for Black Communities

KAMALDEEP BHUI and YVONNE CHRISTIE

Introduction

Black people suffer disadvantage in gaining access to psychiatric services (Littlewood & Lipsedge, 1989; Fernando, 1988; Rack, 1982). Black people are more likely to be admitted to psychiatric hospitals by means of a compulsory order (Rwegellera, 1970; Littlewood & Lipsedge, 1981; Ineichen, 1984; McGovern & Cope, 1987). The police are more likely to be involved in the admission of black people who are described as showing more 'disturbed behaviour' (Scheiffer, 1968; Owens *et al* 1991). The Asian population show inconsistent results in that some studies suggest an over-representation and others an infrequent use of compulsory orders (Pinto, 1970; McGovern & Cope, 1987). Less attention is paid to the Chinese and Vietnamese community. Black patients are more likely to be admitted following a section 136 compared to a white population and less likely to be admitted routinely through their GP (Moodley & Perkins 1991; Hitch & Clegg, 1980). Thus the higher rates of compulsory admission to psychiatric facilities and the differential use of treatments between different racial groups continues to be a matter of importance.

It would not seem unreasonable to conclude that the ability of Black people to have their social and health care needs met is especially compromised; on the one hand they are already a disadvantaged group which has faced difficulties of adjusting to a new way of life, has been exposed to racist persecution and threats of violence and individuals have experienced inequalities of opportunity; secondly they suffer psychiatric disorder which, within the existing health care system, is not identified or treated in the same manner as it is amongst a native English sample (London, 1986; Leff, 1988; Cochrane, 1977; Belliapa, 1991; Rack, 1982). 'Racial discrimination was a strong factor in the treatment of Christopher Clunis. A common pattern emerges in the way in which Clunis was treated' (Francis, 1994). This may be how black people are treated and experience their treatment within the existing system of healthcare. Racism is often institutionalised and hence may become part of the commissioning process. Black people may be stigmatised by their own communities or indeed their own communities may not recognise them to be ill. This can further add to isolation or the instigation unsuccessfully of other coping strategies. Inability to access existing services may be a factor leading to presentation in crisis (Bhui *et al* 1993).

Mental disorder and black people: different rates of disorder

Operationally defined diagnoses of Schizophrenia have been reported to be more prevalent amongst Black people of African and Caribbean origin both in the United States and in the U.K. (Harrison, 1988; Littlewood & Lipsedge, 1989; Adebimpe, 1994; Fernando, 1988). However, in the Epidemiological Catchment Area study in the U.S. there was no difference in the prevalence rates of schizophrenia after correction for age, sex socio-economic status, and marital status (Adebimpe, 1994).

Table 1: *Racial differences in reported rates of schizophrenia in US and UK clinical samples*

Clinical Setting		whites	blacks	black/white ratio
United States		(% of admissions)		
state hospitals		31.5	56.3	1.8
private hospitals		19.2	35.7	1.8
non-federal hospitals		22.7	38.0	1.7
Veterans affairs medical centres		26.4	44.5	1.7
British Psychiatric hospitals		(incidence per 10 000 population)		
Dean et al (1981)	male	1.1	3.9	5.0
	female	1.2	3.3	5.3
Cochrane & Bal (1987)	male	1.2	5.5	3.3
	female	1.0	5.3	2.8
McGovern & Cope (1987)	16–29 y.o.	1.4	11.7	8.4
	30–64 y.o.	1.1	4.7	4.3
Harrison et al (1988)	16–29	2.0	29.1	14.6
	30–44	1.6	19.7	12.3

Table reference: Adebimpe (1994).

The ECA found no difference between blacks and whites in the prevalence rates of anti-social personality disorder, affective disorders, drug dependence and panic disorder. Race related differences were demonstrated for phobic disorders, generalised anxiety disorders and somatisation disorders which were more frequent in blacks; obsessive compulsive disorders were under represented. However, British studies indicate that Black people are less likely to receive diagnoses of anxiety or depression in primary care (Gillam, 1989). This is paradoxical as causal factors in anxiety and depressive disorders are amongst the socio-cultural explanations put forward to account for higher rates of schizophrenia amongst Black people (Lloyd, 1993); consistent with this hypothesis are studies indicating higher rates of anxiety and depressive disorders amongst Black primary care attenders (Kiev, 1965). Burke (1987) suggests that non recognition by GPs is responsible and reported that GPs failed to make a diagnosis in up to 21.3% of black patients and 12.8% of white patients identified as ill by a screening instrument.

A relationship between race, ethnicity and specific diagnosis is also demonstrated in American studies but there appears to be no generalised pattern applicable across racial groups (Flaskerud & Hu, 1992). In some instances diagnoses are clearly related to the historical experience of adversity amongst certain racial, cultural and religious groups. Thus Hinton *et al* (1993) demonstrated that 18.4% of Vietnamese and Chinese refugees had one or more psychiatric disorders. Vietnamese had higher rates of post traumatic stress disorders explained by their experiences of more traumatic events including separation from families. On the whole the data remains controversial as any relationship is likely to be complex and not easily modelled.

Mentally disordered offenders and black people

Black people of African or Caribbean Origin are overrepresented within the criminal justice system as offenders and are under-represented as representatives of various agencies of the Criminal justice system (CJS; NAPO, 1989; NACRO 1991 & 1993; Cope, 1990). Taylor (1986) showed that of all her sample of life sentenced prisoners being supervised in the community, 10% had a diagnosis of schizophrenia and of these 41% were born in the West Indies. Yet very few black people were admitted to Grendon, again suggesting less health care service contact. Black alcoholics in the USA are less often treated in hospital and more often end up in gaol compared to a white population (Pasaminck, 1963). Regional secure units also contain an excess of minorities (Jones & Berry, 1986). This may be explained by Black people being perceived as more threatening (Bolton, 1984) and by difficulties of communication; further factors accounting for this pattern include a failure of interventions/aftercare and situations in which illness is not recognised (Pasamanick, 1963; Lewis *et al* 1979; Dolan *et al*, 1990; Perera *et al*, 1991).

Medication

Black users have voiced their dissatisfaction with excessive doses of medication, the adverse effects of which are often more intolerable than some of the original targeted symptoms (Wilson, 1993). Racial differences in sensitivity to alcohol, response to anti-depressant medication, response to neuroleptic medication and other psychotropics have been demonstrated (Lin *et al* 1989; Takahashi *et al*, 1975; Raskin *et al* 1975; Glazer *et al*, 1994; Yamashita, 1992). The recent changes in practice regarding the prescription of high doses of neuroleptics met with the resistance of many years of clinical experience. Perhaps it is similarly time to challenge views about medication amongst Black people who are known in Britain to receive major tranquillizers and anti-depressants more frequently than White patients, more often as a depot, at higher doses, and less often psychotherapy or counselling. A closer working relationship with pharmacists, systematic drug reviews, and a national standard of care is essential.

Psychotherapy services

'Whilst exact figures on the numbers of black people offered formal psychotherapy have never been published by the Tavistock or the Institute of Psychoanalysis the impression has been that the numbers are very small' (Littlewood, 1988). There has been a greater concern recently that ethnic minorities have difficulty in gaining access to psychiatric services and that such services are not culturally sensitive (Fernando, 1988; Littlewood & Lipsedge, 1989). ' A common statement perhaps muted recently, has been that psychotherapy is essentially culture bound to the western middle class milieu in which it was practised by this class for themselves and that it is not appropriate for the non-European patients who are themselves less verbally sophisticated, less psychologized, preferring to express their distress through a different idiom-somatic, religious or whatever' (Littlewood & Lipsedge, 1989). These notions are examined and discredited by Littlewood and Lipsedge but still seem to influence psychotherapy practice.

'All societies make distinctions between desired and undesired states of being, and have standardised forms of reconstructing experience, through the response of other people to return the individual to a state desired by the individual and community alike. At such a level of abstraction therapy is universal' (Littlewood, 1992). Thus western models of psychotherapy may be unfamiliar to minority groups; this is not the same as a common inference that minority groups because of their lack of historical experience with western psychotherapy lack the ability to use such services.

Nafsiyat, an intercultural psychotherapy centre, has practised intercultural therapy for many years with success. The centre deliberately set itself against ethnic matching except where issues of language made it impossible (Acharya 1989). The gender and racial politics of such matching have been given considerable attention (Littlewood & Lipsedge, 1989; Kareem & Littlewood, 1992; Fernando, 1988). Yet many black organisations still suspect and voice that black experience can not be understood unless the therapist has first hand experience of being black. Should the client's own preference be taken account of? Certainly there exist cases whereby a person asks for therapy to be conducted in the English language despite it being a second language; similarly a refusal to see a therapist from the same ethnic group and culture has often been cited by patients who wish to disclose and discuss acts or events which are taboo within their own culture.

Families

In cultures where an individual's identity and sense of self and personhood are linked to that of the family, distress is likely to be manifest in an interpersonal terms as social dilemmas or family distress (Belliapa, 1991; Marsella & White, 1982). Treating the individual as if he/she were entirely autonomous, a positive attribute of individual personality in the west but not so in many other cultures (Marsella & White, 1982), may be ineffective but also neglects and denies a self defined role of families in many non-western cultures in providing care for ill relatives (Mumford, 1994). Families should be involved in regular meetings to discuss treatment options even if formal therapy sessions are not indicated and such involvement has been demonstrated to be especially important for the families of Black mentally ill people (Lin *et al* 1991). The reluctance of statutory sectors to acknowledge the importance of the family and to develop services to support the dependants in Black families often leaves Black parents unsettled and suspicious of the long term intentions of social and health care service structures (Bushell, 1992).

New services in a changing NHS

Local, more appropriate packages of care should be encouraged. Users must have a channel to influence such developments in the context of scientific advances and epidemiological data which identifies effective interventions related to new medications and innovative psychological strategies. For example linguistically and culturally isolated women may be better cared for at home with either the help of their extended family, if this exists and is comfortably viable, or support from a 24 hour crisis service can be offered. This avoids an enforced admission onto an acutely disturbed, mixed sex and culturally unfamiliar environment. Treatment preferences of black people should be given consideration (however unfamiliar to the professional) with an explicit documented assessment of decision-risk informing the eventual outcome. This is especially important where decisions about detention and compulsory medication are considered as it is in these areas that many black people feel especially aggrieved and unheard (Wilson, 1994). Existing services need to acknowledge their limitations and set targets for improved service delivery for defined groups. Traditional healers and therapies are still used by many alongside consultation with doctors (Bhopal, 1989); it appears that such healers offer Black people a more holistic and generally acceptable solution to their problems of living which may inadvertently be medicalised if doctors are consulted. Paradoxically traditional healers do more often involve families and perhaps it is this component of the holistic approach which facilitates success at recruiting families in a treatment alliance.

We do not know how effective court diversion, prison diversion and care management are for black groups. Already alienated to existing services, the wave of new developments in services not evaluated can only result in further disadvantage. Access to social care may also be prohibitively complex if language and customs inhibit the successful completion of forms and other criteria required by social service offices. Day centres, disability allowances, invalidity benefits, supportive counselling, experience of racism are all issues that require attention. Each of these potential hurdles warrant an evaluation of the progress black people make in negotiating institutionalised barriers.

Information, dissemination and assessments should take account of the diversity of first languages spoken by Black people. A factor often overlooked is that mental health interpreters need special training as do professionals making use of them. Sharing a language is insufficient alone to capture a communication of distress and is fraught with pitfalls (Westermeyer, 1991). Black users highlight their preference for the involvement of bilingual staff rather than interpreters (Wilson, 1994). Potential breaches of confidentiality and the risk of one's community becoming aware about one's mental illness may deter some people from seeking help through an interpreter (or professional) who also belongs to their community; the use of advocates has been encouraged to overcome this problem (Rack, 1982). Organisational audit strategies are essential to continuously monitor the quantity and quality of health and social care offered to those attending statutory services.

Procedures & regulations

Admission procedures and the ward environment should be designed taking account of the cultural diversity of Black people. Units should ensure that religious and cultural practices are supported. This includes the involvement of religious leaders, whose support and care of individuals extends to their spiritual and social needs, as well as attendance at a place of worship. There are diverse religious, spiritual and social needs amongst Black communities and these should be seen as foci for understanding and hence appropriate intervention. For example Black men's over-representation in forensic services and locked units warrants special attention and appropriate initiatives to address inequalities within existing primary and secondary care services (NAPO, 1989; NACRO 1991 & 1993; Jones & Berry, 1986). A similarly bleak example of differential service delivery has been described in the United States where Black alcoholics in the USA are less often treated and end up in gaols (Pasaminack, 1963) and although Black, Hispanic and White offenders in the USA are equally affected by epilepsy or drug abuse, White offenders have more often been in contact with psychiatric services (Novick *et al*, 1977).

Case history 1

Miss K is a 34 year old lady who came to the UK from Hong Kong at her father's request over 20 years ago and is of Chinese origin. She has a diagnosis of schizophrenia for which she is treated with high dose depot medication; she suffers torticollis which is relieved when her medication is reduced. This however, precipitates relapse. She has only been assessed by a Chinese speaking psychiatrist when in crisis; this usually results in admission under a section of the mental health act as she appears hostile and unwilling to talk. She lives on her own. Her mother who lives nearby is her only support. She persists in being rather tearful and falling in love with different members of the team. She is terrified of the Chinese community's response to her and therefore avoids them but also says that she is really English. There are no local facilities for her to see a Chinese psychiatrist or to receive day care travel incorporating something of her own culture and she is too nervous to talk much even with a member of the team; she does not tolerate change well. The team responsible for her care are uncertain of the degree of symptomatology she displays and whether she would be better treated with clozapine. In view of the persistent blood tests however, KL has refused this option. Her history is characterised by relapses often with no certain triggering factors. The whole family's response to this and her own understanding

continued

---

continued

of her illness remains elusive. She remains intensely lonely but any attempt to find real social contacts are resisted for fear of rejection. It may be that the avoidance is related to persistent delusional beliefs. Local day care which takes account of her culture and challenges some of her notions about disability is essential if progress is to be made.

Case history 2

Miss O is a 40 year old single lady who lives with her dog and is of Jamaican origin. She has been known to her local psychiatric service for 6 years and refuses to have any medication fearing that she is being drugged up and losing control. The diagnosis is thought to be one of delusional disorder. She is very lonely and has no trusting relationship always fearing that people are trying to influence her or 'her spirits' and that if 'the spirits' found out she would suffer. She becomes distressed when 'The spirits' become too intrusive or if anyone interferes sexually with her dog; she has accused people of sexually assaulting her dog. On one occasion she has been aggressive with a neighbour and struck him. At times of crisis mental health act assessments have resulted in the approved social worker fearing that her beliefs are culturally consistent and that she may not be mentally ill. She continues to see a counsellor trained in traditional healing techniques at the local women's centre. She feels she has the matter in hand and that she is not ill but lonely and requires clear structures within which to live her life. She reports that her spirits when present are a mechanism to elicit care in a childlike way and that if ignored they result in no harm. Sometimes when the spirits talk to her she is unable to distract herself from them. However, each time mental health services attempt any work with her she refuses contact. When they minimise their contact social services become alarmed or reports from neighbours re-involve them but at no point has an ASW been agreeable to enact a section of the MHA. All psychiatrists are agreed that she has a delusional disorder and her brother's statement that her beliefs are odd confirmed this. When once on a depot she functioned much better and was starting evening classes. The decline since stopping medication is not sufficient to persuade her, the counsellor or social services of her need or right to treatment. She may be denied treatment in an attempt to ensure that she is not inadvertently admitted or she may be admitted under section only to find that enforced medication no longer diminishes her symptoms. The dilemma is not an uncommon one and clearly there are decision risks which need to be evaluated.

Conclusions

The restructuring of health care services has proceeded without due attention to the needs of Black people. Changes in practice require not only information about the potential and effective treatment strategies for any individual but also new strategies for making decisions outside the traditional bio-medical hospital based framework. This will involve all mental health professionals who must question existing standards of care, critically evaluate new directions and potential strategies, engage local Black organisations and users of services and audit progress made not only in terms of illness episodes for the chronically mentally ill but speed of access and satisfaction with services. Clearly it is time for purchasers to address some of the issues raised by Black people. Recommendations are presented below:

Consultation with a range of black communities through:

> Places of worship: Temples, Pentecostal Churches, 7th day Adventists
>
> Black voluntary and community organisations
>
> Ante-natal clinics
>
> Community centres
>
> Youth services
>
> Schools
>
> Local Black radio stations

Directory of local services

> Available for users, staff, families, GPs etc.
>
> Translated in relevant local languages
>
> Access to services
>
> Identify Service users
>
> Quantify & monitor use of services
>
> Examine quality of intervention and its effectiveness based on user satisfaction
>
> Draw upon statutory and voluntary sector expertise
>
> Be prepared to evaluate therapeutic risks
>
> Evaluate the effectiveness of alternative therapy based on client outcomes

Dependants and family therapy

> Availability and use of family therapy for Black communities
>
> The employment of appropriate bilingual staff
>
> Appropriate adaptions of existing therapies taking account of different cultural family norms
>
> Community services which acknowledge and make space for individual's dependants including respite services
>
> The developmental impact amongst children of mental illness in parents and other relatives should be actively addressed without labelling

Treatments

For many years Black people have expressed their disquiet about the sole use of psychotropic medication. The experiences of African Caribbeans is that they receive larger doses of medication and report severe adverse effects which become apparent for many of them.

Pharmacological treatments should be seen as part of the total package of care including alternative treatments

Therapeutic risks should be agreed and evaluated by discussion between complimentary therapists, psychiatrists and patients.

The named responsible medical officer will of course still have ultimate responsibility for the individual and that named practitioner should work in close liaison with the relevant therapist so that a jointly agreed package of care is carried forward

There needs to be built in to community mental health services some assessment of risk factors to allow people to try out some of the complimentary therapies with safeguards

Complementary treatments, which are preferred by Black people, should be evaluated from within the mainstream services, the voluntary and independent services

Only when complimentary treatments are systematically evaluated do successful outcomes for the individual will the whole debate regarding psychotropic medication vs no medication approaches be resolved

Medication can often become the focus of issues around control and autonomy. As such decisions arrived at without consultation with patients may alienate already distressed people

The success of the package of care will be reflected in the trusting partnership between practitioners and patients

Examples of good practice

1 Psychotherapeutic approaches for Black people with persistent psychotic symptoms

The Forward Project (VS)	London
housing, psychotherapies, target severe mental illness	
Mary Seacole House (VS)	Liverpool
Advocacy, user empowerment, day leisure	
The Fanon Project (VS)	London
Day care, meals, psychotherapy, target severe mentally ill	

2 Day care

The Fanon Project (VS)	London
contain and work with severely mentally ill not engaged with statutory services	
The Kingsbury Manor (SS)	London
Day centre for Gujerati community, bilingual staff links with adult education, Asian food, 24 hour cover subject to funding	
The Lambo Day Centre (VS)	London
African & Caribbean people, positive images through museums and library containing African and Caribbean material	

3 Bilingual staff

The Kingsbury Manor (SS)	London

4   *Legal, social and psychiatric advisory & support services*

> Afro-Caribbean Mental Health Association (VS)   London
>
> > integrate advocacy, legal, social and
> > psychiatric second opinions

5   *Male & female specialist services*

> Mandela centre (H)   Nottingham
>
> > men's group, counselling, supportive work,
> > music therapy for men e.g. drumming
>
> Derby City mental health project (SS)   Derby
>
> > Asian women's group, informal settings,
> > people's homes, singing, talking

6   *High support accommodation for black people*

> Effra Trust (independent)   London
>
> > target Black mentally disordered offenders for
> > high support accommodation
>
> Servol Project (VS)   Birmingham
>
> > work with mentally disordered offenders,
> > housing, run a cafe, second hand clothes shop

7   *Community initiatives*

> Birmingham outreach team (H)   Birmingham
>
> > True multidisciplinary team, assertive
> > outreach, include Black families in whole
> > package, attend to social and practical tasks
> > in people's homes
>
> African Caribbean Mental Health Association (VS)   Manchester
>
> > help train professionals, advocacy and
> > negotiate treatment plans with psychiatric
> > services, concentrate on primary care services,
> > user run care, liaison with statutory health
> > services
>
> *continued*

continued

| Chinese Mental Health Association (VS) | London |

avoid focusing on mental illness, encourage
trusting relationship first, holistic approach

| Tulip (VS) | London |

severely mentally ill, psychotherapists,
practical tasks, assertive outreach, care
delivered by all members of team to
anticipate staff turnover

References

Acharya *et al* (1989) *An evaluation of the Nafsiyat centre for Ethnic and Cultural Minorities*. (unpublished manuscript).

Adebimpe, V. (1994) Race, Racism and Epidemiological Surveys. *Hospital & Community Psychiatry*, **45**, no 1: 27–31.

Belliapa (1991) 'Illness or Distress?' *Alternative models of mental health*. Confederation of Indian Organisations.

Bhugra, D. (1993) Setting up services for ethnic minorities. *Chapter in: Dimensions of Community Mental Health Care*. Eds M. Weller & M. Muijen. Saunders. London.

Bhui, K., Sufraz, R. & Strathdee, G. (1993) Asian inpatients in a District Psychiatric Unit. *Int. J. Soc. Psychiatry.* **Vol 39,** No3: 208–220.

Bhopal, R. (1989) Health Education and Ethnic minorities. *B. M. J.* **302**: 1336.

Bolton, P. (1984) Management of compulsorily admitted patients to a high security unit. *Int. J. Soc. Psychiatry.* **30**: 77–84.

Burke, A. (1984) Racism and psychiatric disturbance amongst West Indians in Britain. *Int. J. Soc. Psychiatry,* **30(1&2)**: 50–68.

Bushell, W. (1992) *Black children in care*. A research project for the ethnic study group. Funded by Department of Health.

Chiu, H., Shum, P., Lau, J. *et al* (1992) The prevalence of tardive dyskinesia, tardive dystonia and respiratory dyskinesia among Chinese psychiatric patients. *Am. J. Psychiatry* **149 (8)**: 1081–5.

Cochrane, R. (1977) Mental illness in immigrants in England & Wales: an analysis of hospital admission data. *Soc. Psych.* **12**: 25–35.

Cope, R. (1990) Psychiatry, ethnicity & crime. In: *Forensic Psychiatry*. Eds: Bluglass & Bowden. Churchill Livingston. London.

Dolan, B., Polley, K., Allen, R. & Norton, K. (1991) Addressing racism in psychiatry: Is the therapeutic community model applicable. *Int. J. Soc Psychiatry.* **37 (2)**, 71–9.

Fernando (1988) *Race & Culture in Psychiatry*. Tavistock/Routledge.

Flaskerud, J. & Hu, L. (1992) Relationship of ethnicity to psychiatric diagnosis. *J. Nerv. Ment. Dis.* **180 (**5): 296–303.

Francis, J. (1994) No More Excuses. *Community Care,* **16–22** June: 21–23.

Gillam, S., Jarman, B., White, P &Law, R. (1989) Ethnic differences in consultation rates in urban general practice. *Brit. Med. Journal,* **289,** 953–957.

Glazer, W., Morgenstern, H. & Doucette, J. (1994) Race and tardive dyskinesia among outpatients at a CMHC. *Hospital & Community Psychiatry* **45, no 1**: 38–42.

Harrison, G., Owens, D., Holton, A. *et al* (1988*)* A Prospective study of severe mental disorder in Afro-Caribbeans. *Psychological Medicine* **18 (3)**: 643–57.

Hitch P. & Clegg, P. (1980) Modes of referral of overseas immigrants and native born first admissions to psychiatric hospital. *Soc. Sci. & Med.* **14A**: 369–474.

Hinton, W., Chen, Y., Du, N.. *et al* (1993) DSM III-R disorders in Vietnamese refugees. Prevalence and correlates. *J. Nerv. & Mental Disease.* **181(2)**: 113–22.

Ineichen, B., Harrison, G. & Morgan, H. (1984) Psychiatric hospital admissions to Bristol: I Geographic and ethnic factors. *Brit. J. Psychiatry,* **145**: 600–604.

Jones, G. & Berry, M. (1986) Regional secure units, the emerging picture. In: Edwards, G (ed). *Current issues in clinical psychology* **IV**. Plenum Press. London.

Kareem & Littlewood (1992) *Intercultural therapy.* Themes, interpretations and practice. Blackwell scientific publications. London.

Kiev (1965) Psychiatric morbidity of West Indians in an urban group practice. *Brit. J. Psychiatry.* **111**: 51–56.

Krause (1989) Sinking Heart: A Punjabi Communication of Distress. *Soc. Sci.Med.* **29 no.4**: 563–575.

Leff, J. (1988) *Psychiatry around the globe*: a transcultural view. Gaskell. London

Lewis, D., Balla, D. & Shanok, S. (1979) Some evidence of race bias in the diagnosis and treatment of the juvenile offender. *Amer. J. Orthopsychiatry* **49 (1)**: 53–61.

Lin, K., Miller, M., Polland, R. *et al.* Ethnicity and family involvement in the treatment of schizophrenic patients. *J. Nerv. Ment. Dis.* **179** (10): 631–3.

Lin, K., Poland, R., Nuccio, I. *et al* (1989) *A* longitudinal assessment of haloperidol doses and serum concentrations in Asian and Caucasian Schizophrenic Patients. *Am. J. Psychiatry* **146**: 10 1307–1311.

Lin, K., Miller, M., Polland, R. *et al* (1991) Ethnicity and family involvement in the treatment of schizophrenic patients. *J. Nerv. Ment. Dis.* **179 (10):** 631–3.

Littlewood (1988) 'Towards an Intercultural Therapy'. *Journal of Social Work Practice* **vol 3**, no 3, p 8–19.

Littlewood & Lipsedge (1989) Aliens & Alienists. *Ethnic Minorities and Psychiatry.* Unwin Hyman Ltd.

Littlewood, R. (1992) How universal is something we call psychotherapy. Chapter in: *Intercultural therapy*. Eds: Kareem & Littlewood. Blackwell. London.

London, M. (1986) Mental Illness among immigrant minorities in the United Kingdom. *Brit. J. Psychiatry* **149**: 265–273.

Lloyd, K. (1993) Depression and anxiety amongst Afro-Caribbean general practice attenders in Britain. *Int. J. Soc. Psychiatry.* **39** No. 1–9.

MacCarthy, B. &Craissati, J. (1989) Ethnic differences in response to adversity. *Social Psychiatry.* **Vol 24.**

Marsella & White (1982) *Cultural conceptions of mental health and therapy.* Dordrecht: Reidal.

McGovern, D. & Cope, R. (1987) The compulsory detention of makes of different ethnic groups with special reference to offender patients. *Brit. J. Psychiatry.* **150.** 505–12.

McGovern, D., Hemmings, P., Cope, R. & Lowerson, A. (1994) Long term follow up of young Afro-Caribbean Britons and white Britons with first admission diagnoses of schizophrenia. *Soc. Psychiatry & Psychiatr. Epid.* **29**: 8–19.

Moodley, P. & Perkins, R. (1991) Routes to psychiatric inpatient care in an Inner London Borough. *Social Psychiatry.* **26**: 47–51.

Moorhouse J. (1993) cited in Kareem & Littlewood's Intercultural therapy.

Mumford, D. (1994) Transcultural aspects of rehabilitation. Chapter in: *Rehabilitation for mental health problems.* C. Hume & I. Pullen. Churchill Livingstone. London.

NAPO (1989) Black people and remands into custody. Brief from the criminal justice committee, National Association of Probation Officers. London.

NACRO (1991) Black people's experience of criminal justice. *National Association for the Care and Resettlement of Offenders.* London.

NACRO (1993) Diverting mentally disordered offenders from prosecution. *National Association for the Care and Resettlement of Offenders.* London.

Norvick, L., Penna, R., Schwartz, M. *et al* (1977) Health status of the New York city prison population. *Medical Care,* **15**: 205–216.

Owens, D. *et al* (1991) Ethnic factors in voluntary and compulsory admissions. *Psychological* Medicine **21**: 185–196.

Pasamanick, B. (1963) Some misconceptions concerning differences in racial prevalence of mental disease. *Amer. J. Orthopsychiatry.* **33**: 72–86

Perera, D., Owens, G. & Johnston, E. (1991). Disabilities and circumstances of schizophrenic patients—a follow up study. Ethnic aspects: three matched groups. *Brit. J. Psychiatry.* **159**, Suppl **13**, 40–42.

Pinto, R. (1970) A study of psychiatric illness amongst Asians in the Camberwell area. *MPhil Thesis.* University of London.

Rack P. (1982) *Race, Culture and Mental Disorder.* Tavistock, London.

Raskin, A., Thomas, H. & Crook, M. (1975) Anti-depressants in Black and White Inpatients. Differential treatment to controlled treatment with Chlorpromazine and Imipramine. *Arch. Gen Psychiatry.* **32**: 643–649.

Rwegellera, G. (1970) Mental illness in Africans and West Indians of African Origin living in London. *MPhil thesis.* University of London.

Senior, P. & Bhopal, R. (1994) Ethnicity as a variable in epidemiological research. *BMJ* Vol 309, 327–330.

Scheifer, C. *et al* (1968) Clinical change in jail referred mental patients. *Archives of general psychiatry* **18**: 42–46.

Takahashi R., Sakuma, A., Ito, K. *et al* (1975) Comparison of efficacy of Lithium Carbonate and Chlorpromazine in Mania. Report of Collaborative Study Group on the Treatment of Mania in Japan. *Arch. Gen. Psychiatry* **32**: 1310–1318.

Taylor, P. (1986) Psychiatric disorders in London's life sentenced prisoners. *Brit. J. Criminology.* **26**: 63–78.

Turner, T., Ness, M. & Imison, C. (1992) Mentally disordered persons found in public places. *Psychological Medicine,* **22**: 765–774.

Westermeyer A. (1991) Working with an interpreter in psychiatric assessments. *J. Nervous and Mental Disease.* **Vol 178**: No 12, 745.

Wilson, M. (1993) Mental Health and Britain's Black communities. *NHS Management Executive:* Mental Health Task Force & Kings Fund Centre.

Wilson, M. (1994) Black Mental Health: A dialogue for change. *NHS Management Executive:* Mental Health Task Force.

Winett, R., King, A. & Altman, D. (1989) *Health Psychology and Public Health.* Pergamon Press.

Yamashita I. (1992) Transcultural psychopharmacology. *Psychiatric Bulletin.* **16**: 732–733.

0 Lessons from the Mental Health Task Force London Project

RICHARD MOORE

Introduction

During the spring of 1994 the Mental Health Task Force London Project visited and reviewed mental health services provided to the populations of the 12 Inner London health districts comprising the London Initative Zone (LIZ). The review was commissioned by the Secretary of State as a result of concerns raised in the Ritchie Report and the Biennial Report of the Mental Health Act Commission. A brief visit to each district comprising meetings with purchasers, providers, users, local authority departments, carers and voluntary organisations was followed by the preparation and agreement of an action plan. This chapter outlines some of the main themes to have emerged from these visits and plans.

Needs assessment for London

The Project combined a qualitative review (visits and discussions) with some quantitative analysis. The latter took two forms, preparation of a comparative report by the Inter Authority Comparisons Consultancy (IACC) at the University of Birmingham, using nationally available sources of data, and a survey by Conrane Consulting using data provided by the 12 districts on a pro-forma designed for the project. A number of the districts visited had recently completed their own strategy review or needs assessment. The teams found considerable variation in the approach of different districts to the assessment of what needed to be done, and in the vocabulary used to describe services.

There had been an expectation amongst team members that one of the principal problems which services encountered would be that maintaining contact with people with severe mental health problems, because those people were highly mobile. Early in the visiting programme a psychiatrist in one of the Districts visited made the point to the visiting team that the people who make the most demand on mental health services are well known to practitioners in the local context and not particularly mobile. As the visits progressed this view was echoed a number of times by other practitioners, and by service users and local authority staff. One of the most consistent recommendations to be made during the work of the Project was formulated at this stage. This was that in assessing the mental health needs of their local population, health authorities might be well advised to begin by identifying those people who are known to make the most use of services 'now' and to use the aggregated knowledge as a basis for determining priorities for service development.

The intention was not that this should be a sophisticated research exercise, but one which tapped the knowledge of people working in the services, sharing information and identifying groups of need based on the experience of working with known clients. The Care Programme Approach (CPA) forms a natural basis for doing this, whilst some authorities also maintain a register of people with long-term mental health problems. The recommendation seems logical and straightforward, although not all accepted that the task is as easy as some consider it to be. 'But ...' some districts asked and "how should we define 'long term severe mental health problems?'". The Project advised that the definition should be made locally, and based on the needs of the population reviewed as outlined above. The basis for this was simply that if people with mental health problems are consistently in contact with services, and regularly make use of expensive resources such as in-patient beds, then their problems must be considered long-term and severe.

Any assessment of the problems faced by those people most consistently in contact with services is likely to illustrate a spectrum of need. This will include people who have:

- a periodic need for care during an acute phase of illness

- been in contact with the judicial system

- housing problems or are homeless

- has not been successfully engaged by services in the past

- enduring social and other problems exacerbated by their mental illness.

It is helpful to group some of these characteristics when looking at the use made by people of different parts of the service. Unless this is done, the use made of services by (i.e.) mentally disordered offenders may not be differentiated from the use of acute services by people who have not been in contact with the judicial system, thus distorting one set of analysis and obscuring the need within another.

Some districts have looked specifically at the needs of mentally disordered offenders, including those people from their area who are currently in the special hospitals or other specialised provision with a view to seeing what is needed for them in the local context.

An outline analysis of the most significant issues might focus on the following:

- distinguish between different groups within the overall (eg. MDOs, people with challenging behaviours)

- look at the specific needs of people from different racial and cultural backgrounds

- find out why people are coming into, and remaining in, hospital

- identify the range of services available to meet the range of treatment and social needs.

Meeting differing needs

Identifying and addressing different needs is essential both to the management of existing services and planning for change. For the management of existing hospital services this will include finding out why people have been admitted to hospital, why they remain there, and how this relates to their care in the community.

Hospital beds in London are intensively used. In a number of Districts the London Project recommended, or agreed with the local Commission's assessment that additional beds were required, at least in the short term. Commissioners of services and providers alike have been keen to see that as the most expensive resource available to meet the needs of people with mental health problems, beds are used effectively.

Commissioners have approached this in a number of ways, focusing on routes into hospital, management of resources within hospital and on the resources necessary to enable people to leave hospital at the right time.

The project found broad agreement amongst the districts it visited that early access to help in the community and the existence of consistent support networks would have enabled some people to continue to function outside hospital. At the other end of the spectrum there was clear evidence that some people were remaining in hospital beyond the time when it would have been right for them to leave because the necessary social support was not available for them.

Attention to these two dimensions could significantly alter the pattern of acute bed usage. Housing and meaningful daily activity are two aspects of social support which are regularly cited by service users as being of central importance to their well-being, in addition to good clinical care. Housing departments are therefore crucial to the effective functioning of a mental health service, and welcome the active engagement of health commissioners and providers. The nature of this engagement is dependant on the local circumstances. In the case of long-stay hospital closure programmes, the housing department will be able to assist with the identification of places for some people with LA commissioned housing. They may be able to broker relationships with housing associations or reserve places within new social housing schemes for people with mental health problems. The earlier they are involved the better, so that they can gain an understanding of the needs of the people to be housed upon discharge from hospital and work with health and social services colleagues to meet these.

Acute care has, of course, a relatively fast pace, and some districts have found difficulty in working closely in this area. A rapid response to housing needs is of central importance to maintaining a persons' social stability, however, and housing should therefore be seen as part of the on-going process of agreeing and reviewing a care plan. If the contribution of housing is seen in this way rather than as a hurdle to be jumped only at the point a person is ready to leave hospital, then unnecessary pressure of time can be avoided. In a number of cases the early intervention of the housing department may avoid the type of crisis which can lead to a person's accommodation being jeopardised in the first place.

Resources

The Project found that London DHAs spend widely differing sums per head of population on mental health services, and that this variation cannot always be explained in terms of relative need. This is not perhaps surprising, and neither is it at variance with the Audit Commission's observations in 'Finding a Place'. Expenditure is more often a reflection of inheritance than needs assessment.

Although able to specify the proportion of their total budget spent on mental health, not all DHAs were able to identify the separate components of this expenditure. The Project felt that had they been able to do so this would have been useful in terms of tracking expenditure on the priority area—people with a long-term severe mental health problem. Once again the recommendation to purchasers followed from this viewpoint, so that it was suggested that DHAs attempt to identify expenditure on:

- all mental health services
- services for adults
- services for MDO's
- services for the older people
- services for children and adolescents.

An analysis of expenditure on these groups would enable commissioners to focus on the comparative costs within services and between services. This would help to establish not only whether expenditure is following the agreed service priorities, but also assist in reaching commissioning decisions in terms of value for money.

Analysis of the recipients of mainstream NHS expenditure will enable consideration of the appropriateness of current placement of contracts or singly purchased episodes of care. The range of possible beneficiaries is summarised below:

- local providers
- other NHS general providers
- NHS specialist providers
- independent sector providers.

Since variations in expenditure are likely in part to be related to the level of provision or expenditure by other agencies and organisations it is necessary also to work with colleague agencies to establish the totality of expenditure and provision of services within the District. An exercise of this type will also increase the level of understanding about the range of services available to the population served and the relationship between those funded by each agency. A package of indicators commissioned by the Project provided a basis for comparing expenditure between the London districts using the expenditure and activity levels and Jarman scores.

Working with other agencies

Effective joint working between agencies is one of the pre-requisites of good mental health services. In London the complex network of relationships between Health Authorities, London Boroughs, NHS Trusts and voluntary organisations presents a major challenge. This was most frequently highlighted in the implementation of the Care Programme Approach (CPA) and Care Management because of the need to reach agreement between NHS providers and Social Services Departments in agreeing policies and procedures. Not only this, but the agreed priorities have to follow from the commissioning priorities of the Social Services Departments and their Health Authority partners.

A number of specific issues emerged in relation to this area of work:

- The CPA must be implemented for all people referred to the specialist psychiatric services, but it can be implemented in phases;

- Sometimes the implementation of the CPA is hampered by over-bureaucratic procedures;

- Sometimes problems in implementation are the product of underlying problems with the existing service;

- Full integration of CPA and Care Management will take a long time to achieve and may not be the best solution.

Some particular lessons are outlined further below:

(i)   The CPA must be implemented for all people referred to the specialist psychiatric services, but it can be implemented in phases

Many DHAs welcomed the guidance of the Project to the effect that implementation of the CPA could be gradual, in line with commissioning priorities. Implementation would thus normally begin with those people who have a long-term severe mental health problem. Implementation could then be extended to other groups.

The form of implementation will vary in accordance with the varying needs of different groups, so that whilst a person with significant and complex needs of both a treatment and social nature may need a full multi-agency CPA, a person with significant treatment needs but no other complications may have a care plan drafted only in partnership with their practitioner.

(ii)   Full integration of CPA and Care Management will take a long time to achieve and may not be the best solution

A number of Authorities were striving to achieve a comprehensive and fully integrated CPA/Care Management system. This is laudable, and is an objective felt by many to have been implicit in the original guidance, but can be extraordinarily difficult to achieve in practice. The Project also found examples of districts where the two systems were being implemented separately by their respective authorities, but in a coherent and complementary way.

Under this latter arrangement the system most appropriate to a person's needs could be applied, with a key worker from the most appropriate agency. Thus a person who does not have needs for social care would not need care management. People with the most severe and complex needs would be offered a comprehensive care plan with care management, drafted in discussion between themselves and workers from the range of professions and agencies necessary to achieve the desired outcomes. A key worker would be identified and would be the main point of contact between the person using the service and other workers as per the original guidance.

A variety of approaches to the allocation of a key worker were found across the Districts visited. In some the identity of the key worker changed at each transition in a person's care. Under this arrangement the following would apply:

- Care plan whilst in the community: ⇒ Key worker 1
- Admission to hospital: ⇒ Key worker 2/named nurse
- Day hospital: ⇒ Key worker 3
- Discharged from day hospital: ⇒ Key worker 4

In other systems the agencies aimed to identify a single key worker with the authority to negotiate all care arrangements, clinical and social, for the client. This seems an ideal arrangement in terms of identifying a single 'broker' for the client, although it does confront some difficult practical issues regarding resource commitments.

A third arrangement again identified a single keyworker for the client, but did not attempt to negotiate the authority to commit resources across agencies. A key worker would be identified from health and Social Services would identify a care manager, but only one of these would be the 'key worker' for purposes of the care programme with the client. This has the advantage of giving the client a single point of contact, but simplified the administrative arrangements behind this.

The most important recommendation of the Project was that the agencies should work together to ensure that their care management and care programme systems are compatible and coherent, rather than seeking the perhaps elusive goal of full and comprehensive integration.

(iii) Sometimes problems in implementation are the product of underlying problems with the existing service

Occasionally service providers told Project members that it was impossible to prepare a care programme before a patient was discharged from hospital because of the short duration of their in-patient stay. One of the problems encountered in this situation was said to be the difficulty of bringing together the multi-professional team to discuss the programme. It seemed to Project members that this kind of problem stems from two underlying service issues:

1   admission to hospital being seen as a discrete event rather than part of a continuing care programme;

2   an assumption that care programme always requires full multi-professional team involvement.

Whilst there will be occasions where a person becomes known to local agencies only when in crisis and requiring admission to hospital, this is not routinely the case, and it would clearly be more helpful for all concerned for admission to hospital to be regarded as a necessary part of an overall care plan.

On the second point, it is a requirement that all patients discharged from hospital should have a proper discharge plan. Whilst it may be that the initial arrangements may need to be re-visited to incorporate the recommendations of other professionals in who were not available at the time, any problems of bringing people together should not be a reason for failing to agree at least a basic care plan.

Working with voluntary organisations

Voluntary sector, or not-for-profit providers, are an increasing part of the overall range of provision for people with mental health problems, and in a number of Districts are now the subject of formal contracting relationships in the same way as any other NHS or LA contracted provider. One of the reasons for their success lies in their ability to respond to need in a way which is accessible and acceptable to the people who need the services they offer. Some successfully bridge the range from social to psychological needs whilst others exist specifically to meet one of these dimensions.

Voluntary sector organisations were consistently found to have the ability to attract and engage service users who would not readily be engaged by the statutory agencies. This was particularly true of organisations run by and for people from minority racial and cultural backgrounds, and in a number of cases this advantage had been acknowledged by the statutory agencies in the form of funding and recognition.

Those which employ therapeutically qualified staff and offer a range of treatment options can provide some of the services which might otherwise be vested in a CMHT.

Voluntary organisations across London expressed concern about the nature of their funding. This concern was related to the short term nature of funding not to the degree of confidence expressed in their ability by the statutory agencies. A degree of confidence that the Health Authority or Social Services Department will contract with you next year is not the same as a two or three year rolling contract, such as those enjoyed by most NHS Trusts. The absence of a firm commitment to continued funding makes it difficult for voluntary organisations to attract and retain staff or to enter into other agreements, such as the leasing of property. In recognition of this, Lambeth, Southwark and Lewisham Health

Commission has agreed a financial principle that any voluntary organisation with which it has a service agreement of more than a certain value will be offered a two-year rolling contract.

Summary

During the course of the visits to the 12 inner-London Districts, Mental Health Task Force London Projects members saw many services in both the statutory and voluntary sectors which offer excellent, focused, and cost effective services to people with severe mental health problems. Many of these are identified in the *two reports* published by the Mental Health Task Force London Project, and also in the video 'Care in the Capital'. These examples quoted above are drawn from the experience of all visits, and have been selected to highlight the real issues being faced by practitioners not only in London, but elsewhere as a means of illustrating some of the recommendations of the visiting Teams.

References

Department of Health (1994). *Mental Health in London: Priorities for Action.* 1515 IN9/94.

Department of Health (1995). *Mental Health Task Force London Project: Follow-up Report.* NHS Executive. 26051P1.SK.

1 Cost Information for Commissioners

JENNIFER BEECHAM & PAUL McCRONE

1 Introduction

Better information and better use of existing information can aid development of mental health care. Recent reports from the House of Commons Health Committee, the Mental Health Foundation, the Audit Commission and the Mental Health Task Force stress the central role information plays but give less attention to requirements for costs information. Yet these data are vital to commissioning and purchasing decisions[1].

This chapter illustrates how research and practice generated data can inform cost-related decisions. It summarises information presented during one session of the *Purchasing Mental Health Services* conference, and is structured around four 'cost principles'. These principles were originally developed to guide the use of costs data in research (Knapp and Beecham, 1990), but are shown to be equally applicable in the world of purchasing and providing care:

- costs measures should be comprehensive and should range over all services likely to be used by people with mental health problems;

- costs will vary—exploring the reasons for such variations will illuminate the implications of commissioning decisions;

- when comparing costs, care should be taken to ensure comparisons are made only on a like-with-like basis; and

- costs information should not be used in isolation, in particular combining costs with outcomes data can provide measures of efficiency.

2 Comprehensive costs

We know that people with mental health problems require an array of support services, provision of which tends to cross traditional organisational boundaries. The Mental Health Foundation (1994), for example, cites the following dimensions of needs: an appropriate place to live; an adequate income; a varied social life; employment and other day activities; help and support; respect and trust; and consultation and choice. At the individual level, services should be carefully compiled into 'packages' of support through case-level coordination mechanisms such as care programming or care management. Where these processes occur alongside a devolved budget, purchasers clearly link provision of care to service costs.

---

[1] We take commissioning "to refer to the decisions taken by health and local authorities about the aggregate levels of service to be available in their locality. We retain the word purchasing to refer to the decisions taken by local care managers and others to acquire appropriate services for specific individuals" (Mental Health Foundation, 1994, para 4.16).

It is, of course, difficult for purchasers or commissioners to obtain good quality information on the likely costs of all the components of a community mental health service, particularly given the spread of local provision. Nationally applicable costs data can provide a useful benchmark and unit costs for some 50 community care services are provided by Netten and Dennett (1995). These data are supported by a clear methodological approach based on economic theory (Allen and Beecham, 1993). Some specialist services, particularly the more expensive facilities, will require more detailed examination to help ensure resources are deployed in the most efficient manner.

The results from one service costing exercise have been presented by Hyde and Harrower-Wilson (1995). The authors calculated the direct costs of providing a 12-bed psychiatric intensive care unit (PICU) over a six month period, identifying fixed and variable costs. The former were those elements independent of short-term changes in patient numbers, and comprised nursing and other medical staff salaries, hotel costs, overheads, and miscellaneous costs. Variable costs were defined as those which fluctuate with the number of patients treated and included expenditure on drugs, intensive staff supervision and staff time spent handling violent incidents, and patient injuries. (In the long-term, of course, all costs are variable.) In this study, the average cost of a PICU day was found to be £284 with an average cost per admission of £3488 (1993–94 prices). Fixed elements accounted for 93 per cent. Over the study period there were 170 aggressive or violent incidents, each of which incurred extra supervision and/or drug costs. Intensive supervision accounted for three quarters of the variable costs. Sixty-five of the incidents required 'rapid tranquillization' for patients at a cost of £366 over the study period. Eleven patients (out of 101 admissions, 83 individuals) were responsible for more than half of all incidents.

Many research studies which consider use and costs of mental health services have focused on the measurement of direct costs (for further discussion of this approach see McCrone and Weich, 1995). We advocate a comprehensive approach which allows the 'knock-on' costs of service options to be recognised. Services such as psychiatrists, community psychiatrists, day treatment and acute beds are undoubtedly important in treating and supporting clients, but so too are residential services, day care services, home helps, general health care staff, social workers and support services for informal carers. Mind (1995), for example, pinpoint care for people facing a crisis as a fundamental component of a comprehensive community mental health service and indicate that provision of a crisis service can offset the high cost of hospital care (quoting Cobb, 1995). However, users of crisis team services will still require shelter, food and an income as well as a range of other health and social care services. Three categories of costs can be identified:

- *core service costs* which are those incurred by the deployment of specific mental health services (health or social care) in hospital or community settings;

- *the costs of extra-core services* which are those available to the general population;

- *hidden costs* which can arise as a result of time foregone by clients who must travel to, wait for and use the services. This final category is not considered in this chapter.

At the individual care package level, a comprehensive approach means that the cost implications of all elements of clients' support are included. Such a perspective, which covers all agencies and organisations, aids decision-making by providing information on both the direct *and* wider costs associated with a particular intervention, treatment or care delivery mode. Comprehensive costs data are of paramount importance to help balance the mental health budget with identified needs through contracting services to meet those needs.

3 Exploring costs variations

The Hyde and Harrower-Wilson study highlights one factor which caused variation in the costs of intensive psychiatric care—aggressive or violent incidents—showing that higher costs accrued to some service users. Descriptive information, therefore, goes part way to explaining why costs vary—our second costs principle. When taking a client rather than service-based perspective it is unusual to be able to isolate just one cause of variation. More sophisticated statistical techniques are needed to help tease out the many factors (often inter-related) which have an effect on service utilisation and costs (Knapp, 1984). McCrone and Strathdee (1994), for example, have categorised cost determinants as follows (examples are given in brackets): patient-related determinants (employment, symptoms); social factors (social networks, attitudes of others); service determinants (type of setting, gatekeeping influences); and outside influences (unemployment rate, level of urbanisation).

Techniques which allow the full exploration of cost variations require large-scale and detailed data-collection, and careful analysis and interpretation. Day-to-day pressures mean these tasks are difficult to undertake within commissioning or provider bodies. There is a growing body of research which has explored the multi-faceted influences on costs for various groups of users. One example was presented at the conference by a member of the team for Psychiatric Research in Service Measurement (PRiSM).

In this long-term study, the costs and effects of a new configuration of community mental health services will be compared with traditional hospital-based care for people with a psychotic diagnosis living in South East London. Preliminary results from the examination of comprehensive service receipt and costs data *before* the new services came on stream show that the study members (n=101) had used over 40 different service types over the six-month period prior to data collection. The average cost of care was £7226 per person for the period (1992/93 prices). However, the range of costs was considerable—the most expensive care package costing about 20 times more than the least costly.

What accounted for this variation? Differential service use is the simple answer but care packages should be put together in response to client needs. Client-level information, therefore, should be the starting point for any exploration of costs variation. As undertaken in previous mental health care studies (see

Knapp, 1995, for a summary) multivariate analysis was used to tease out the factors which influenced variations in the total costs of care (a summary measure of the services used). Using information assembled from case-notes prior to the period covered by the costing exercise, the findings showed that thirty per cent of the variation in costs could be 'explained' by variables describing the age of the user, their marital status and broad indicators of social functioning and self-care.

Information about the way costs vary in response to client characteristics is vital to service providers and purchasers, and can help them estimate prices. Commissioners require a broader level of information at their fingertips as they must focus not on individual clients but on the whole resident population. Commissioners must decide what services should be available to respond to local needs and should, therefore, take on board information which recognises clients will use many different services over a period of time, that they are likely to use those services in different combinations which, in turn, will have different cost implications.

4   Like-with-like comparisons

Reporting costs data and cost variations invites comparisons—this client is more expensive to support than another, for example. As we saw above, the total costs of support are sensitive to individual differences as measured along a number of dimensions. Knowledge of these dimensions can guide purchasers in the disbursement of their budgets by providing information with which to identify clients who may cost more or less than the average. Again we see that commissioners require a broader view—their focus must be on contracting services for *groups* of clients. Importantly, such groups must comprise 'similar' clients; they should be based on 'like-with-like' comparisons. In turn, the results of multivariate client-level analyses can inform such comparisons.

To date, limited use has been made of such tools in psychiatric research as analyses have tended to focus on broader categorisations. Studies in the United States (English *et al*, 1986; Frank and Lave, 1985; Wood and Beardmore, 1986) and in the UK (Oydebode *et al*, 1990) have explored the potential of diagnostic-related or health-care resource groups but found them to be poor predictors of either cost or service utilisation. In regional health authority statistics, diagnosis is often the only clinical data recorded yet McCrone and Phelan (1994) found this level of categorisation to be inadequate in explaining resource use.

Research undertaken in 1992 on community care for former psychiatric hospital inpatients in North London supports this view and found more variation *within* diagnostic categories than *between* them. No significant difference was found between diagnosis groups in either service use or costs one year after discharge, however, within the research study a wide range of data were available for the period prior to the clients' move to community-based services. The total costs of community care for 217 people one year after discharge were influenced by a number of underlying clinical symptoms (neurotic syndrome score, negative symptoms, delusions and hallucinations) and other characteristics (such as abnormal behaviour ratings, requirements for daily nursing care and size of social networks). Demographic data also played a part in 'explaining' 35 per cent of costs variation: marital status, age, gender and the length of time spent in psychiatric hospital (Knapp *et al*, 1995). Such data can be used in two ways. First, they help identify the client-related dimensions which will influence costs, therefore some of the dimensions along which needs assessments data can be collected. Secondly, they can help identify casemix groups which may have similar cost implications. Casemix groups identified by these analyses appear to be more useful than broader clinical typologies and may considerably aid commissioners in both predicting mental health resource requirements and in targeting those resources on *needs-related* groups (Knapp *et al*, 1992). The use of more detailed routine data collection schedules, such as that developed within the Health of the Nations Outcomes Study (Wing *et al*, 1994), will facilitate such work.

5   Combining costs and outcomes data

Commissioners should not, of course, focus entirely on costs. Commissioners have a duty to make the most *efficient* use of available resources—maximising outcomes for a given level of expenditure or minimising costs to achieve a given level of outcomes. The reprovision service in North London referred to above, for example, was found to be a cost-effective alternative to hospital care (Beecham, 1991). At the service level, Dr Paul Mallett has shown how information on the effectiveness of interventions was used by commissioners in Wales to help prioritise expenditure. The *Mental Health Protocol* was developed to identify treatments which had proven effectiveness for particular conditions; rather than identify whether neuroleptic treatment, for example, was effective *per se*, effectiveness would be examined separately for schizophrenia, mania and other illnesses. On the basis of research evidence (particularly results from randomised controlled trials), treatments were ranked according to the committee's consensus opinion on their effectiveness and it was felt that only those treatments ranked highest should be purchased routinely.

This exercise used specific client-based outcomes (changes in psychiatric symptons, social functioning and the like), to guide decisions about resource allocation to services. Generic outcomes measures can also be used and members of one fundholding general practice specifically linked such measures to expenditure information. The *Health Investment Portfolio*, described by Wendy Sunney, is a 'market portfolio' of health care programmes for different diagnosis or conditions. Each programme incorporates concepts of utility (well-being) and cost (deployment of resources) and is aimed at helping patients achieve their optimum quality of life. Eight strategic objectives were identified for each programme: assessment; preventative care; maximising potential; cure; rehabilitation; maintaining independence; support in crises; and palliative care and bereavement support. Traditionally, resource allocation in general practice has favoured the curative, rehabilitative, maintenance and crisis support functions. By examining expenditure according to the achievement of these objectives, the practice could develop purchasing strategies to move their 'profile' in the desired direction—to improve both patient health *and* patient independence. The author suggests *dis*investment in types of supportive, curative and palliative care which encourage high levels of patient dependence and *greater* investment in screening and educational programmes, and methods to help patients self-manage their condition.

Research findings from economic evaluations can also inform decision-making. Economic theory suggests the relative costs and benefits of service options can be examined using cost-utility analysis, cost-benefit analysis or cost-effectiveness analysis. In mental health research, it is the latter model which is most commonly found. Simple comparisons of the costs and benefits emanating from two or more service options can be revealing but if outcome measures do not move in concert, or if the results are ambiguous, the findings may be less easy to interpret. Again, analytic techniques developed by economists can help tease out the links between resource inputs and client outcomes, identifying for who and under what circumstance particular arrangements might be more cost-effective (Beecham *et al*, 1991).

6   Guiding principle for commissioners

We have suggested *four principles* to guide commissioners in their use of costs data. *First, commissioners should ensure they have costs information relating to all services which clients might require.* Joint commissioning, across health and local authorities, can be helpful in this respect as a view over the whole mental health budget will facilitate recognition of the wider cost implications of particular service choices and can reduce the potential for both gaps and overlaps in provision (Department of Health, 1993).

Second, the commissioners' cost perspective should not only encompass average costs data. They should be aware that costs will vary within services, between service options, and within and between groups of clients. Information on the sources of cost variation can inform purchasing plans at two levels; in the distribution of budgets between individuals and, at the macro-level, to better inform predictions of resource requirements for client sub-groups.

Our third rule suggests that when comparing cost information commissioners should remember that only like-with-like comparisons are fully valid. Grouping clients according to needs and characteristics which influence costs will help commissioners predict budget requirements and contract the most appropriate quantities and types of services. The Audit Commission's resource allocation model moves toward this approach, specifically linking client needs, costs information and budgets with priorities and eligibility criteria (House of Commons, 1993). The model has six components:

- estimate the needs of each client group in broad categories;

- determine the average cost of a 'typical' package of services for a client at each level of need;

- calculate the total cost of supplying such a package to the numbers of people identified at each level of need;

- compare total costs, resources and service requirements with existing provision;

- prioritise and revise eligibility criteria to bring total cost into line with the budget; and

- allocate the resources according to the revised set of eligibility criteria.

Costs information should not be used in isolation of data on clients outcomes—this is our fourth costs principle. By using costs data in conjunction with outcomes (client specific or generic) commissioners can ensure that resource inputs are deployed to create or maintain services to generate improvements (or at least, prevent deterioration) in clients' welfare. Each of the conference papers incorporated into this chapter clearly shows the central role cost data play in today's care environment. Driven by both research and practice needs, the findings show how costs data can be used to inform the purchasing or commissioning activities which form the foundation of the mental health care market.

Acknowledgements

We take this opportunity to thank the participants of the workshop on *The Economic Cost of Providing Mental Health Services* at the conference on *Purchasing Mental Health Services* in September 1994. The conference was jointly organised by PRiSM, the Department of Health, the Royal College of Psychiatrists, and Lambeth, Southwark and Lewisham Health Commission. This chapter draws heavily on papers presented by Clive Hyde, Paul McCrone, Paul Mallet and Wendy Sunney to whom particular thanks are extended.

Jennifer Beecham is Lecturer in Mental Health Economics at the Centre for the Economics of Mental Health and Paul McCrone is Lecturer in Health Economics at PRiSM (Psychiatric Research in Service Measurement). This paper is lodged as Working Paper 047, Centre for the Economics of Mental Health, Institute of Psychiatry, London.

References

Allen, C. and Beecham, J.K. (1993) Costing services: ideals and reality, in A Netten and J Beecham (eds) *Costing Community Care: Theory and Practice*, Ashgate, Aldershot.

Beecham, J.K., Knapp, M.R.J. and Fenyo A.J. (1991) Costs, needs and outcomes, *Schizophrenia Bulletin*, **17**, 427–439.

Cobb, A. (1995) Community crisis services cost less than hospital care, *Openmind*, February/March, p8.

Department of Health (1993) *Community Care Monitoring Study: Mental Health Services*, HMSO, London.

English, J.T., Sharfstein, S.S., Scherl, D.J., *et al* (1986) Diagnosis-related groups and general hospital psychiatry: the APA study, *American Journal of Psychiatry*, **143**, 131–139.

Frank, R.G. and Lave, J.R. (1985) The psychiatric DRGs: are they different? *Medical Care*, **23**, 1148–1155.

House of Commons Health Committee (1993) *Community Care: The Way Forward,* Sixth Report, Volume II Minutes of Evidence and Appendices, HMSO, London.

Hyde, C. and Harrower-Wilson, C. (1995) Resource consumption in psychiatric intensive care: the cost of aggression, *Psychiatric Bulletin*, **19**, 73–76.

Knapp, M.R.J. (1984) *The Economics of Social Care*, Macmillan.

Knapp, M.R.J. (1995) Costs and outcomes; variations and comparisons, in M Knapp (ed) *The Economics of Mental Health Services*, Arena, Aldershot.

Knapp, M.R.J. and Beecham, J.K. (1990) Costing mental health services, *Psychological Medicine*, **20**, 893–908.

Knapp, M.R.J., Beecham, K.J. and Gordon, K. (1992) Predicting the community costs of closing psychiatric hospitals: national predictions, *Journal of Mental Health*, **1**, 315–525.

Knapp, M.R.J., Beecham, J.K., Hallam, A. and Fenyo, A.J. (1995a) Predicting costs from needs and diagnoses: community mental health care for former hospital inpatients, *British Journal of Psychiatry*, **166** supplement, 10–18.

McCrone, P. and Strathdee, G. (1994) Needs not diagnosis: towards a more rational approach to community mental health resourcing in Britain, *The International Journal of Social Psychiatry*, **40**, 79–86.

McCrone, P. and Weich, S. (1995) Mental health care costs: paucity of measurement, *Social Psychiatry and Psychiatric Epidemiology* (in press).

McCrone, P. and Phelan, M. (1994) Diagnosis and length of psychiatric in-patient stay, *Psychological Medicine*, **24**, 1025–1030.

Mental Health Foundation (1994) *Creating Community Care: Inquiry into Community Care for People with Severe Mental Illness*, MHF, London.

Mind (1995) *Mind's Model of a 24 Hour Crisis Service,* Mind Publications, London.

Netten, A. and Dennett, J. (1995) *The Unit Costs of Community Care 1995*, Personal Social Services Research Unit, University of Kent at Canterbury.

Oydebode, F., Cumella, S., Garden, G., *et al* (1990) Diagnosis-related groups: implications for psychiatry, *Psychiatric Bulletin*, **14**, 1–3.

Wing, J., Curtis, R. and Beaver, A. The Health of the Nation: measuring mental health outcomes, *Psychiatric Bulletin*, **18**, 690–691.

Wood, W.D. and Beardmore D.F. (1986) Prospective payment for outpatient mental health services: evaluation of diagnosis-related groups, *Community Mental Health Journal*, **22**, 286–291.

22 Effectiveness of Interventions for Mental Illness and Implications for Commissioning

MEL CONWAY, GEOFF SHEPHERD and DAVID MELZER

Introduction

The effectiveness of different treatment interventions and different models of service organisation should be important influences on purchasing decisions. This chapter will;

- describe the effectiveness of *individual* treatments and interventions for people with mental illness

- discuss the technical limitations of the evidence and the problems of translating research into practice

- present other important commissioning issues for both clinicians and commissioners.

The effectiveness of different models of service organisations will not be discussed. A large number of good quality evaluations have demonstrated beneficial outcomes from comprehensive and co-ordinated community based care (for example, community treatment teams, case management etc.)[1]. This will be covered elsewhere. Purchasers need to be familiar with this research to ensure that not only effective interventions are purchased, but that these are provided from effectively organised services. This review will therefore concentrate on the individual elements of services rather than the service 'system' as a whole.

The effectiveness of treatments

A wide range of treatments are needed for the diverse array of mental disorders that present to the health service. In general, specialist staff (psychiatrists, psychologists, mental health nurses, social workers, occupational and other therapists, and community support workers) treat a different range of mental disorders than do general practitioners and other primary health care workers. Many of the most difficult commissioning decisions relate to the care of moderately ill patients who are not clearly the responsibility of either specialist or primary care.

Primary care

Mild mental disorders affect about 30% of the population each year. Most people are looked after solely by general practitioners[2]. Around half of all cases are self-limiting, but the remainder may experience enduring symptoms, largely anxiety and depression. General practitioners correctly identify anxiety and depression in about half of those presenting[3] and these are more likely to receive specific mental health interventions. They are also more likely to have better outcomes than non-recognised cases[4].

Drug treatments

(a) Depression

Two main groups of drugs are effective in the treatment of depression: tricyclic and related antidepressants (TCAs) and selective serotonin reuptake inhibitors (SSRIs). There has been considerable debate over the relative merits of these two groups of drugs, partly prompted by the rapid increase in prescribing of the substantially more expensive SSRIs. A comprehensive meta-analysis of randomised controlled trials suggests that TCAs and SSRIs have equal efficacy[5]. The overall drop-out rate from treatment for each drug was about the same, but slightly more people taking TCAs stopped because of side effects (18.8%, as opposed to 15.4% for SSRIs). Two large scale reviews have therefore recommended that SSRIs should **not** be used as first line treatment in depression[6,7].

Despite similar efficacy, SSRIs and TCAS do have a different profile of side effects. SSRIs can cause nausea and insomnia and TCAs can cause sedation and heart problems. SSRIs are relatively safe in overdose (unlike TCAs) and may be preferable in the treatment of some depressed people who are at higher risk of suicide. As it may be difficult to predict accurately which individual is most at risk of self-harm, some practitioners have advocated a more extensive use of SSRIs. However, a recent cost-effectiveness analysis has evaluated the impact of deaths from suicide of prescribing SSRIs as a first line treatment for depression and concluded that routine prescribing with SSRIs would only save 300 to 450 deaths a year at a very high cost of life year gained[8].

This illustrates the importance of distinguishing between *population* treatment strategies and *individual* clinical decisions when commissioning services. Not using SSRIs as a first line treatment for depression in a population does not negate using them as the initial treatment for some people. However, while SSRIs clearly have a place in the treatment of some depressed patients, uncritical prescibing is likely to produce only a marginal benefit and divert resources away from other priority areas.

Of course, effective treatment of depression in primary care entails more than just choosing an appropriate drug. Maximising the recognition of psychological disorders by GPs can increase the number of people who are effectively treated and improve patient outcomes[4,9]. Furthermore, there is good evidence that specific education packages can enhance diagnostic accuracy which is then maintained over time[10]. Effective treatment also relies on the prescription of appropriate therapeutic doses. Milder depression in general practice is frequently treated with inadequate levels of medication and without proper consideration for the need for maintenance therapy. Psychological treatments may also be effective in postponing relapse (see below).

(b) Anxiety

Anxiety disorders compromise a range of syndromes, including generalised anxiety disorder, panic, phobias and minor emotional disorders[11]. Benzodiazepines are still widely used to treat anxiety, but should not be prescribed for more than 2–4 weeks because of the risk of dependence[12]. Anxiety often coexists with depression in patients presenting to primary care[4] and these cases may benefit from treatment with antidepressants. Antidepressants may also be effective in the treatment of panic disorders[13], however psychological treatments for anxiety and panic are probably the more effective alternative to drugs in the primary care setting[12].

Psychological treatments

Psychological treatments may be used in combination with, or as an alternative to drug therapy. For the purpose of commissioning mental health services, most psychological treatments can be considered in three categories: counselling, cognitive and behavioural psychotherapies, and psychodynamic therapy. A brief description of each is outlined in box (1).

Box 1: Glossary of terms

Counselling

The term 'counselling' tends to be used very loosely. It may describe the process of general empathic support and information giving that one would expect to be part of every clinical encounter. More often, it refers to a discreet clinical process, involving counsellors or other mental health professionals. A wide variety of interventions may be provided, from unstructured 'tea and sympathy' through to more specific cognitive and behavioural techniques. Many counsellors have received only limited formal training.

Cognitive and behavioural psychotherapies

These therapies are structured, time limited and focused on achieving specific goals. Cognitive therapy attempts to teach patients to control psychological symptoms by adjusting erroneous beliefs and disordered ways of thinking. Behaviour therapy teaches patients how to alter unhelpful and maladaptive ways of coping (for example, the avoidance of anxiety provoking situations). The two approaches are commonly combined as a single therapy—(CBT).

Psychodynamic therapy

This is often long term and focuses on the understanding of previous subconscious experiences and working through emotional difficulties through a transference relationship with the therapist.

(a) Counselling

Subjective accounts suggest that counselling is identified with a high degree of satisfaction in patients and GPs, but evidence of improved clinical and social outcomes is less convincing[14,15]. There is no evidence that non directive and unstructured techniques, applied by counsellors, are superior to routine GP care[16]. Structured problem-solving counselling can, however, be superior to routine GP care[17] and can be effectively administered by GPs, once trained in the technique[18].

There is, therefore, considerable potential for using staff with only basic training to provide general structured support in primary care. More structured interventions, for example, marital therapy[14] and post natal depression[19], should be targeted to people with specific problems and provided only by those with the relevant training.

Commissioners might also consider a variety of other cost-effective community based interventions, such as self-help groups, self-instruction manuals, videos etc.[20].

(b) Cognitive and behavioural therapies

CBT has been used effectively for a variety of problems[21,22]:

- depression

- panic disorder

- generalised anxiety disorder

- social phobia

- obsessive compulsive disorder

- marital problems.

Numerous studies have shown that cognitive therapy is one of the most effective psychological interventions for depressive disorders[23]. Cognitive-behavioural therapy (CBT) can produce similar results to drug therapy in non-psychotic depression, even with moderately severe cases[21,24,25]. Some studies suggest that CBT might be more effective than drug therapy[26] particularly in delaying or preventing relapse[24,25,27]. Cognitive therapy has been recommended as first line treatment in preference to pharmacotherapy for mild depression[28,29], however, there is no evidence that CBT is effective in the most severe and psychotic forms of depression[30]. This is more likely to respond to medication and electroconvulsive therapy (ECT).

Cognitive-behavioural therapy can also be an effective alternative to drug treatment for panic disorders, social phobia, agoraphobia, and generalised anxiety disorder[12,31,32]. It tends to produce longer-term benefits in these conditions than medication or other psychological therapies[21,33,34]. Once again, non specific interventions for generalised anxiety disorder (such as relaxation) are not likely to be effective[31].

Behaviour therapy can also be effective in the treatment of obsessive compulsive disorders (OCD), with long term symptom reduction of 50% or greater[35].

(c)   Psychodynamic therapies

Many studies of psychodynamic therapy are methodically flawed, with inadequate control groups and diverse psychological techniques[36]. There are no controlled trials which favour dynamic psychotherapy over other active treatments. Two meta-analyses concluded that short-term psychodynamic therapy was superior to 'no treatment' (waiting list controls) but no more effective than drugs, behavioural therapies, or counselling[37,38]. This conclusion has been supported by other reviews[30,39]. There are no studies of dynamic psychotherapy lasting longer than a year, but in one review of 2,400 patients, the maximum effects of psychotherapy were estimated to occur by one year (52 weekly sessions)[40].

(d)   Cognitive analytic therapy (CAT)

A relatively new intervention—cognitive analytic therapy (CAT)—attempts to combine the principles of psychodynamic therapy with those of cognitive therapy[41]. An initial period of unstructured listening helps to define treatment goals. These are then dealt with using cognitive techniques. As yet, there is little evidence of its effectiveness from controlled trials.

Specialist services

Specialist mental health services treat the majority of people with serious mental disorders, such as schizophrenia, manic-depression, and other psychoses. They also treat a number of people with serious neurotic disorders who require more intensive treatment and monitoring than can be provided in primary care.

Most disorders treated by specialist services are characterised by severe symptoms, but also, impaired social functioning and disability in addition to, and independent of these symptoms. Marked social disability can persist, even when symptoms are well controlled. Interventions, therefore, need to address both symptoms **and** social disabilities, and need to be provided over a long period of time, in accordance with the long-term nature of these disorders. Maintaining continuity and co-ordination of care is essential and can be achieved by well-organised multidisciplinary teams.

The interventions discussed in the previous section are also used within specialist mental health services but there are a number of additional treatments whose prescription and monitoring require specialist levels of expertise and training.

Electroconvulsive therapy

Electroconvulsive therapy (ECT) involves inducing convulsions by the application of an electric current to the head, in fully anaesthetised patients.

There has been a decline in the use of ECT and it is generally reserved for severely depressed patients and for those who are resistant to drug therapy[42].

ECT is a highly effective treatment for depression, with 80–90% of patients showing a good response to bilateral administration[43-46]. When ECT is limited to patients who have not responded to an adequate course of antidepressant medication, response rates fall to 50%. Cognitive dysfunction, particularly memory impairment, is a significant adverse effect of ECT. The effectiveness of ECT is highly dependent on the treatment schedule, including the dose, frequency of application, total number of treatments administered, and type of ECT equipment used[43,47]. The training and skill of anaesthetists and psychiatrists are also important influences on its effectiveness.

Drug therapies

Antipsychotic drugs, also known as 'neuroleptics' and (misleadingly) 'major tranquillisers', are the mainstay of treatment in schizophrenia, mania and other acute psychoses. When used in equipotent doses, all neuroleptics are potentially and equally effective, but there are considerable individual differences in drug response. Medication generally produces greater improvements in the 'positive' symptoms of schizophrenia (hallucinations, delusions, disordered thinking, and paranoia), than the 'negative' symptoms (deficits in social interaction, emotional expression, and motivation)[48]. Some patients do not respond to drug treatment and up to 40% of people with schizophrenia relapse whilst on medication.

Compliance with medication is a particular problem in the long-term control of schizophrenia. Antipsychotic drugs have a number of disabling side-effects which may contribute to a poor compliance. For example, acute extrapyramidal syndromes (involuntary tremors and slowed movement) develop in up to 75% of patients receiving traditional neuroleptics[49]. Tardive dyskinesia (facial grimacing etc.) is a particularly serious side effect and may be permanent, even after withdrawal of the drug.

Other compliance problems may stem from the patients' inability or unwillingness to accept their need for medication. This is easily dismissed as lack of 'insight', but in fact is part of the complex psychological process of coming to terms with a major mental illness. Specific psychological counselling should be provided to deal with these personal adjustment issues.

A large proportion of patients with severe mental illness will need continued maintenance treatment with neuroleptic drugs to reduce the incidence of relapse and many of the classic neuroleptic drugs are available as 'depot' preparations, with a single injection providing sufficient treatment for 2–4 weeks. This may aid compliance with some groups of patients, especially those with chaotic life-styles, but needs to be carefully monitored in order to prevent long-term overprescribing.

Atypical neuroleptics

Clozapine is the most extensively evaluated of the new neuroleptic drugs[50]. It is at least as effective as other antipsychotic drugs in schizophrenia but, in addition, is effective in a substantial proportion (30 to 50%) of patients who are resistant to classic antipsychotic therapy[51]. Clinical studies have shown clozapine to be effective in suppressing both the positive and negative symptoms of schizophrenia and to be associated with an extremely low incidence of extrapyramidal side effects, especially tardive dyskinesia[52]. A major factor restricting the drug's wider use in psychiatric practice is the potentially fatal side-effect of agranulocytosis (reduced blood cells) that can occur in 1–2% of patients[53]. Currently, clozapine is only licensed for treatment resistant schizophrenia, and its use must be monitored by the Clozaril Patient Monitoring Service[54]. It is substantially more expensive than typical neuroleptics.

Lithium

Lithium is effective in up to 60% of acute manic episodes but is less effective in atypical or more severe presentations of manic-depression. The long-term outcome of manic-depression is not necessarily improved by prophylactic lithium therapy, and like other serious mental illness, carefully organised programmes of care, including psychosocial support, are needed.

Flexible (targeted) drug treatments strategies

Research on flexible drug treatment strategies has attempted to balance the need for long-term maintenance therapy with the disabling side-effects associated with such therapy. Studies have examined methods of predicting schizophrenic relapse, and the effectiveness of alternative management strategies.

There is some evidence to suggest that a number of largely non-psychotic symptoms usually herald the onset of schizophrenic relapse[55]. Although the nature and timing of these symptoms usually varies markedly between individuals, each person appears to have their own specific and consistent pattern. Up to 70% of patients and 90% of carers report prodromal symptoms within the week prior to relapse[56] and a small pilot study concluded that monitoring such early signs was a useful method of predicting relapse[57].

Obviously, if relapse can be predicted accurately, then early intervention with drugs or psychosocial therapy may attenuate the severity of the subsequent course of illness. It may also be possible to maintain patients on low doses of drugs, which are then augmented when relapse seems likely. Unfortunately, consistent results have not been found in relation to the prediction of relapse and it appears that 'early warning signs' may lack specificity[58].

A number of randomised controlled trials have compared the effectiveness of different medication management strategies for people with schizophrenia[59,60]. In one study[59], the experimental group did not receive maintenance therapy but were prescribed neuroleptic drugs intermittently when prodromal symptoms suggested an imminent relapse. The control group continued to receive maintenance medication, plus additional therapy as indicated by prodromal symptoms. After the first year of follow-up, the experimental group had experienced more prodromes and more relapses, but these were judged to be of a trivial nature. The experimental group received much lower overall doses of neuroleptic medication and experienced fewer side effects. However, these promising results were not maintained by the second year of follow-up[61]. The experimental group experienced greater psychotic and non-psychotic morbidity, more frequent hospitalisation, and no overall gains in social function. Although they also experienced fewer side effects, the incidence of the more serious tardive dyskinesia was similar between experimental and control groups.

In contrast to the earlier pilot study[57], monitoring of the early symptoms in this trial was not particularly predictive of relapse. In the first year, although 73% of all relapses were preceded by episodes of prodromal symptoms, only one in five of such episodes were followed by relapse. By the second year of follow-up, only 25% of relapses were preceded by prodromal episodes.

A number of important points can be concluded from this study. Firstly, continuous neuroleptic prophylaxis appears to be important in the treatment of most patients suffering from schizophrenia. In fact, completely intermittent therapy (i.e. stopping and starting doses of medication) is probably the most ineffective approach in terms of symptom control and minimising side effects[60]. Continuous, low dose depot medication with additional oral doses at times of stress might be a more effective treatment regime. Secondly, there is poor evidence that early signs monitoring can reliably predict relapse, but focusing on patients' symptoms may have other beneficial consequences in the therapeutic relationship. Thirdly, psychosocial and psychoeducational approaches were used to instruct patients and their carers about schizophrenia and the early signs of relapse, and these seemed integral to the overall outcome. The disappointing results of some of the early intervention strategies may therefore be related to a concurrent need for ongoing and more intensive family and psychoeducational approaches.

Many patients themselves have developed idiosyncratic coping strategies to deal with symptom changes. These include manipulation of drug dosage, cognitive strategies (focusing or ignoring), relaxation and other physical activities[56,62]. A similarly wide range of coping strategies has been developed by people with persistent, non-drug responsive, psychotic symptoms[63]. Further trials are needed to identify these methods and to elucidate the specific conditions under which each may be most effectively used.

Psychosocial therapies

Since the 1980s, there has been increasing interest in the potential role of psychological therapies as an adjunct to neuroleptic medication; these have largely been limited to patients with schizophrenia. It is well established that neuroleptic medication in schizophrenia lengthens the period of symptom remission, but does not entirely prevent relapse. Adding psychological therapies may further postpone relapse in some cases.

The different types of therapy which have been evaluated are (a) family interventions with and without social skills training, and (b) cognitive strategies (e.g. CBT). These therapies are generally termed 'psychosocial', but are not distinct. Each contains a slightly different package of educational, behavioural and cognitive elements.

The family interventions current in schizophrenia are based on two premises. Firstly, certain types of interactions between people with schizophrenia and family members are likely to increase the probability of relapse, notably, high levels of critical or emotionally over-involved communications. Secondly, many severely mentally ill people do not have the social skills necessary to handle stressful relationships and situations. The aims of the intervention are therefore to improve the emotional 'climate' in the family and help patients and carers cope with the stresses associated with long term mental illness[64].

The cognitive strategies are a straightforward application of CBT approaches to psychosis. Thus, the therapist attempts to identify 'faulty' or dysfunctional cognition, analyse their frequency and patterns of occurrence, and think up competing explanations and behavioural responses.

Family interventions

Studies of family interventions provide the strongest evidence for the effectiveness of psychosocial intervention. However, the link between high 'expressed emotion' (EE) and relapse is complicated. It appears to be stronger among families where the schizophrenia is well established and relatively weaker in the first onset cases[65]. This suggests that the stress and burden to families of caring for a relative with schizophrenia may itself lead to high levels of expressed emotion[64]. It is then likely that worsening symptoms interact with increased family stress resulting, in turn, in further symptom exacerbation.

Evaluations of family therapy have used different treatment models. Most successful models include[66];

- a structured approach with trained therapists and close liaison with other members of the clinical team;

- the provision of information about the nature of schizophrenia and its management;

- the use of behavioural psychological techniques to develop and break down goals into manageable steps;

- the use of problem-focused techniques to reduce expressed emotion and enhance coping in the home environment;

- a genuine working relationship between the therapist and the family;

- encouragement of respect for interpersonal boundaries within the family;

- improving communication between the family members.

Results are available from six controlled trials of family therapy, conducted with recently discharged, stable patients with schizophrenia living in high 'EE' households[66]. The family intervention was provided for at least 9 months, in addition to usual neuroleptic medication, and patients were followed up for two years. The trials confirmed that family interventions reduced schizophrenic relapse at nine months and one year to rates comparable with those of low EE households[66]. The frequency of hospital admission was also reduced. Medication compliance was improved in patients receiving family treatment, but was unlikely to be the sole mechanism of reduced relapse since the relapses were also less frequent among patients receiving family therapy but who were not compliant with drug treatment[67]. Some studies demonstrated improved social functioning and adjustment for both patients and family members. Family therapy was also found to be more cost effective, even though it involved greater amounts of staff-time than the control treatments[66,68].

Over the course of the two year follow-up, the proportion of patients who relapsed while receiving family treatment increased. However, in one trial, lower relapse rates persisted at two years[67]. This suggests that family interventions delay, rather than prevent, relapse and that ongoing treatment may be necessary to maintain improvements in patients' functioning. Schizophrenia causes life-long disability for many patients and time-limited interventions will probably produce only transient improvements.

Two further trials of family intervention have included subjects from non-high EE families[69]. These were conducted in China, where a greater proportion of patients with schizophrenia live at home compared with Western cultures. They confirmed a lower rate of hospitalisation in the treatment group and this finding was independent of improved drug compliance. However, the family therapy was accompanied by improved follow-up procedures and the relative contribution of each to the improved patient outcomes is not clear.

Family interventions that are limited to brief educational packages (omitting a behavioural component) may result in improved knowledge about the nature and management of schizophrenia and better engagement in management programmes, but are likely to have little impact on relatives' or patients' behaviour and rates of relapse[66,70].

Social skills and training

Social skills training (SST) uses highly structured educational and behavioural techniques. The aim is to improve the deficits in social functioning that often accompany severe mental illness, even when symptoms are well controlled[71]. Unlike family interventions, SST is not restricted to people living in family households. The content of skills training programmes may include specific training in assertiveness, conversational skills, problem solving and medication management. Homework assignments are used to encourage patients to apply newly acquired skills in real-life situations[72].

SST appears promising in that it is a simple approach and directly tackles the problems that are most relevant to mentally ill people. However, the methods used to evaluate SST in most studies are not of high quality and so information about effectiveness is limited.

Four different types of outcome have been evaluated:

- changes in the patients' feelings and attitudes;

- changes in the patients' social behaviour;

- changes in the patients' social functioning.

- responses of other people to the patient.

Results show that SST can reduce the amount of anxiety and discomfort experienced by the patient. It can also improve the quality of social behaviours, such as the use of eye contact, the initiation of conversation, and responsiveness. Two meta-analyses of social skills training have concluded that the specific behavioural changes can generalise to different settings, and that improvements are maintained over time[73,74]. Few studies have evaluated the impact of altering these behaviours on social functioning or quality of life, but the limited evidence does not appear promising[64,71].

Studies provide little information about the optimal frequency and duration of training, and the setting in which it should take place. It is likely that the most seriously ill patients will only benefit from SST if it is integrated into long-term programmes of support and management, hence the connection between social skills training and family interventions.

Recently, some principles of cognitive therapy have been incorporated into social skills training[64]. Many patients with schizophrenia have problems with cognitive functions, such as memory, attention span, and problem solving, and these deficits may be responsible for the disappointing lack of impact of SST on social functioning. It has, therefore, been argued that adding cognitive-based, problem-solving training would help patients to use newly acquired skills in a wider range of situations. Although this assumption is plausible, preliminary results from a small number of studies provide little supporting evidence.

THE TECHNICAL LIMITATIONS OF 'EVIDENCE-BASED' COMMISSIONING

Several factors limit a purchasers' ability to commission mental health services based on effectiveness. These include;

- the quality of the research evidence

- the context of the research may differ radically from local services

- competing priorities may reduce the feasibility of purchasing otherwise effective interventions.

Quality of the evidence

The efficacy of drugs is tested in rigorous, randomised controlled trials. In every-day situations, their effectiveness may be modified by a wide range of other variables. For example, the illness process may affect drug compliance, and failure to address this will ultimately result in poor patient outcomes, regardless of the efficacy of treatment.

Psychological mental health interventions and service models of care are much more difficult to evaluate in trials. The main methodical problems include the difficulty in defining the intervention precisely and in controlling for modifications that might occur when the intervention is applied in different contexts[75]. Consequently, much of the evidence on which purchasing decisions depend, is derived from methodologically flawed studies, or consensus and expert opinion.

Many well conducted studies often provide only limited information because the range of outcomes evaluated is narrow. It is now well accepted that psychological symptoms and social functioning are potentially independent and effective treatment in relation to one outcome is not necessarily correlated with improvements in other outcomes[75]. The implication for commissioning is that the service objectives need to be very explicit. Serious mental illness cannot be 'cured' and important interventions that improve the quality of life and social functioning, but do not influence symptomatic outcomes, may be perfectly legitimate service goals.

It is also important to distinguish between therapeutic interventions and supportive care that is required for everyday living. Adequate housing, financial assistance, and social occupational activities are regarded by service users and their families as probably the most important components of care[76]. The fact that such services have not received much empirical support does not mean that they are ineffective. The exact form in which such services are provided, however, can be tested (for example, the relative effectiveness of different types of supported housing).

The context of care provision

'Effectiveness' is not an absolute property of a treatment intervention: it is conditional on how the intervention is implemented. Purchasers, therefore, need to understand how their local services are organised and how local conditions influence outcomes. For example, community mental health teams cannot be expected to deliver effective psychological interventions if patients are in inadequate housing, with no money and nothing to do. Treatments do not operate in isolation: they require integration and support from other agencies in order to maximise their effectiveness and achieve continuity of care.

In everyday practice, interventions may also be provided simultaneously. Treatment effects can be synergistic, the effectiveness of one aspect of care influencing the outcome of another. For example, adding psychological treatment to drug therapy will generally produce better outcomes than either therapy delivered alone.

Training may also be an important limiting factor for the effective delivery of treatment. Thus, interventions may be effective only when applied to particular groups of patients by specifically trained personnel. This is most relevant to the use of psychological therapies, because these tend to be used most uncritically. For example, two randomised controlled trials compared GP care with psychological treatment provided by community mental health nurses (CPNs), and reported different conclusions[77,78]. In one trial where CPN treatment was superior, only patients with enduring symptoms were targeted, behavioural techniques (of prior proven effectiveness) were employed, and nurses were specifically trained to apply these procedures[77]. In contrast, in the second trial, patients were not selected for enduring symptoms and nurses used unstructured, client-centred counselling as the psychological intervention, and there was no difference with standard GP care[78]. Health Commissions, therefore, need to be satisfied that service specifications include a degree of operational detail indicating that treatments are going to be 'targeted' and delivered by properly trained professionals.

Competing priorities

National policy clearly defines severely mentally ill people as the priority group for mental health services[79]. The limited resources available for specialist mental health services cannot realistically be expected to help the numbers of people estimated to suffer from mental disorders in community surveys. Thus, there is always a danger that if services are not targeted on the most severely disabled psychiatric patients, their needs will be displaced by the more articulate demands of those with less severe disorders[80]. Commissioners therefore need to be very clear about how they will apportion resources to different client groups and how they will monitor this allocation.

Most of the purchasing decisions facing commissioners are not absolute, i.e. whether or not a service should be purchased at all. Choices will be marginal, 'trading off' different disorders and different groups. All choices entail some value judgements, since the evidence is always imperfect and has to be subjectively interpreted and weighted. Also, for each intervention, not only the cost and effectiveness needs to be considered, but also the 'opportunity costs' of the treatments **not** purchased as a consequence. These are the difficult choices at the heart of the commissioning process. Commissioning mental health services, therefore, requires a sound knowledge of the effectiveness of interventions, but this is only one source of information that will influence the final purchasing decisions.

COMMISSIONING ISSUES FOR CLINICIANS AND COMMISSIONERS

We have already noted some of the limitations of the 'evidence-based' approach to commissioning. Of course one would wish that services are based on the best evidence of effectiveness but, as indicated, 'evidence' tells you what works best for a particular group of patients in a particular context, while clinicians are confronted with decisions about specific individuals in specific contexts. They therefore have to interpret and weigh the evidence in the light of their knowledge of individual differences and the influence that the service context may have on outcomes. These judgement are not 'scientific' and may reflect nothing more than simple prejudice and long standing 'custom and practice', however, they do have to be taken into account when formulating commissioning policies. It is pointless to try to persuade busy clinicians in an heterogeneous English city to adopt a service model based on a semi-rural, mid-Western, US town. They simply will not listen. There has to be a 'dialogue' between the 'evidence' and the clinical realities and commissioners have to strive to understand these 'clinical realities'.

To achieve this, commissioners and clinicians have to find a language with which they can communicate. Most commissioners are intensely frustrated by what they see as the lack of information coming back from clinicians regarding exactly what the money is being spent on. Conversely, many clinicians are equally frustrated regarding what they see as the rather trivial, and often inaccurate data which are currently used to monitor contract performance. One of the central challenges facing mental health services is therefore the formulation of valid and widely used methods to monitor contract performance and, until these are available, commissioners and clinicians will have to sit down at a local level and agree some meaningful indices. This process in itself may be a useful exercise.

Finally, for all the reasons outlined above, the relationship between commissioners and clinicians is often strained and both sides may have difficulties in learning to respect and trust the other. Clinicians may suspect—with some justification—that their commissioners have little time and little expertise to devote to mental health services. On the other hand, commissioners often see their provider clinicians as simply defending professional vested interests and traditional ways of working which bear little relationship to the available evidence and accepted 'best practice'. The difficult relationship has to be 'worked at'. There is validity in both points of view and it takes considerable patience and good will for each side to recognise the other's distinctive contribution and to move forward together. The purchaser-provider 'split' thus sometimes resembles a separated couple squabbling over custody and access to the children and, as in this situation, the 'partners' must strive to minimise the inherent potential for damage and concentrate on identifying what they have in common, rather than what divides them. Therein lies the road to a constructive partnership and more effective services.

Conclusions for commissioning

- The effectiveness literature now contains substantial evidence on many individual interventions. Studies of models of service organisation are beyond the scope of this paper, but are important in designing local services. All people require some social resources, including income, food and housing. The need to provide these for the more disabled patients who cannot obtain them themselves is self evident and essential.

- There are a number of effective interventions which are not widely available: most purchasers would benefit from reviewing the local provision of cognitive and behavioural therapies, family management therapy and the use of Clozapine for certain people with schizophrenia.

- There is good evidence that, with more targeted treatment regimes, many patients could be maintained on lower overall doses of neuroleptics. This would have substantial benefits with reduced adverse drug effects. The use of neuroleptics should be reviewed and could be a useful audit topic.

- Social skills training can be an effective technique but needs to be integrated with comprehensive psychosocial interventions.

- ECT is an effective intervention, but only if administered with the correct procedure and equipment. Requiring an audit of ECT may therefore be helpful.

- There are also a number of therapies for which effectiveness studies have not been supportive. Reviewing services offering non-specific counselling and psychodynamic psychotherapy may be worthwhile.

- The overall management and targeting of local services is as important as the individual interventions on offer.

References

[1] Conway, M., Melzer, D., Shepherd, G. & Troop, P.A. *A companion to purchasing adult mental health services.* Cambridge: Anglia and Oxford Regional Health Authority, 1994.

[2] Goldberg, D. & Huxley, P. *Common mental disorders: a biosocial model.* London: Routledge, 1992.

[3] Goldberg, D. & Gater, R. *Estimates of need. Psychiatric Bulletin* 1991; **15**:— 593–595.

[4] Ormel, J., Van Den Brink, W., Koeter, W.M.J., *et al. Recognition, management and outcome of psychological disorders in primary care: a naturalistic follow up study.* Psychol Med 1990; **20**; 909–923.

[5] Song, F., Freemantle, N., Sheldon, T.A., *et al. Selective serotonin reuptake inhibitors: meta-analysis of efficiency and acceptability.* BMJ 1993; **306**: 683–687.

[6] *Effective health care bulletin: The treatment of depression in primary care.* University of Leeds, 1993;

[7] *Selective serotonin reuptake inhibitors for depression. Drug and Therapeutics Bulletin* 1993; **31(15)**; 57–58.

[8] Freemantle, N., House, A., Song, F., Mason, J. & Sheldon, T.A. *Prescribing selective serotonin reuptake inhibitors as a strategy for prevention of suicide.* BMJ 1994; **309**: 249–253.

[9] Rutz, W., Von Knorring, L. & Walinder. J. *Long term effects of an educational program for General Practitioners Given by the Swedish Committee for the prevention and treatment of depression. Acta Pschair Scand* 1992;**85**: 83–88.

[10] Paykel, E.S., Priest, R. *Recognition and management of depression in general practice: a consensus statement.* BMJ 1992; **305**: 1198–1202.

[11] Lader,M. *Treatment of anxiety.* BMJ 1994; **309**: 321–324.

[12] *Psychological treatment for anxiety—An alternative to drugs? Drug and Therapeutic Bulletin* 1993: **31, No19**: 73–75.

[13] Tyrer, P. *Treating panic* BMJ 1989; **298**: 201–202.

[14] Corney, R. *The effectiveness of counselling in General Practice. Int Rev psychiatry* 1992; **4**: 331–338.

[15] Corney, R.H. *Counselling in general practice—does it work? Journal of the Royal Society of Medicine* 1990; **83**:253–257.

[16] Ashurst, P.M. & Ward, D.F. *An evaluation of counselling in general practice; Final report of the Leverhulme counselling project.* London: Mental Health Foundation, 1983.

17 Catalan, J., Gath, D.H., Anastasiades, P., Bond, S., Day, A., Hall, L. *Evaluation of a brief psychological treatment for emotional disorders in primary care. Psychol Med* 1991; **21**: 1013–1018.

18 Mynors-Wallis, L.M. & Gath, D.H. *Brief psychological treatments. Int Rev Pyschiatry* 1992; **4**: 301–305.

19 Holden, J.M., Sagovsky, R. & Cox, J.L. *Counselling in general practice setting: a controlled study of health visitor intervention in treatment of post natal depression* BMJ 1989; **298**: 223–226.

20 Hughes, I., Russell, K. & Rollnick, S. *Walk free: a service for panic and phobia sufferers. Behavioural and Cognitive Psychotherapy* 1995; **23**: 187–191.

21 Hollon, S.D. *Cognitive-behavioural therapy. Current Opinion in Psychiatry* 1993; **6**: 348–352.

22 Andrews, G. *Psychotherapy: from Freud to cognitive science.* Med J Aust 1991; **155**: 845–848.

23 Scott, J. *Cognitive therapy of depressive disorders. Current opinion in Psychiatry* 1994; **7**: 233–236.

24 Hollen, S.D., Shelton, R.C. & Loosen, P.T. *Cognitive therapy and pharmaco-therapy for depression. J Consult Clin Psychol* 1991; **59(1)**: 88–99.

25 Stravynski, A. & Greenberg, D. *The pschological management of depression. Acta Psychiatr Scand* 1992; **85**: 407–414.

26 Dobson, K.S. *A meta-analysis of the efficacy of cognitive therapy for depression. J Consult Clin Psychol* 1989; **57(3)**: 414–419.

27 Westbrook, D. *Aspects of behavioural and cognitive therapy. Current opinion in Psychiatry* 1990; **3**: 355–358.

28 Wexler, B.E. & Cicchetti, D.V. *The outpatient treatment of depression. Implications of outcome research for clinical practice. J Nerv Ment Dis* 1992; **180**: 277–286.

29 Dunler, D.L. *Depression: challenges for the future. J Clin Psychiatry* 1991; **52 Suppl**: 44–51.

30 U.S. Department of Health and Human Services. *Depression in primary care: treatment of major depression.* Rockville: AHCPR publications, 1993;

31 Mattick, R.P., Andrews, G., Hadzi-Palovic, D. & Christensen, H. *Treatment of panic and agoraphobia. An integrative review. The Journal of Nervous and Mental Disease* 1990; **178(9)**: 567–576.

32 Durham, R.C. & Allan, T. *Psychological treatment in generalised anxiety disorder. A review of the clinical significance of results in outcome studies since 1980. Br J Psychiatry* 1993; **163**: 19–26.

33 Criaghead, L.W.C. *Behaviour therapy: recent developments. Current Opinion in Psychiatry* 1991; **4**; 916–920.

34 Dubbert, P.M., Payne, T.J. & Mosley Jr, T.H. *Recent developments in behaviour therapy. Current Opinion in Psychiatry* 1992; **5**: 849–853.

35 Greist, J.H. *Treatment of obsessive compulsive disorder: psychotherapies, drugs and other somatic treatment. J Clin Psychiatry* 1990; **51 Suppl**: 44–50.

36 Milton, J. *Presenting the case of pyschoanalytic psychotherapy services. An annotated bibliography.* London: Association for pyschoanalytic psychotherapy in the NHS and Tavistock clinic 1993;

37 Crits-Christoph, P. *The efficacy of dynamic psychotherapy: a meter-analysis. Am J Psychiatry* 1992; **149**: 151–158.

38 Svatberg, M. & Stiles, T. *Comparative effects of short-term pyschodynamic psychotherapy: a meta-analysis. Journal of Consulting & Clinical Pyschology* 1991;

59: 704–714.

39   Andrews, G. *The evaluation of psychotherapy. Current Opinion in Psychiatry* 1991; **4**: 379–383.

40   Howard, K., Kopta, S., Krause, M. & Orlinsky, D. *The dose-effect relationship in professional psychotherapy. American Psychology* 1986; **41**: 159–164.

41   Ryle, A. *Cognitive-analytic therapy: active participation in change. A new integration in brief psychotherapy.* Chichester: Wiley, 1993.

42   Devanand, D.P., Sackeim, H.A. & Prudic, J. *Electroconvulsive therapy in the treatment-resistant patient. Psychiatr Clin North Am* 1991; **14(4)**: 905–923.

43   Shapira, B., Calev, A. & Lerer, B. *Optimal use of electorconvulsive therapy: choosing a treatment schedule. Psychaitr Clin North Am* 1991; **14(4)**: 935–946.

44   Parker, G., Roy, K., Hadzi-Pavlovic, D. & Pedic, F. *Psychotic (delusional) depression: a mata-analysis of physical treatments. J Affect Disord* 1992; **24(1)**: 17–24.

45   Fink, M. *Combining Drugs and Electroconvulsive Therapy: Safe and/or Effective? J Clin Psychopharma*col 1993; **13**:85–86.

46   Monroe, R.R. *Maintenance electroconvulsive therapy. Psychaitr Clin North Am* 1991; **14(4)**: 947–959.

47   Pippard, J. *Audit of Electroconvulsive Treatment in two National Health Service Regions. Br J Psychiatry* 1992; **160**: 621–637.

48   Levison, D.F. *Pharmacologic treatment of schizophrenia. Clin Ther* 1991; **13**: 326–352.

49   Casey, D.E. *Clozapine: neuroleptic-induced EPS and tardive dyskinesia. Psychopharmacology Berl* 1989; **99 Suppl**: S47–S53.

50   Pickar, D. *Prospects for pharmacotherapy of schizophrenia. Lancet* 1995; **345**: 557–562.

51   *Clozapine and Loxapine for schizophrenia. Drug and Therapeutics Bulletin* 1991; **29(11)**: 41–42.

52   Buch, D.L. *Clozapine: a novel antipsychotic. Am Fam Physician* 1992; **45**: 795–799.

53   Fitton, A. & Heel, R.C. *Clozapine. A review of its pharmacological properties, and therapeutic use in schizophrenia. Drugs* 1990; **40**: 722–747.

54   Kerwin, R.W. *Clozapine: back to the future for schizophrenia research. Lancet* 1995; **345**: 1063–1064.

55   Herz, M.I. *Course, relapse, and prevention of relapse. In: Talbott J.A. ed. The Chronic Mental Patient: Five years later. Orlando: Grune & Stratton*, 1984;

56   Birchwood, M. *Early intervention in schizophrenia: theoretical background and clinical strategies. British journal Clinical Psychology* 1992; **31**: 257–278.

57   Birchwood, M., Smith, J., Macmillan, F., *et al. Predicting relapse in schizophrenia: the development and implementation of an early signs monitoring system using patients and families as observers, a preliminary investigation. Psychol Med.* 1989; **19**: 649–656.

58   Malla, A, & Norman, R.M.G. *Prodromal symptoms in schizophrenia. Br J Psychiatry* 1994; **164**: 487–493.

59   Jolly, A.G., Hirsch, S.R., McRink, A. & Manchanda, R. *Trial of brief intermittent neuroleptic prophylaxis for selected schizophrenic outpatients: clinical outcome at one year. BMJ* 1989; **298**: 985–90.

60   Schooler, N. *Maintenance medication for schizophrenia; strategies for dose reduction. Schizophr Bull* 1991; **17**: 311–324.

61 Jolly, A.G., Hirsch, S.R., Morrison, E., McRink, A. & Wilson, L. *Trial of brief intermittent neuroleptic prophylaxis for selected schizophrenic outpatients: clinical and social outcome at two years. BMJ* 1990; **301**: 837–842.

62 Birchwood, M., Shepherd, G. *Controversies and growing points in cognitive-behavioural intervention for people with schizophrenia. Behavioural Psychotherapy.* 1992; **20**: 305–342.

63 Fallon, I. Talbot, R.E. *Persistent auditory hallucinations: coping mechanisms and implications for management. Psychol Med* 1981; **11**: 329–339.

64 Bellack, A.S. Meuser, K.T. *Psychosocial treatment for schizophrenia. Schizophr Bull* 1993; **19**: 317–336.
1991; **17**: 311–324.

65 Stirling, J., Tantam, D., Thomas, P., *et al. Expressed emotion and early onset schizophrenia: a one year follow-up. Psychol Med 1991; **21**: 675–685.*

66 Lam, D.H. *Psychosocial family intervention in schizophrenia: a review of empirical studies. Psychol Med* 1991; **21**: 423–441.

67 Hogarty, G.E., Anderson, C.M., Reiss, D.J., *et al. Family psychoeducation, social skills training, and maintenance chemotherapy in the aftercare treatment of schizophrenia. Arch Gen Psychiatry* 1991; **48**: 340–347.

68 Brooker, C. *Expressed emotion and psychosocial intervention. Int J Nurs Stud* 1990; **27(3)**: 267–276.

69 Kavanagh, D.J. *Family interventions in mental disorder. Current Opinions in Psychiatry* 1995; **8**: 130–133.

70 Smith, J.V., Birchwood, M. *Specific and non-specific effects of educational intervention with families living with a schizophrenic relative. Br J Psychiatry* 1987; **150**: 645–652.

71 Wallace, C.J., Nelson, C.J., Liberman, R.P., *et al. A review and critique of social skills training with schizophrenic patients. Schizophr Bull* 1980; **6**: 42–63.

72 Heirholzer, R.W., Liberman, R.P. *Successful living: A social skills and problem solving group for the chronic mentally ill. Hosp Community Psychiatry* 1986; **37**: 913–918.

73 Corrigan P.W. *Social skills in adult psychiatric populations: a meta-analysis. Journal of Behaviour Therapy & Experimental Psychiatry* 1991; **22**: 203–210.

74 Benton, M.K. Schroeder H.E. *Social skills training with schizophrenics: a meta-analytic evaluation. Journal of Consulting & Clinical Psychology* 1990; **58**: 741–747.

75 Ruggeri, M., Tansella, M. *Evaluating outcome in mental health care. Current Opinion in Psychiatry* 1995; **8**: 116–121.

76 Shepherds, G., Murray, A. & Muijen, M. *Relative Values.* London: Sainsbury Centre for Mental Health, 1994.

77 Marks, I.M. *Psychiatric nurse therapists in primary care.* London ISBN 0–902606–87–5: Royal College of Nursing, 1985.

78 Gournay, K. Brooking, J. *An evaluation of the effectiveness of community psychiatric nurses in treating patients with minor mental disorders in primary care: final report to the Department of Health.* Health Care Studies, Middlesex University: Queensway, Enfield, EN3 4SF, 1992;

79 Department of Health. *The Health of the Nation Key Area Handbook: Mental illness; 2nd edition.* London: Department of Health, 1994;

80 Harrison, G., Eaton, W. *Targeting effective health care. Current Opinion Pyschiatry* 1995; **8**: 107–108.

23 Performance Indicators in Mental Health Services

GYLES GLOVER & EDNA KAMIS-GOULD

Introduction

Performance Indicators are operationally defined, indirect measures of selected aspects of a system which give some indication of how far it conforms with its intended purpose. They are ratios designed to reflect levels of performance, mostly through comparisons against established yardsticks, against other organisations operating in the same field, or over time. Indicators can be relatively concrete, for example, measures of cost per unit of service or active case load. They could also be proxies for complex concepts, such as services in least restrictive setting, or of intended policy implementation. In the context of health or mental health care, performance indicators have a range of uses.

Clinical audit often entails both cross sectional comparison among clinical teams and longitudinal comparison over time. Managers need to make simple comparisons of and derive information about providers, mostly around costs and benefits. In competitive situations such information may be used for marketing. Health care funders may wish to assure themselves that interventions are necessary, parsimonious and effective. Regulatory bodies may consider a range of measures indicative of the extent to which a provider unit reaches acceptable quality standards. Performance indicators are a good vehicle for these and other assessments.

Performance Indicators have developed to a far greater degree of sophistication in the United States than in Britain. This chapter will begin by reviewing the theoretical framework which has emerged there, focusing on one State, Colorado, which has developed a particularly sophisticated system of performance indicators. It will go on to look at indicators with relevance to mental health care in the English Department of Health's Health Service Indicators package and to consider how far these fulfill the requirements of sound performance assessment. Finally, it will consider the steps which would be required for the English position to be substantially advanced.

Theoretical aspects

Performance Indicators are reflections of attributes of interest. They can be used to measure:

1   What managers and the public want to see, e.g. clients' improvement

2   What managers and the public do not want to see, e.g. barriers to services

265

3   Levels of performance, and

4   The degree of conformity of a system to its intended purpose.

They can address relatively objective aspects, such as costs, or value-based policies and the degree to which performance attests to policy implementation. Some aspects of the performance of the organisation may be relatively uncontentious. Individuals who need care should have access to services at reasonable cost. In the same vein, providers should be productive. Greater specificity about ease of access, quality and outcomes of services provided are desirable, but more difficult to operationalize, measure and develop relevant norms for. Other aspects, such as the relative weight to be assigned to costs versus the importance of the clinical gain, are similarly more contentious. Numerous measurement and procedural aspects of assessment may also be questioned. For example, the issue of who should measure is value laden. Managers and public bodies, such as health authorities or external regulators, may consider that they should make inspections of clinical work, while professionals may consider this an intrusion and feel that examinations should be left to them. If a system of performance indicators is to achieve broad acceptance, all these issues must be explicitly debated and workable compromises achieved from the outset.

Because of these dynamics and debate, each system's and/or organisation's values should be identified and articulated clearly and unambiguously. The varying perspectives, for example, of clinical and public health outcomes or of primary and secondary level care styles must be understood in order to assure that future assessment will reflect on adherence to those values.

Kamis-Gould (1995) has recently proposed a model for evaluating providers and systems of care in the US. In her model, most providers are likely to be private; the perspective emphasized in the assessment, however, is tailored to mental health care and promotes principles of public health and mental health. The assessment considers two broad aspects of an organisation or a system: its capacity and its performance. Capacity covers such issues as human and financial resources available, the ability of managers to provide the necessary leadership and innovation, the comprehensiveness of range and quality of clinical facilities, the technical capacity to run, coordinate and monitor all aspects of the organisation's functions and finally its financial viability.

The comprehensive performance of the organisation is considered in three distinct dimensions:

1   Responsiveness and accessibility. The extent to which those who must look to the organisation for care, get it when they need it. This issue is of particular relevance for poorly served groups. The congruence of service utilization with the local assessed need, cultural sensitivity to relevant minority groups and the promptness and sensitivity of response to clients are measures of this issue.

2   Efficiency. Levels of productivity, cost containment, occupancy rates and other measures of efficient use of resources.

3   Effectiveness. Client and systems outcomes. Clients' outcomes encompass health and mental health status (functional levels,

symptomatology and substance abuse), quality of life and satisfaction with treatment. Provider outcomes cover satisfaction of staff with the environment and constraints in which they work and their personal effectiveness.

Within a model of this type the Performance Indicators which comprise the building blocks of capacity, responsiveness/accessibility, efficiency and effectiveness should all share a number of features.

1   They should relate clearly to an agreed organisational goal.

2   Operational definitions of measures should be clear and should fit well within dimensions of performance and be reliable and valid.

3   Where possible, data required should be derived from operational information systems, because special data collection is costly and invites manipulation.

4   Indicators should always be expressed as ratios; never as raw numbers. In some instances, ratio denominators may require complex estimation. For example, treatment rates for refugee populations require estimation of local population size. Similarly, accessibility, or congruence between true and treated prevalence require epidemiological estimation of true prevalence of mental disorders and need for services.

5   The desired direction for each indicator should be clear. For example, the number of Mental Health Act approved social workers per unit population would be a poor indicator since too low a figure would be undesirable, indicating likely problems with availability, while too high a number would suggest that many would be unlikely to have sufficient ongoing experience to maintain skills. An example of clear desired direction could be client's outcomes, because the higher the client's functioning, the better the outcome.

6   The nature of reasonable comparators should be established. For issues such as population based admission rates, the nature of some types of area will inevitably imply greater need. A mechanism will be required to adjust for this. This may either take the form of some type of statistical standardisation (similar to age adjustment of death rates) or selection of appropriate comparators, such as by use of the area types recently defined by the Office of Population Censuses and Surveys (1995).

7   Indicators should measure features of the service sufficiently universal for comparison with other services to be realistic.

8   Finally, judgement about the extent of deviation ascribable to random fluctuation, and thus how big a difference will be required to be considered relevant should be determined.

In addition to these mandatory features, several other properties of Performance Indicators are also desirable. They should be equally applicable to all types of mental health provider, public or private. Indicators of possibly opposing concepts such as cost and effectiveness should be set together so that published compilations indicate possible trade-off effects. Indicators should be relatable to the development of performance standards, such as those produced by the

267

Clinical Standards Advisory Group (Wing *et al*. 1995). They should be structured to illustrate the nature of the organisation as a functioning system; thus where shortened in-patient stays lead to higher community nursing case loads, such patterns should be apparent. Managerial, financial and quality aspects should be integrated. Finally, mental health indicators should be associated with a wider structure of indicators of related types of care, health and social services, because more often than not, persons with mental disorders have multiple service needs.

Developments in Colorado

The development of a Performance Indicator system for state funded mental health systems began in Colorado about ten years ago (Barrett *et al*, 1992). In conditions of increasing financial stringency, state legislators wanted justification for the funding used by mental health services. In the same climate, the number of staff available in the state office to monitor the performance of publicly funded services had reduced. A performance indicator programme was seen as a way forward.

A lengthy process of indicator development was undertaken by a steering group made up mainly of representatives of the State (as the health care purchaser) and relevant provider organisations. They undertook a five step process. Relevant values were identified, appropriate detailed concerns underlying each value were crystallized. Measurement strategies for each concern were developed; (this component of the work was undertaken by a separate technical working group). Over the last few years data has been collected, analysed and reported widely. Finally, in 1995 and for the first time, the fifth step, financial reward for performance documented by the indicators has been initiated.

The Colorado system emphasised five dimensions. Mental health centres should be financially viable, satisfactorily productive, responsive to their community's needs, comprehensive in their service provision and client outcomes should be satisfactory. Detailed indicators of a range of issues relating to each dimension were developed and have been measured for some years. Measurement of outcome is undertaken by both professionals and service users. For the former, a simple standardised seven point scoring system, similar to the HoNOS scales (Wing *et al* 1994) was devised. User feedback is elicited through two programmes, one run by care providers, one by users themselves.

The eventual allocation of financial incentives has been based on a set of four indicators drawn from this wider pool. User satisfaction and the average change score from start to end of treatment episodes in the standard scale provide an outcome component. Two process measures are also included. One measures the extent to which care agencies within the community cross refer; this is seen as an indicator of the quality of multi-agency working. The other is the ratio of non-hospital residential places managed, to hospital beds used by the centre. This is a measure of the provision of a comprehensive service configuration.

In the first year $50,000 additional funding was allocated to the mental health centre with the most consistently satisfactory performance across these four measures. The State mental health authority hopes that this approach will encourage greater productivity and more outcome focused care.

Performance indicators in the national health service

A set of numerical indicators of the activity within the National Health Service has been produced since the early 1980s, first by the statistics division and most recently by the Finance and Performance Division of the Department of Health. The figures are based on numerical information returned routinely by provider units and district health authorities in line with national reporting requirements, now set out in the NHS Data Manual.

The scope and detail of the set of indicators has evolved over the years reflecting changing concerns. With the introduction of the internal market some indicators continue to be published on a population base whereas others have moved to a provider unit base. Following the publication of *The Health of the Nation* (Secretary of State, 1992) a set of population health outcome indicators was added.

The indicators are produced on floppy disks and circulated widely within the Health Service. Curiously, until the publication of the most recent set, they seem never to have achieved the status of 'league tables' though for many indicators the rank order of districts or provider units has always been published. The computer software accompanying the indicators will produce output in several forms including histograms and charts showing the position of districts in terms of the percentiles of the whole distribution. In most years, the data has also been published as Lotus-123 format spreadsheets to permit maximal flexibility in its analysis.

The Health Service indicators are not widely known. Their use is largely restricted to administrative circles reflecting the bias of the Korner data sets on which they are largely based (Korner, 1983). There is a degree of scepticism about the accuracy of the information on which they are based.

The indicators can broadly be divided into five categories, though those related to the mental health service mostly fall into the first three.

1   A range deal with population based rates of service use. Examples include measures of treatment incidence; the number of admissions of district residents to psychiatric in-patient care, or the numbers of first contacts by community psychiatric nurses per unit population.

2   Some detail aspects of the process such as the percentage of patients or episodes in which compulsory detention under the Mental Health Act is involved. Profiles of the stay length in episodes of hospital admission falls under this category.

3   A further set of indicators describe the cost of care in various settings in relation to the number of patients using that type of care during the course of the year.

4   A small number track specific policy initiatives. For example, the percentage of all psychiatric admissions of individuals in a district

population where treatment occurred outside the district is included to monitor the rate of development of local in-patient units as reprovision for old hospitals.

5	A further series pull together all available national information with relevance to the Health of the Nation Targets. In the case of mental health the only target effectively addressed is C2, the general suicide rate, which is supplied at district health authority level.

A high proportion of the indicators seen in this set falls short of the criteria described above. The only critereon of a satisfactory indicator all meet is that they are calculated from routinely collected data. For the most part the indicators do not sit in a clear policy framework. The only exception to this are those relating to *The Health of the Nation*. They are largely descriptive, rather than evaluative and do not represent a conceptual, multi-dimensional and comprehensive model of performance assessment.

There are no sufficiently detailed statements of the organisational goals of the mental health services for indicator development along the lines proposed earlier in the chapter to be realistic at this stage. However some approximations may be surmised. It seems reasonable to expect that indicators calculated at purchaser level should give a measure of the pattern and volumes of service provision available. This should be standardised according to some measure of likely population based need. At provider level indicators should demonstrate the extent to which clinical care is performed in line with policy directives such as the *Care Programme Approach* (Department of Health, 1989). Clinical outcomes and consumer satisfaction for patients treated should also be covered. At both levels, issues of efficiency should be tackled in a manner which considers the treatment of patients and individuals rather than abstract entities such as admissions which may be more susceptible to manipulation.

Recently a small number of specific performance management indicators has been developed to monitor progress in particularly high profile initiatives such as the Care Programme Approach and Supervision Registers. These have mostly required the setting up of new *ad hoc* reporting systems.

To move performance indicators in the NHS to a position closer to the theoretical ideal, broadly three developments would be required.

1	A detailed and widely accepted series of organisational goals would need to be developed,

2	A multi-dimensional model of most important aspects of performance and performance indicators within each dimension should be developed, and

3	Data sources would have to be substantially improved.

The first task is made very difficult by the size of the organisation. Policy documents inevitably either take the form of apparently distant advice or very 'top down' directives. Somehow the co-operative concensus feel, for example of the Mental Illness Service Strategy for Wales (Welsh Office, 1989) seems hard to achieve at the scale of the English NHS.

The deficiencies of available data fall under the headings of scope and quality. Currently, data collected centrally relate to episodes or volumes of care. Linkage of the various inputs to each patient is not technically feasible. Activity covered relates primarily to hospitals. Social Services and care provided in the voluntary sector, important parts of modern multi-disciplinary mental health care, are not addressed at all. A number of aspects of treatment such as the use of sophisticated modern drugs are also omitted. Perhaps most important, no consumer outcomes and/or feedback is incorporated. The quality of data is almost certainly a reflection of the limited use made of it. Technical work to address these deficiencies is currently being undertaken both at the level of the information base (Glover 1995) and of the overall performance management framework. Thus this set of problems may soon be addressed.

However if the UK is to have a modern and humane mental health service in the long term, these are issues which cannot be avoided. The quality of care provided in the increasingly dispersed network which characterises a modern mental health service must be monitored in an objective and widely comparable ways if standards are to be maintained. The constant search for value for money cannot and should not be avoided if the benefit of available resources is to be maximised. Finally, the justification of expenditure in terms of results will be a necessary condition if adequate levels of funding are to be achieved and sustained.

References

Barrett, T. J., Berger, B. L. & Bradley, L. A. (1992), *Performance contracting: The Colorado model revisited*, Administration and Policy in Mental Health, **20 (2)**, 75–85.

Department of Health, (1989) *Caring for people with a mental illness:* The Care Programme Approach. (Abstract).

Glover, G. R. (1995) *Mental health informatics and the rhythm of community care.* British Medical Journal, **311** 1038–9

Kamis-Goulde, E. (1995) *A model of indicators for State Mental Health Agencies assessment of mental health plans and system performance.* Presented at the National Conference on Mental Health Statistics, 1995 (Abstract).

Korner, E. (1983) *Report of a working party on information requirements in the National Health Service*, London: HMSO.

Department of Health (1992) *The Health of the Nation: a strategy for health in England* London: Cm 1986, HMSO.

Wallace, M., Charlton, J., Denham, C. (1995) *The new OPCS area classification.* Population Trends, 15–30.

Welsh Office (1989) *Mental Illness Services. A strategy for Wales.* Welsh Office Publicity Unit.

Wing, J. K., Curtis, R., Beevor, A. (1994) *'Health of the Nation': measuring mental health outcomes.* Psychiatric Bulletin, **18;** 690–691.

Wing, J. K., Rix, S., Curtis, R. (1995) *Protocol for assessing services for people with severe mental illness.* Volume 2, C.S.A.G. Schizophrenia report. (Abstract).

Related references

Bartlett, J., and Cohen, J. (1993), *Building an accountable, improvable delivery system*, Administration and Policy in Mental Health, **21 (1),** 51–8.

Birch, S. and Maynard, A. (1986) *Performance indicators and performance assessment in the UK National Health Service: Implications for management and planning*, International Journal of Health Planning and Management, **1**, 143–156.

Kamis-Gould, E. (1987) *The New Jersey Performance Management System: A state system and uses of simple measures*, Evaluation and Program Planning, **10**: 249–255.

Leff, H. S., Mulkern, V., Lieberman, M., and Raab, B. A. (1994) *The effects of capitation on service access, adequacy, and appropriateness*, Administration and Policy in Mental Health, **21 (3)**, 141–160.

McCarthy, P. R., Belber, S. and Duggar, D. E. (1993) *Outcome measurement to outcome management; The critical step*, Administration and Policy in Mental Health, **21 (1)** 5968.

4 National Standards for Mental Health Care: Making Community Care Work

CHRISTINA PERRING & JENNY WILLMOT

Community care: problems and solutions

We can only consider the roles of health service purchasers in the context of a national mental health service based on need. If we neglect this full picture, our mental health care will continue to be:

- patchily and unequally provided on the basis of geography, personal characteristics of service users (gender, ethnicity, class, sexual orientation) and the particular attributes of local services or referral routes;

- oriented towards control rather than care, support and treatment: control occurs increasingly when true community care fails, especially given understandable fears of high profile news stories and a national climate that stresses tough 'law and order' responses to social problems;

- characterized by the misallocation of resources to outdated institutions or to newer mini-institutions, rather than to community-based care set up to meet locally assessed need that is informed by user and carer perspectives;

- one in which local planning ends up as a convoluted rationing device.

Four major reports (1) in the last two years on mental health care provided in the community identify similar reasons for failures—poorly distributed resources, poor inter-agency working and planning, inadequate user and carer involvement, differential (worse) treatment for Black people and women. Reports also agree on the overall policy framework of community care—with the exception of supervision registers. We see further consensus about underlying principles and how and what we want to achieve by community care. There is less agreement about how to turn our mental health services into community care that really works.

This chapter offers a systematic approach for progress towards integrated and comprehensive national mental health care. By emphasizing a legal framework and national minimum standards it strikes a balance between a prescriptive and simplistic 'blueprint' and a laissez-faire approach. The first neglects diversity, local context and expertise and would disempower all involved. The second leaves the ground open either to the 'survival of the fittest' (where the 'fittest' are those most equipped to survive on this particular terrain) or to local rationing decisions. Both of these neglect the least powerful in the planning and service structures—service users and their carers, and the less powerful among paid or unpaid workers. We can seek balance by:

- valuing the diversity of different professional specialisms, ethnic groups, social classes, geographical locations;

- using agreed principles to guide service planning and delivery. In 1994, MIND set out four principles—Respect, Justice, Helping not Harming, Entitlement—from which it developed examples of possible national standards (Pfluger and Sayce, 1994);

- assessing medical and also social, cultural and personal need, and then creating responses to meet need, rather than perpetuating existing service activity;

- focusing on how we achieve community care (process) and on what we want to achieve (outcome) in relation to assessed need and health gain by moving towards entitlement—the right to receive community-based care;

- establishing local cycles of constant feedback and monitoring that are compatible with life in an ever changing world, and building flexibility in to our processes, structures, attitudes, professional skills;

- remaining sensitive to local contexts;

- avoiding a narrow definition of 'standards' which attend to service activity, but neglect health gain.

On this basis we can make proposals at four levels in society—national, regional, local and individual—to ensure adequate national mental health care for the next century.

A national framework

Nationally agreed standards, some with the force of law behind them, will help us meet the most frequent and damaging criticisms of current community care by achieving the following: statutory rights to mental health care for people in greatest need, effective inter-agency working, effective user and carer involvement, guaranteed minimum level of funding of mental health care, and an agreed allocation of financing between community-based and other mental health services.

Since the 1960s, government community care policies and legislation have been hampered by a predominantly laissez faire approach which has not worked fast or well enough. Even the intense activity of the last five years has produced only the unsatisfactory and far from 'seamless' patchwork we see today. It is time for a new approach.

New legislation: entitlement to care
Existing legislation

The NHS and Community Care Act 1990 provided an important legislative framework, but its 3-year time scale for implementation and its compartmentalised approach to mental health care have led to the logjams predicted in 1991 (Sayce). It could have introduced Cabinet ministerial responsibility for community care for national co-ordination, as recommended in the government's own White Paper (Griffiths, 1988). It could have ringfenced or safeguarded resources to ensure that capital and revenue from old institutions were transferred to new community mental health care. The predicted difficulties arising from distinctions between 'health' and 'social' care have impacted seriously on those needing care. It suspended the section on carers' needs in the Disabled Persons (Services, Consultation and Representation) Act 1986, and it has taken a Private Member's Bill (presented to Parliament by Malcolm Wicks in March 1995) to seek proper support to the seven million or so carers, without whom community care would break down. Even if this becomes law, there is no provision for additional money nationally to provide the support.

The Mental Health Act (1983) is increasingly recognised as an inadequate framework for mental health care provided mainly from community bases rather than from hospital in-patient wards. The Act concentrates on compulsory treatment in hospital rather than ensuring care—not through compulsion—in the community. There is a duty on social services and health authorities to provide aftercare for patients who were detained in hospital for treatment (section 117) but this is rarely properly implemented. The problem is that the duty is not clearly enforceable and is non-specific, both in respect to who should carry it out and what after-care services should be provided. The government's Mental Health (Patients in the Community) Bill will introduce compulsion on patients to accept those section 117 services that are offered—yet more unnecessary and unsuitable coercion when existing measures have not been supported as fully as they might by, for instance, national standards and appropriate resources. What is needed is not compulsion on service users but an enforceable right to essential services.

A revised Mental Health Act or the Community Care [Rights to Mental Health Services] Bill 1995 introduced to Parliament as a Private Member's Bill by Tessa Jowell could place local authorities under a duty to provide services for which people have been assessed. They would also provide for national minimum standards and principles for assessment and provision of services and therefore lead to a greater and better range of community care services. Without such a national legal framework, users and their carers have no recourse when they are failed by inadequate community care. Instead, we see victims of these failures coming together to campaign for change and justice, for example through the Zito Trust.

Further evidence of failures come from media reports of tragedies involving mental health service users. These exaggerate risks from people experiencing acute episodes of mental distress and underreport other tragedies, such as the fact that over 5000 people a year commit suicide, that many people are dying following prescription of psychiatric medication or that many people seek and are refused treatment. Bootham Hospital, York has set more stringent criteria for accepting users during acute episodes of distress, apparently to ration bed spaces. Some community services are reporting that there is now nowhere for users to go: refused by hospital, and too disturbed to be accepted by existing community services. The Ritchie report (1994) documents repeat refusals met by Christopher Clunis when he sought support. Nationally, we must ensure that people in need of both continuing and acute care are entitled to receive it.

Existing implementation is failing in yet another way, for service users need protection from abuses in mental health settings. Coercive practices, use of dangerous 'cocktails' of medication or levels over BNF recommended dosages, failure to provide adequate information about treatments available, failure to allow users access to single sex wards, exploitation of clients by some counsellors or psychotherapists, failure to facilitate users' informed consent to treatment (Sayce, 1995): users are abused in these and other ways in psychiatric settings. All can be and must be prevented and we need a clear legal framework for this to happen.

Further legislative steps forward will be to overcome society's failure to allow evidence from service users to be fully accepted in courts and elsewhere. The present law is framed to protect professionals and others from patient's allegations of criminal or wrongful conduct. Section 139 of the Mental Health Act 1983 provides that no civil or criminal proceedings can be brought in respect of things done under the Act without leave of the High Court or the Director of Public Prosecutions. The common law (i.e. the law found in the decisions of judges) also provides that juries should be warned that it is dangerous to accept the evidence of patients in special hospitals. The effect of such provisions is to reinforce a system in which users are powerless and are not taken seriously. Evidence from patients at Rampton Hospital at the inquest of a patient's death was unvalued in court proceedings, and is lost sight of in reports referring to this incident (e.g. Rampton Health Advisory Committee, 1995).

Guidance and charters

Current government policy favours national guidance and charters, but not legislation and national standards. Guidance and charters are not powerful enough to bring about the scale of improvement needed, fast enough.

The most comprehensive guidance for mental health care is contained in the Department of Health's 'Health of the Nation Key Area Handbook on Mental Illness' (1993). Produced jointly with Social Services Inspectorate, it is heavily oriented towards medical care and neglects social care and the roles of service users and carers. This partial picture hampers implementation. Significantly, it makes no recommendations about resourcing services. There are useful sections on advocacy, user involvement, but while acknowledging the distinct needs of women and ethnic minorities it falls short of addressing underlying problems such as those highlighted by Harris (1994). He reports common experiences for Black people, such as admission to hospital outside the catchment area, and the Ritchie report's relegation 'to obscurity the dominant factor' (p25) of institutional racism.

A second example of guidance concerns supervision registers, an inappropriate and unnecessary response brought about by the climate of the times and reactions to media stories rather than by considered policy positions. Opposed by many professional and most user and carer groups and not implemented under Scottish law, supervision registers appear to break European and English and Welsh domestic law. The upshot is unnecessary administration which adds to the fear and stigma of accepting mental health care. When so-called 'non-compliance' of service users remains a concern, it is odd to introduce a measure almost designed to drive people away. More widespread concerns (eg. Nuffield Institute Conference, 1994) include confidentiality; the right to independent appeal; emphasis on control at the expense of care and treatment; difficulties in assessing 'dangerousness' and risk; inter-agency communication; resourcing issues; risks of increased stigma and of keeping people in hospital longer than necessary. These criticisms echo those raised against earlier proposals about community treatment orders, again opposed by professional and user organisations.

Two different approaches to Patients' Charters are seen in guidelines from the Department of Health (1994) and from the Mental Health Task Force's User Group (1994a). The latter sets out ten rights, which could be reinforced by national charter standards, as has happened in the US with a Patients' Bill of Rights (Harris, 1994). A national conference on Citizen's Charter (1995) emphasised only local charters, apparently driven by an aggressive stance for local autonomy and by a government abdicating responsibility. In practice, this is likely to disadvantage individual service users and carers who will be unable to guarantee equal access across the country, and national service providers (like Methodist Homes, Mencap Homes) which have to negotiate with different purchasers to their differing standards.

Policy must be adequately supported by fully implemented and resourced legislation which provides both a right to care and also protection from psychiatric abuse. Guidance and charters cannot compensate for a lack of proper legislation. They do not have the force of law and are necessarily partial when compared with legislation that balances the interests of different parties.

Inter-agency working

Piecemeal approaches to mental health care hinder full participation of the various professionals involved in housing, work or leisure activity, treatment and care, forensic needs. This fragmentation is magnified by lack of proper consultation with users and carers, an over-reliance on medical approaches and white eurocentric assumptions which disregard authoritative critiques from Black perspectives (e.g. see Harris, 1994). Community based care was intended to be an integrated system meeting a full range of human need, and not merely the relocation of hospital-type care (O'Donnell, 1989). Instead we see a range of mismatches created when methods and structures appropriate to one form of care (hospital) are transferred uncritically to a quite different form of (community) care (Sihota, 1995). Research has shown a greater gap between the views of different professional workers than between the views of some professional workers, users and carers (Perring, 1991; Shepherd, Murray and

Muijen, 1994). Yet, unless new professional relationships are put in place, we risk a vacuum to be filled by existing professional and other interests (Pilgrim and Rogers, 1994). Without agreement about the sort of treatments that work well, we will receive only a version of hospital-type care, rather than radically different community care.

A particularly wide gap exists between statutory and the increasing range of effective user-controlled services. These have usually been marginalized as 'low-level' support by statutory agencies and planners, and workers within user-controlled services have not been treated as equal partners. A new initiative in Leeds may help to redress this imbalance. Funding has been set aside for user-controlled crisis services.

One unifying move will be to focus on measures of mental health gain rather than service activity and ensure that service providers and service users and their carers enter into equal partnerships. Above all, to provide true community services (rather than re-located hospital-type services) we have to start from people's mental health and 'ordinary' social or personal needs (Perring, Willmot & Wilson, 1995). We will then end up with a highly complex web of interlocking 'services'. Just how complex is suggested in work on diversion from custody (Staite, Martin, Bingham and Daly, 1994).

A new approach to resourcing: guaranteed minimum resources for mental health care and an agreed balance between institutional and community care

Inadequate resourcing is one frequent reason given for patchy or poor community care. However, the issue is rarely defined clearly enough to ensure that it is properly addressed. Here, we look at just two aspects of resourcing: the absolute level of resources allocated to mental health, and the allocation of resources as between different mental health services. Without national agreement on these two aspects of resourcing, 'local implementation' will continue to mean 'rationing', and fully planned community services will continue to elude us.

Some resourcing issues were outside the control of the NHS, such as a collapse in property prices in England. More were not. An important opportunity was missed when the NHS and Community Care Act failed to ringfence the capital and revenue used in the old institutions. It has proved difficult to trace the extent of any leaching of resources from mental health services and anecdotal evidence is at odds with formal requests for information. Further loss of capital and revenue from mental health services can still be prevented by ringfencing resources for the rest of the closure programme. Double running costs for many Authorities have not been offset by money to introduce new services through Mental Illness Specific Grant or through loans. West Midlands Health recommends setting up a specific reserve fund to cover 'double running' (Elkin, in preparation).

Despite such setbacks, authorities are succeeding in shifting resources across. Trent Health reports 38% of its mental health expenditure is now spent on the old outdated institutions, as against national figures of more than half of the

£2 billion NHS expenditure on mental health (Holmes, Barnes and Jenner, 1994). This is in contrast to an earlier figure of 72% of spending on in-patient care (Thompson and Pudney, 1991).

Resourcing requirements are not as yet specified at national level. One recent extrapolation suggests a gap of £226m (Holmes, Barnes and Jenner, 1994, p147). The House of Commons Social Services Committee (1990) called for an additional £267m for the years 1990–95, to cover the transition from hospital to community care. MIND called for an immediate injection of £300m in 1993, to allow for inflation and the fact that the House of Commons' recommendation had not been implemented. In 1994, the Mental Health Foundation reported that some national funding has been made available—£36m Mental Illness Specific Grant in 1994–95; £68m through the Capital Loans Fund; £250,000 through the Mental Health Task Force; £10m for community mental health services in London; £3m through the Sainsbury Centre for Mental Health (p31)—far short of the gaps identified above. Given the financial constraints on budget setting we cannot imagine how such a shortfall can be made up without national intervention. This failure to allocate resources to national community care policies suggests governmental lack of commitment and a preparedness to rely on unpaid informal care or 'cardboard box' 'solutions'.

Further risks are inherent in the powers of GPs as fundholders, who may purchase services out of their local area or town. This will make local planning more difficult, and increase risks of patchy provision nationwide. A counterbalance to such a trend could be provided by the accrediting of GPs, as proposed by Elkin (in preparation).

Regional support

The new Regional Offices of the NHS continue to clarify their roles. There is an opportunity for them to include nationally agreed standards of care and resourcing in their contractual arrangements with commissioners and providers. This has already been introduced by Trent Health, over Department of Health guidance for supervision registers by October 1994. The apparently limited impact is likely to be due more to the strength of local concerns about supervision registers than the mechanism itself.

A second way of promoting implementation is being developed by West Midlands Health (Elkin, in preparation).

A regional support team could:

- accredit agencies such as Trusts and fundholding GPs to ensure best practice and aid planning

- conduct performance management of Chief Executives of health commissioners

- oversee the build up of a revenue reserve for 'double running' of services

- provide a framework for local purchasers and joint commissioning.

Mechanisms for change emphasise 'dialogue' and offer guiding principles rather than an 'imposed blueprint of services'. They include a networking linkage to a 'smart card'-type system so that dispersed workers from different disciplines can share information swiftly, for which adequate security would have to be introduced. Of greater concern are moves towards 'market testing services' in summer 1995. Proposed as a 'lever' to focus on outcomes they could, in the current climate, herald the privatization of health care.

NHS Regional Offices could use national minimum standards to strengthen their work to:

- promote good practice

- provide training

- emphasize constructive ways of interagency working

- be a watchdog for user involvement

- retain and enhance the CHCs' role in complaints, and thus eliminate the need for a separate complaints' system proposed in March 1994

- ensure diversity of care locally

- attend to equality of access and outcome

- ensure local need assessment

- specify quality in contractual arrangements between purchasers and providers

- specify and monitor local planning arrangements—to ensure full user and carer involvement, and perhaps a full 'menu' of services for each local area

- provide costed evaluations of different services against medical and social outcomes.

At the moment, we have seen what is effectively a selective introduction of national standards for supervision registers through guidance and monitoring, whilst other aspects of a mental health service are seemingly ignored.

Local implementation

Four dimensions of purchasing for health gain are identified by Holmes, Barnes and Jenner (1994): needs assessment, commissioning and planning, monitoring outcomes and healthy alliances.

Services will ideally be driven by comprehensive assessment of individual need aggregated up to focus on how to meet assessed need rather than on existing services. Planners and commissioners services map existing services and provide decisions about which are to be retained and developed and which are to be replaced by more appropriate services. Commissioners can specify a range of care options and introduce standards within services. Providers, if they have not already done so, can ensure that they monitor their services on the basis of outcomes which reflect health gain. Users and carers can contribute to every stage of planning and monitoring of outcome of and satisfaction with services, which is then fed back into assessment. Thus, each local area will have a constantly improving cycle of quality—in line with the process set out in the NHS and Community Care Act, 1990.

Needs assessment: for individuals and for local areas

Comprehensive and sensitive needs assessments are keys to appropriate mental health care and support. Too often, diagnosis automatically dictates treatment. Social and personal need is ignored in favour of medical treatment, and assessment remains incomplete, because practitioners are unaware of, or know there are no, services to meet a particular need. A further risk is that of low expectations, common amongst many people used to little support (Perring, 1991).

Different ways of assessing the scale of local need include aggregating data from individual assessment, conducting a specific local needs assessment and using published data. A comprehensive survey of local need that incorporates users and carer perspectives (Hagan and Green, 1994; Perring and Hagan, 1995) provides a methodology and reports on the scale of need in one geographical area. Thirty-eight percent of a postal sample of 2210 people scored as possible 'cases' on the General Health Questionnaire, although 15% of these felt in no need of help. The study also provided details on where people prefer to receive mental health care (at home and at the GP's surgery); what care they prefer (an informed choice from among options, with an emphasis on talking treatments); and when it should be provided (with as little delay as possible, with a 24-hour, 7-day-a-week access point).

The Key Area Handbook presents epidemiological data on mental distress. It estimates prevalence of between 23,000 and 58,000 and service contact figures of between 43,800 and 54,350 for a district population of 500,000 (includes 70,000 people over the age of 65; Department of Health, 1993, p15. Emphasis on diagnosis can be misleading and unhelpful so we report only summary figures here.)

National standards can support needs assessment:

- Purchasers and providers should not deny people a service on the grounds of diagnosis. For instance, people deemed to be 'worried well' or as having a 'personality disorder' have real needs that should be assessed and met.

- An assessment should be available within seven days, or immediately in urgent cases. Individuals should be informed of the outcome within two days.

- Assessments for health care and social care should be conducted at the same time, with a single nominated person co-ordinating the process.

Ideally, all assessed need would be met. However, the current climate sees an increasing shift towards rationing in various forms. This both disadvantages people in need, and also emphasises short term solutions over longer term investment in services. Voucher or brokering systems are of particular concern, for they would favour more informed, vocal and assertive users and carers above people new to mental health care and those least able to express their needs. Arguments about promoting user and carer choice can be better served by addressing the well known lack of information and alternatives among services from which users and carers can select. A voucher system is likely only to reduce access.

A better approach to containing financial expenditure will be to ensure that services are evaluated for cost effectiveness (e.g. Cobb 1995a) so that need can be met by services that work well, are preferred by users and their carers, and also represent 'good value for money'. Users' entitlement, framed by an Act of Parliament such as Tessa Jowell's Private Members' Bill or a revised Mental Health Act, can further support local assessment of need.

Commissioning and planning: the range and scale of services

At best, planning translates need assessment into a comprehensive and integrated ('seamless') system of local services. However, joint and integrated commissioning is as yet a comparatively new activity that we all have to learn—in contrast with expertise of provision which resides with Trusts. Some progress can be made by streamlining the administration of different agencies (such as planning cycles) while other problems to solve are more deep rooted.

The Care Plan includes both the range and scale of services that should be in place, and can be informed by data from different sources. So far, many Care Plans have described existing services, rather than specified them as part of a local approach to meeting need by focusing on health gain. Pointers from

Anthony's (1993) 'recovery oriented mental health system' with its emphasis on outcome for user, service role and category are useful here.

Commissioners and purchasers have now to work with an increasing range of providers with the diversification of providing that follows from the NHS and Community Care Act. Traditional health providers (mostly Trusts) and social service provision (becoming 'enablers') compete with independent providers who may be private, not-for-profit, or larger or smaller scale voluntary. One type of provision that is often overlooked is self help or user-controlled services which both in Britain and the US can meet needs which remain unmet in traditional (White) services (Lindow, 1994a). The Mental Health Task Force has endorsed this approach, but mental health purchasers will need to adapt to make the most of these radically different ways of meeting need in the community (Lindow, 1994b).

Services to meet specific needs

Mental health service users have many needs which can be met in a variety of ways. In 1983 MIND identified a range of possible services for a new mental health service, based on comprehensive and local services in the community. This range is reflected in six areas of service activity—information, service planning and co-ordination, treatment, accommodation, individual support and development and user, carer and community involvement (Mental Health Task Force, 1995). A 'typical' range of services can be drawn up from individual and local assessments, but this should not override or dictate individual users' views about the amount and type of care and support required. Services must move away from a 'production line' approach where a single designated response is triggered by a narrow psychiatric assessment. For instance, Villeneau (1992) describes different ways of meeting which housing needs can be met. There are numerous different forms of talking treatments. MIND's model of crisis services (Cobb, 1995a) sets out some costed options for crisis care, and demonstrates that acute hospital care is only one of several alternatives (in Perring, 1995). There is no one way to meet assessed needs and purchasers are in a powerful position to specify new ways of meeting need or adaptations to existing services to meet the needs of Black users and all carers, who still typically lack information, support at home and respite care.

Examples of standards which would address the most commonly reported gaps include:

- Health and social services authorities must make available a 24-hour access point for help and make it clear how people contact it.

- If assessment establishes a need, then authorities must (under the Community Care, Right to Services Bill) meet the needs and offer options including 24-hour crisis services, support in the home, counselling and psychotherapy.

- Purchasers and providers must be aware that people need access to housing, work, money, leisure, education and many other basic rights and opportunities; and should help them secure them.

Sensitive services to respect diversity

Phrases such as 'the mentally ill' collude with the myth that there is a homogeneous group of service users. Twenty-first century society will continue to become more diverse, and commissioners and purchasers can be guided by work on, for instance, the needs of women and Black and minority ethnic people. Mental health needs further vary according to economic status, physical health, age, presence of dependent children. Where people are unused to being fully consulted and listened to, it will be particularly difficult for planners and purchasers to envisage new directions for care, and special initiatives (e.g. Black User Forums) can help to influence an appropriate range of sensitive services.

There are two main ways of providing fully sensitive services, both with risks and advantages. The first might be termed an 'equal opportunities' approach and aims to open out access to existing services by improving access. This has been very slow at achieving the necessary change. The second provides tailor-made services that arise from the needs of specific groups in society. Risks follow from this, for funding has been temporary and insecure, such projects may attract additional stigma that already surrounds mental health services, and we may end up with a health and social care 'apartheid'. Planners and purchasers need to decide on a balance between these two ways of providing services for, for instance, people from Black and minority ethnic groups in their area.

Some examples of standards aimed at ensuring that service planning and purchasing is geared towards meeting users' expressed needs are:

> • Users and carers should have the opportunity to be involved in planning and managing all mental health services. This will require finance to cover users' and carers' expenses, planning of meetings to ensure they are accessible and meaningful for all attending, and training to provide skills for full participation.
>
> • Purchasers of health and social care should include some services that change traditional power balance between professionals and users—for instance self-help and user-run initiatives.
>
> • Providers should take positive steps to adapt their services appropriate to different needs: for instance, people whose first language is not English should be offered a service in their own language or with a properly trained interpreter; people with children should receive a service that takes account of child care needs.

Monitoring outcomes: for constant quality improvement and health gain

Monitoring, both for providers and commissioners will ensure constant improvement in quality. MIND proposes the following standards to enhance the process set out in the NHS and Community Care Act:

- Services in each area must monitor the harmful effects of psychiatric treatments—for instance rates of tardive dyskinesia—and take action to reduce them.

- Service users should have the opportunity to be involved in all auditing and monitoring procedures.

- Purchasers must use the feedback from users to plan for services which people find therapeutic: for instance, many users value Hearing Voices groups and non-hospital crisis facilities.

- Purchasers should develop educational and research activities which help promote positive mental health and which add to knowledge about mental distress and how to respond to it.

Mental Health Task Force User Group's Guidelines for local charters for users proposes similar rights, including no prescription above British National Formulary (BNF) standards, right to reject ECT in some circumstances, full information about all aspects of care and treatment, and a right to be involved in monitoring the quality of services.

Healthy alliances and inter-agency working

The importance and difficulty of achieving effective inter-agency working was mentioned above, and it is in the local area that 'on the ground' multi-disciplinary working has to work. Onyett (1992) refers to conflicts that can arise from issues of responsibility and accountability and proposes operational policies to overcome some areas of difficulty in the context of case management. Pilgrim and Rogers (1994) provide a broader framework for understanding the sociological tensions that may exist.

Inter-agency working covers more than the relationships between professional disciplines with their own philosophies, structures and hierarchies. It extends to include voluntary, not-for-profit and independent (private) agencies. Fundamental differences between agencies, such as the philosophy of 'protest' underlying some user-controlled alternatives to mental health care, can provoke resistance from some professional workers (Lindow, 1994a). To some statutory agencies, 'consultation' means only an opportunity to comment on the final draft of a document, and 'partnership' means only a last-minute invitation to a conference. Good relationships do not just 'happen'. They depend on focused and continuous work. Perhaps local relationships in the twenty-first century can aim for equal relationships based on mutual respect, so that no party feels used or abused by any other.

Individual relationships

Relationships between individual service users and practitioners will be improved by applying standards derived from MIND's four principles of

Respect, Helping not Harming, Justice and Entitlement (Pfluger and Sayce, 1994).

Respect: partners in care

Respect is a mark of equality in a relationship. A respectful relationship will not allow users to be treated unnecessarily against their will. It will ensure users are given enough high quality information to make informed decisions about their treatment. They will be listened to and their views will be taken seriously as the relationship between worker and user becomes one of 'equal partners in care'.

Traditional views of the capacity of service users have often excluded users from making decisions. In 1995, there is more understanding that acute distress usually lasts for only comparatively short periods of time, and that between episodes users are well able to express an informed preference for or against particular services with 'living wills'. The Law Commission has introduced proposals for a new law governing substitute decision making for those with 'Mental Incapacity'. The proposed framework would enshrine respect for personal autonomy, for example by requiring adherence to a person's wishes expressed in advance or through a person appointed by them to make decisions, should they be unable to. The proposals do not extend to the law on consent to medical treatment for medical disorder. Similar principles would give legal force to crisis cards and advance directives. This legal debate is opening up the issue and practitioners can use cards and directives to show their respect for people's wishes.

Some of MIND's standards offer ways of achieving respect through informed consent:

- Users must be able to exercise choice over what services they get.
- In order to be able to choose, users must be given full information on available services and treatments.
- Users must have a say in who their psychiatrist or keyworker is.

Respect implies confidentiality. MIND hears of many examples of breaches of confidentiality which are unthinkable in most areas of life—but which do occur in the mental health field. A woman receiving care at a general hospital for a physical condition found that a psychiatric interview had been arranged for her, without her knowledge. No attempt had been made by medical staff to find out what she wanted or needed. In fact, following previous experiences of psychiatry she had set out to learn other ways of keeping her mental health on an acceptably even keel (personal caller to Trent and Yorkshire MIND, 1994). Current debates about supervision registers reiterate concerns about confidentiality (e.g. Russell, 1994).

Other ways of building respect into personal relationships include a National Patients' Charter modelled on the rights listed in the Mental Health Task Force's Guidelines (1994, p12), and use of published codes of conduct and ethics from the British Psychological Society or the British Association of Counselling. Local charters or codes modelled on other principles and unsupported by national legislation, will be less effective.

Finally, full respect will be achieved when service users are fully involved in planning and delivery of mental health services, and when activities and funding fully support empowerment and self-determination.

Justice: equal access

Access to and receipt of services are not yet evenly distributed. Secure hospitals hold disproportionate numbers of Black people, too rarely offered decent community services at an earlier stage of their distress. A critique of the Ritchie report (Harris, 1994) again highlights institutional racism. ECT appears to be more widely used among older women that other groups (Cobb, 1995b). Service users must be able to access and obtain a range of services to meet their needs, and have the right to complain and appeal without fear. These rights need the support of national legislation and standards such as:

- Mental health services must not discriminate against people on the grounds that they are old; nor that they are from certain ethnic groups; nor that they are gay; nor on any other irrelevant grounds.

- People should be able to refuse a service and have access to immediate appeal through a fair and agreed process if this refusal is ignored.

- People should be able to complain about a service without prejudice, through an agreed procedure.

Helping not harming: an end to treatments with dangerous adverse effects

A mental health service must be therapeutic and avoid harming the person who receives the service. Psychiatric medicines can have adverse effects such as addiction or tardive dyskinesia. Practitioners must ensure the safe prescribing of all psychiatric medication, with no unnecessary polypharmacy and careful adherence to BNF levels. MIND has introduced a scheme similar to the 'Yellow Card' scheme by which GPs record adverse drug reactions, to collect users' own views on adverse effects of medication. This can feed into local monitoring of services. At least one death a week is associated with psychiatric medication and many report personal memory loss following receipt of ECT (Cobb, 1993). MIND receives reports of physical, emotional, sexual and racial abuse within mental health services. The way in which some talking treatments are delivered have harmed, rather than helped, recipients (Wood, 1993). Codes of practice and careful accreditation of counsellors and psychotherapists are essential. In addition, a nationally agreed standard can support the therapeutic benefits of all personal relationships:

- services should have in place policies and staff training to prevent abuses of service users, and to deal strenuously and sensitively with them if they occur. Users and staff must know they can complain or 'whistle blow' without fear of reprisals; management must be prepared to take firm disciplinary action against any staff found to be responsible; and everyone must be clear that racial and sexual harassment, bullying and other abuses are totally unacceptable.

Entitlement: the right to care to meet need

Services must be provided according to people's need and not on a solely professional assessment, on ability to pay or on local rationing of services. Even when a full range of options covering basic needs is in place, users may need support in securing that care and support—through advocacy and adequate information:

> • users should have access to an advocate for the assessment, at no cost; this means purchasers must make available independent advocacy services.

Carers continue to find it difficult to acquire the right forms of help. They have, in their own right and simply as a 'carer' for another person, needs for emotional support, domestic care, information and respite care. Many of the standards could be adapted to ensure a less demanding and exhausting life for carers. Standards will help to eradicate old abuses by supporting—not restricting—a national mental health service and framing relationships so that individuals are treated well as human beings and workers follow their professional codes to the best possible standards.

Conclusion

This chapter recognises well known limitations of how community care is being implemented. Attention to many existing areas of good practice could eventually improve the situation. For a more equitable and prompt resolution, we propose a systematic and integrated approach that attends to what is needed at every level, in ways that are not narrowly prescriptive.

National minimum standards will help to guarantee quality and equality of access and of treatment and outcome across the country. By insisting on a choice of high quality services that users support, we can aim for informed consent and reduce so-called 'non-compliance'—where often users are refusing treatments they believe to be harmful rather than beneficial. To focus only on the role of commissioners and purchasers is a partial solution which at best shifts a national responsibility to local level. At worst it colludes with the assumption that we need no national framework to ensure that provision is comprehensive, integrated and properly resourced.

National minimum standards that attend to process and components of a comprehensive service will also improve working relationships between those involved in making community care work. Standards based, as MIND proposes, on user and carer perspectives, will also promote user and carer empowerment. We will thus be able to improve the implementation of policies that have widespread support but which are under attack from simplistic demands to keep open the old, outdated institutions.

Standards will work to maximum benefit when supported by the force of a law which provides an entitlement to mental health care. What is most obviously missing is a national expression of will to introduce Legislation and to tackle resourcing issues. It is time to try something different: a combination of new legislation and systematic implementation to move us all closer to a community based national mental health service for the twenty-first century.

Acknowlegements

The authors are grateful to Liz Sayce and Kate Harrison for their advice and comments on an earlier draft of this chapter.

Notes

(1)   The four reports are:

Audit Commission (1994) Finding a Place: *A Review of Mental Health Services for Adults*. London: HMSO.
House of Commons Health Committee (1994) First Report: *Better Off in the Community*, (vol **1**). London: HMSO.
Mental Health Foundation (1994) Creating Community Care: *report of the Mental Health Foundation Inquiry into Community Care for People with Severe Mental Illness*. London: Mental Health Foundation, 37 Mortimer Street, London W1N 7RJ.
Ritchie, J., Dick, D. and Lingham, R. (1994) *The Report of the Inquiry into the Care and Treatment of Christopher Clunis*. London: HMSO.

References

Anthony, W.A. (1993) Recovery from Mental Illness: The Guiding Vision of the Mental Health Service System in the 1990s. *Psychosocial Rehabilitation Journal*, **16** (no **4**: April), 11–23.

Citizens Charter Quality Seminar on Community Care (1995), Citizens Charter Unit, House Guards Road, London SW1P 3AL.

Cobb, A. (1993) *Safe and Effective? MIND's Views on Psychiatric Drugs, ECT and Psychosurgery*. London: MIND.

Cobb, A. (1995a) *MIND's Model of a 24 Hour Crisis Service*. London: MIND. Granta House, 15–19 Broadway, Stratford, London E15 4BQ.

Cobb, A. (1995b) *Older Women and ECT*. London: MIND.

Department of Health (1993) *The Health of the Nation: Key Area Handbook–Mental Illness*. London: Department of Health.

Department of Health (1994) *A Framework for Local Community Care Charters in England*. London: Department of Health.

Department of Health and Welsh Office (1990, 1993) *Code of Practice: Mental Health Act 1993*. London: HMSO.

Hagan, T. and Green, J. (1994) *Mental Health Needs Assessment: The User Perspective—Summary Report*. Wakefield: Wakefield Health Care, White Rose House, Wakefield WF1 1LT.

Elkin, K. (in preparation) *Spotlight on Commissioning Mental Health Services*. West Midlands Health.

Griffiths, R. (1988) *Community Care: Agenda for Action*. London: HMSO.

Harris, V. (1994) *Review of the Report of the Inquiry into the Care and Treatment of Christopher Clunis: A Black Perspective*. London: Race Equality Unit, 5 Tavistock Place, London WC1H 9SN.

Holmes, S.P., Barnes, S.B.B. and Jenner, D. (1994) *Health Gain Investment Programme for People with Mental Health Problems (Part One)*. Sheffield: Trent Health Regional Authority and London: Centre for Mental Health Services Development, King's College, University of London, Institute of Health, Campden Hill Road, Kensington, London W8 7AGH.

House of Commons Social Services Committee (1990) *Eleventh Report: Community Care: Services for People with a Mental Handicap and People with a Mental Illness*. London: HMSO.

Lindow, V. (1994a) *Self-Help Alternatives to Mental Health Services*. London: MIND.

Lindow, V. (1994b) *Purchasing Mental Health Services: Self-Help Alternatives*. London: MIND.

Mental Health Foundation (1994). *Creating Community Care: report of the Mental Health Foundation Inquiry into Community Care for People with Severe Mental Illness*. London: Mental Health Foundation, 37 Mortimer Street, London W1N 7RJ.

Mental Health Task Force (1995) *Local Systems of Support: A Framework for Purchasing for People with Severe Mental Health Problems*. London Department of Health, NHS Executive.

Mental Health Task Force User Group (1994a) *Guidelines for a Local Charter for Users of Mental Health Services*. London: Department of Health.

Mental Health Task Force User Group (1994) *Advocacy: A Code of Practice*. London: Department of Health.

MIND (1983) *Common Concern: MIND's Manifesto for a comprehensive mental health service*. London: MIND.

MIND (1994) *Community Care (Rights to Mental Health Services) Bill*. London, MIND.

Nuffield Institute (1994) *Care Programme Approach and Supervision: Overcoming the Obstacles*. Conference Report, 21 July, Priority and Community Services Group, Nuffield Institute for Health, University of Leeds, 71–75 Clarendon Road, Leeds LS2 9PL.

O'Donnell, O. (1989) *Mental Health Care Policy in England: Objectives, Failures and Reforms*. Centre for Health Economics, University of York, Heslington, York YO1 5DD.

Onyett, S. (1992) *Case Management in Mental Health.* London: Chapman and Hall.

Perring, C. (1991) How do former psychiatric patients fare in the community? In J Hutton, S Hutton, T Pinch and A Shiell (Eds) *Dependency to Enterprise.* London: Routledge.

Perring, C., Twigg, J. and Atkin, K. (1990) *Families Caring for People Diagnosed as Mentally Ill: The Literature Re-examined.* London: HMSO.

Perring, C. and Hagan, T. (1995) Breaking through to Meet Need, *Openmind* (**73**, February/March) 9.

Perring C, Willmot J & Wilson M (1995) Reshaping the future: MIND'S Model for Community Mental Health Care. London, MIND.

Pfluger, A. and Sayce, L. (1994) *National Minimum Standards to make Community Care Work.* London: MIND.

Pilgrim, D. and Rogers, A. (1994) *A Sociology of Mental Health and Mental Illness.* Buckingham: Open University Press.

Rampton Hospital Advisory Committee (1995) *Annual Report of the Hospital Advisory Committee.* Rampton Hospital.

Russell, P. (1994) Supervision Registration: Rights and Civil Liberties. In *Care Programme Approach and Supervision: Overcoming the Obstacles.* Report of Conference held on 21 July 1994: from Priority and Community Services Group, Nuffield Institute for Health, University of Leeds, 71–75 Clarendon Road, Leeds LS2 9PL.

Sayce, L. (1991) *Waiting for Community Care.* London: MIND.

Sayce, L. (1995) An Ill Wind in a Climate of Fear. *The Guardian, Society* 18.1.95, pp 6–7.

Shepherd, G., Murray, A. and Muijen, M. (1994) *Relative Values: The Differing Views of Users, Family Carers and Professionals on Services for People with Schizophrenia in the Community.* The Sainsbury Centre for Mental Health, 134–138 Borough High Street, London SE1 1LB.

Sihota, S.K. (1995) *Knowing about Asking: Meeting the information needs of Mental Health Service Users and their Carers.* Trent and Yorkshire MIND, 44 Howard Street, Sheffield S1 2LX.

Staite, C., Martin, N., Bingham, M. and Daly, R. (1994) *Diversion from Cutody for Mentally Disordered Offenders.* London: Longman.

Thompson, D. and Pudney, M. (1991) *Mental Illness: The Fundamental Facts.* London: The Mental Health Foundation, 8 Hallam Street, London W1N 6DH.

Villeneau, L. (1992) *Housing with Care and Support: A Quality Action Guide.* London: MIND.

Wood, D. (1993) *The Power of Words: Uses and Abuses of Talking Treatments.* London: MIND.

5 Quality and Monitoring in the Statutory and Non-Statutory Sectors

MIKE FARRAR

About Quality

> *Quality is sacred. Like apple pie and human rights, who can be against it? The difficulties lie in its application and even its pursuit.*
>
> Williams H (1992) [1]

Defining a framework to understand quality in mental health care

Much has been written about the theory of quality and its pursuit. The success of the quality movement can be measured by the number of times that Maxwells six dimensions of quality[2] or Donabedian's framework of 'structure, process and outcome'[3] are used to frame strategic plans and objectives. The danger with such widely used models is that organisations begin to see quality as an 'off the shelf' product without applying the thought processes necessary to genuinely improve the experience of service users as a result of the pursuit of high quality performance.

For this reason, this chapter adopts a different approach to the understanding of quality, drawing on the theory of its pursuit, but attempting to place the learning firmly in the practices of purchasing mental health care and its subsequent impact on service provision.

It is possible to summarise the theory by outlining a small number of definitions of quality that emerge consistently throughout the literature:

(i)   Quality as conformance with requirements,

(ii)   Quality as the absence of faults or failures,

(iii)   Quality as the avoidance of waste or duplication,

(iv)   Quality as an ideal customer service,

(v)   Quality as continuous improvement.

Each definition introduces a distinct dimension to the understanding of quality as an entity. *A genuine approach to pursue high quality performance must embrace each of these dimensions.* Translated into the practice of purchasing and providing mental health care these dimensions would cover:

(i)   Provider conformance with purchasing/funding mental health specifications or contracts,

(ii)   Provider avoidance of service failures (e.g. deaths, untoward incidents, unplanned readmissions etc.),

(iii)   Provider compliance with specified and coordinated processes of service delivery (e.g. CPA, Supervision Registers),

(iv)   Coordination between service providers,

(v)   Provider focus on customer satisfaction

(vi)   Commissioner involvement of the public in the commissioning process,

(viii) Commissioner and provider partnership on improving mental health care as an evolutionary process.

These dimensions thus provide a framework within which to explore and understand the pursuit of high quality mental health care. *These are explored through the perspective of those individuals and organisations charged with the responsibility to commission, purchase and fund mental health care.*

Statement: If it ain't broke don't fix it.
Retort: Is that your theory of aircraft maintenance

---

i   Provider conformance with purchasing/funding specifications or contracts.

Specifications and contracts

The notion that this dimension could be used as a basis for the establishment and assessment of a high quality mental health service assumes that purchasers/funders have set out clear and detailed specifications and/or contracts. Information provided by a current survey of commissioning documentation would suggest that this is unlikely to be the norm (HAS/Birmingham University 1995)[4]

The NHS Executive is clear in its guidance for NHS Commissioners that effective contracts are one of the fundamental components of the purchasing function (Mawhinney and Nichol 1993) [5] It is therefore essential that *Commissioners have discreet contracts for mental health services,* and preferably for the individual sub specialities or patient groups (e.g. Child and adolescent services, secure psychiatric services etc.) which should have their roots in a clear overall specification or strategic framework for mental health.

Producing meaningful specifications relies on the bringing together of a number of important elements;

Figure 1: *Drawing up the service specification*

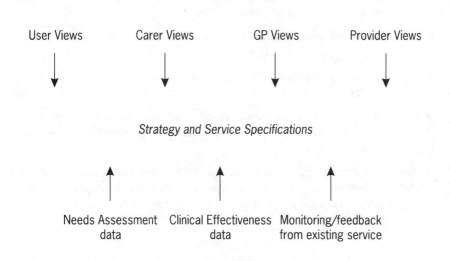

Many Commissioners have been prompted to develop detailed specifications to support their expressed intention to invite providers to compete for the provision of a mental health service. In many instances this has been associated with the reprovision of mental health care from long stay hospital sites. In such cases the specifications produced and contracts won have formed a solid base for the setting and monitoring of quality standards. However, good practice in this respect need not be restricted to the process supporting competitive tendering.

Primary care contracts and equity

Towards a primary care led NHS (EL (94) 79 NHS Executive 1994)[6] sets out a course by which General Practitioners will increase their role in the direct purchasing of health care. Robust service specifications will form an essential base to ensure a clear strategic direction for purchasing by GPs and the setting and maintaining of quality standards. Such foundations will be the key to ensuring an equitable health service for all users and carers.

Contracting with the non statutory sector

The non statutory sector provides a large element of the overall service provision for people with mental health problems. Recent evidence gathered in the process of assessing Child and Adolescent Mental Health Services highlighted the inefficient methods by which the non statutory sector was funded or purchased suggesting that this important element of provision is not being facilitated to contribute to its full potential and that purchasers are unable to use conformance with contracts as a basis to define and enhance the quality of care provided by the sector (Health Advisory Service 1995)[7]. The dangers in this area are:

- extensive use of Extra Contractual Referrals offering no basis for setting quality standards or monitoring their achievement,

- one-off unplanned grants to organisations with financial performance returns the only stipulation,

- short term contracts which overspecify the expected returns distracting providers from the undertaking of desired activity,

- short term contracting frameworks that create instability in non statutory providers and have a detrimental effect on their overall ability to meet specified activity.

Avoidance of these practices is desirable and should be possible. A number of models for contracting with the non statutory sector have been proposed and are operational in certain parts of the country (Farrar, 1994) [8].

Another day gone,
All targets met,
All systems fully operational,
All customers satisfied,
All staff keen and well-motivated,
All pigs fed and ready to fly.

---

ii   Avoidance of service failures

Defining failures

It is possible, as suggested in the previous section, to define service failure as non conformance with service specification or contract requirements. However, given the progress required to achieve effective contracts and the view that the overall public perception of service performance may be governed by a small number of high profile service failures, there is probably a specific subset of 'failures' that night be targeted separately by purchasers. These might include;

- homicides by mentally ill people,

- suicides by mentally ill people,

- high profile disputes and delays for the admission of mentally disordered offenders into NHS facilities,

- unplanned readmissions into acute psychiatric beds caused by poorly judged discharges,

- absconders from secure psychiatric services,

- admission of children under 16 to adult psychiatric wards.

Learning from failures and improving quality

Commissioners have an important role in relation to service failures. In the case of homicides and suicides the role of the Health Authority is specified in NHS Executive Guidance (EL (94) 27)[9] requiring them to report the incidents to the Confidential Inquiry into Homicides and Suicides by Mentally Ill People, set up an investigation and, if in contact with specialist services, ensure a full multi-disciplinary audit is carried out by the provider. Commissioners may also be able to make quality improvements by;

- assessing the reasons for failure in the context of future service planning,

- developing an ongoing problem solving relationship with the provider or in extreme cases using the evidence to consider competitive tendering,

- testing and reviewing local audit procedures,

- setting higher or more rigorous quality standards or outcome targets,

- assessing the impact on local Health of the Nation targets for suicide prevention and considering additional investment.

The success of identifying 'specific failures' as a means to assess and upgrade the quality of services will depend on the maturity of the relationship between purchasers/funders and providers. A strong partnership will lead to effective communication and a timely and accurate flow of information.

iii   Provider compliance with specified and coordinated processes of service delivery.

Health Authorities are currently guided by the NHS Executive [9] to place contracts which should govern a number of key processes;

- explicit and clear requirements to implement the Care Programme Approach (CPA),

- explicit and clear arrangements for management accountability for the CPA,

- explicit and clear requirements for CPA information (including the number of people covered by CPA, collected at least quarterly),

- explicit and clear processes for monitoring and auditing CPA,

- explicit and clear mechanisms to review the facilities necessary for the discharge of patients; which are reflected in subsequent purchasing plans,

- the maintenance and development of a mental health system, including supervision registers,

- staffed adequately trained in the CPA and risk assessment and management,

- suitable arrangements for the management and clinical supervision of staff in community mental health teams,

- audit of suicides

- agreed procedures in the event of a homicide or assault by a patient subject to the CPA.

Most of these processes *are equally relevant to contracts which are negotiated by GP Fundholders.*

In addition there are a number of other important processes which should be considered as requirements of commissioners;

- routine customer satisfaction surveys by providers,

- wide application of clinical and medical audit,

- general information flows on activity, including prescribing data,

- clear processes for handling Mentally disordered offender placements by the courts and Home Secretary in view of the Health Authorities' responsibilities under Section 39 Mental Health Act from April 1996,

- general contract monitoring processes, including measures for provider self assessment of performance.

Most people would succeed in small things if they were
not troubled by great ambition

H W Longfellow

---

iv   Coordination between service providers

Key Interfaces

The large number of potential providers in the mental health field means that there are a number of interfaces between services for users to cross. Poor coordination has often been cited as the main reason for service failures rather than a lack of skill and commitment in the professionals concerned (SETRHA/NETRHA 1994)[10].

Of all the potential interfaces, a number are worthy of review to ensure that the experience of the service user is one of a single coordinated response. These include the interfaces between statutory and non statutory agencies; primary and secondary care; health and social care systems; health and criminal justice systems (mentally disordered offenders); health, social and education systems (children and adolescents); local and highly specialised regional or national services; and health, social and housing systems.

Commissioners may utilise a variety of means to ensure they are purchasing an integrated package of care;

- developing protocols for transfers, referrals and discharges between providers,

- commissioning specific liaison posts to 'manage' the boundaries,

- encouraging joint audit of shared cases,

- encouraging forms of shared care,

- encouraging joint training programmes.

The NHS Executive have recently produced a guide to facilitate interagency working as part of the Secretary of State's Ten Point Plan to improve services for the severely mental ill. The Inter-Agency Guide (DoH 1995) [11] considers these interfaces and proposes a number of methods to promote coordination of care between agencies.

A customer is not an interruption of work;
he is the purpose of it.

L. L. Bean Co. Ltd. USA

---

v Provider focus on customer satisfaction

Commissioners and providers share a common concern to ensure that the provision of care is focused on customer satisfaction. There are three reasons why this should be so;

(i) When patients or clients are treated as customers (in the sense of people with choices whose satisfaction determines organisation performance), a very different set of priorities emerge,

(ii) Orientation towards patients as customers permeates throughout the organisations culture and established the notion of internal customers (creating interdepartmental and interpersonal notions of supplier and customer) which can act as a catalyst for quality improvement,

(iii) Satisfied patients are more likely to follow medical advice and treatment instructions and to have a clearer grasp of medical information leading to better health outcomes [12].

Commissioners should, as a minimum, be confident that providers with which they contract have an orientation towards customer satisfaction. Confidence could be established through;

- ensuring providers have regular customer satisfaction surveys and sampling returns,

- regular consultation with local service user groups,

- benchmarking performance through visiting other providers or comparing progress against patients charter standards,

- learning from specialist reviews (e.g. HAS, MHAC),

- ensuring providers have appropriate complaints procedures that are audited regularly,

- encouraging providers to include clients in clinical audit

Commissioners have the opportunity to learn from research on customer satisfaction that has attempted to predict the components which create satisfied customers. Hardy and West (1994) [13] described the predictors for customer satisfaction in in-patient care settings;

Patient Satisfaction Area	In-patient Care Predictors (Ranked in decreasing order of importance)
Quality of Care (General satisfaction)	Nursing information Ward cleanliness Medical information Socialisation processes Secondary care staff attitudes Patient participation Ward facilities Nursing attitudes
Health Understanding and management of health and illness	Medical information Nursing information Socialisation processes Secondary care staff attitudes
Feelings (Psychological well being)	Medical information Socialisation processes Patient participation Ward cleanliness Secondary care staff attitudes

Quality is not a single thing but an aura, an atmosphere,
an overwhelming feeling that an organisation is doing
everything with excellence

John Walsh, Chief Executive, General Electric USA, (1980)

vi Commissioner involvement of the public in the commissioning process

Responsiveness to local populations is another of the fundamental requirements of the commissioning function (Nichol and Mawhinney, 1993)[5]. Its achievement will be driven largely by public involvement in the whole of the commissioning process from assessment of need through to the evaluation of services. This task highlights the central importance of the public as the recipients of services in defining and achieving high quality performance.

Figure 2: *The centrality of the public in the achievement of high quality performance*

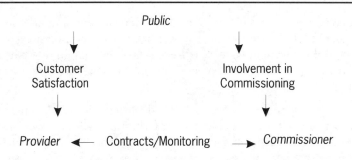

As for the other dimensions of quality, there is a substantial amount of reference materials that can inform Commissioners on good practice in this arena. For many Commissioners generalised findings are difficult to place within the context of widely differing local groups, relationships and consultation processes. However it may be helpful for Commissioners to assess their own performance on user involvement by testing it against the following list of commonly found barriers to successful involvement of users:

- poor or partial information to users/public,

- inability to accept user voice as representative when users disagree with service planners,

- inability to provide financial support to sustain and maximise users' contribution,

- development of overbureaucratic procedures and/or unnecessarily technical language that confuses users and/or marginalises user views,

- frustration of user views by extending or failing to communicate timescales,

- inability to recognise the sometimes separate voices of users and carers,

- playing user views off against carers or each other, leaving the commissioner voice to dominate.

We want...to become an organisation where people come to work each day in a rush to try something they woke up thinking about the night before.
We want them to go home from work wanting to talk about what they did that day, rather than trying to forget it. We want factories where the whistle blows and everyone wonders where the time went and someone wonders aloud why we need a whistle.

Corporate Vision. General Electric Co. USA

vii   Commissioner and provider partnership on improving mental health care as an evolutionary process

This final and essential dimension of the understanding of quality in mental health goes beyond the timeframe within which the other dimensions primarily operate. In this case there is a clear emphasis on the notion of a partnership between purchaser and provider set firmly in 'a timeless journey towards the pursuit of excellence'.

Many Commissioners have been restricted, since their establishment, to the purchasing of health care within a short term framework centred on annual business and performance management cycles. Such approaches have had some value but, even when this process has been undertaken well, have been unable to deliver the basis for a sustained long term improvement in quality. When the approach has been undertaken badly, without the context of an overall strategy, it has often contributed to a number of problems;

- overambitious and unrealistic demands on providers, leading to an increase in staff turnover and burn out,

- underambitious expectations of providers, leading to an absence of a credible strategic direction,

- confused priorities and rapid shifts in resource allocation on a seemingly ad hoc basis,

- inability to provide space and time for providers to manage organisational change,

- short sighted policies, creating future gaps in knowledge and shortages in key staff positions.

In contrast the partnership approach may provide a significant contribution to overcoming these problems. This approach has three basic elements;

- the creation of a climate for innovation and development,

- investment in people,

- an organisation-wide commitment to quality.

Commissioners and providers embarked on such an approach would be characterised by;

- high level of investment in research and development,

- organisation-wide use of audit,

- personal development plans for all staff,

- modelling of drive and innovation by senior managers,

- high levels of investment in staff training,

- robust performance appraisal systems and rewards recognising both individual and team performance,

- willingness to subject the organisation to external scrutiny or peer review (particularly involving users or customers),

- good systems of lateral and vertical communication between staff,

- delegated responsibility coupled with effective project management,

- orientation to customer satisfaction.

All of which would be set in the context of a mature purchase/provider relationship with an honest and open flow of information.

The dominant culture in most organisations demands punishment for a mistake no matter how useful, small, invisible. This is especially ironic because the most notable ancestor of todays business rationality was called scientific management. Experimentation is the fundamental tool of science.

Peters and Waterman (1982) [14]

About quality in the commissioning organisation....

Whilst the previous section set out a framework to assess and improve the commissioning process and its impact on the quality of provision, the ability of Commissioners to deliver such improvements will be dependent on the resources available in the organisation itself. The following self assessment questions offer a means by which the organisation be it Health Authority, Social Services Department or GP Fundholder can identify their strengths and weaknesses on mental health;

- Which officer has responsibility for mental health?

- At what level of seniority in the organisation are they?

- What level of commitment and leadership on mental health is provided by;

    Chief Executive/Director

    Non Executive Directors

    Members

    Board/Council/Partnership as a whole

- What level of knowledge on mental health does the organisation have?

- Can the organisation reliably identify its current spend on mental health?

- What is the organisations level of spending on mental health consultancy or improving the corporate knowledge of mental health matters?

- Does the organisation know that mental health is one of the NHS Executives top priorities?

- How would your organisation rank the following in levels of importance,

Coronary Heart Disease	Community Care	Child protection
Cancer	Acute waiting times	Elderly
Mental Health	Patients Charter	Health Promotion

Design in quality rather than inspect out error. If a part can be inadvertently put in upside down redesign it so that it will only fit one way. If cleaners are prone to use dirty water while mopping floors, redesign the bucket to hold enough water for one room.

Harold S Williams (1992)

About monitoring...

The current system of monitoring performance in the NHS can be summarised as follows:

Figure 3: *Current Monitoring System*

Individual

- at a personal level, users and carers need to know about services, their development and changes. They also need to know about treatment events.

Organisational

- *providers* need to monitor service performance, costs, overall effectiveness and user views,

- *purchasers* need to monitor providers performance against contract and user views,

- *NHS Executive* needs to monitor overall NHS performance in order to inform

- *Ministers*, who are accountable to Parliament.

The system as it relates to mental health will only be able to provide a robust and challenging monitoring framework when a number of success criteria are applied:

- information collected should be reliable, accurate and timely based on a common definition and interpretation of questions asked,

- information requested should be reduced to that which accurately indicates true performance,

- routine information used by clinicians and managers to monitor service effectiveness and efficiency should be the quarry from which others take what they need.

- the information used to monitor should be in harmony with the rhythm of clinical practice,

- the further the distance from clinical activity, the higher the level of indicator, but the lower the volume of information collected,

- information collected should be based on better use of existing data rather than adding unnecessarily to the overall volume collected.

In addition there are a further two criteria that relate to the effect of the monitoring system for mental health as an element of the overall monitoring of NHS performance in general:

- the system must rank mental health performance as a priority that is not seen to be subsidiary to along list of competing priorities,

- the system must include an appropriate mechanism for correcting poor performance rather than simplistic punitive approach.

Monitoring tools

A number of options are open to Commissioners to undertake monitoring of mental health performance by providers. These might include;

Data submissions

A general process where evidence is requested from providers such as; activity data as specified in contracts, results of audits, customer satisfaction surveys, outturn reports etc.

Thematic reviews or studies

A detailed study of provider practice in specific performance areas such as CPA implementation, supervised discharge arrangements etc. The reviews would typically involve interviews with members of the organisations at all levels and often include both customers and consumers of services.

User and Carer Surveys

Detailed appraisal by users and carers undertaken by Commissioners to validate provider evidence of customer satisfaction

Comparative studies

Studies often requiring considerable research technology to consider comparative performance by providers working with similar populations. This can be particularly relevant to monitoring the care provided to minority groups.

The comparative studies can be used to set benchmarks for performance by providers.

Provider Self Assessment Models

Providers are required by Commissioners to complete regular self assessment schedules against agreed criteria set by Commissioners. Commissioners may choose to sample results or returns at specified or random intervals, using quantifiable measures may set the basis for an accreditation system of providers or a list of preferred providers. In a similar vein Commissioners may choose to instigate their own self assessment procedure to assess their competence as Commissioners of mental health services.

Examples of self assessment tools and quality measurement techniques for Commissioners and Providers

- Quartz System.
  A total quality management package aimed primarily at service providers.
  Devised by: Sainsbury Centre for Mental Health
  (0171 403 8790)

- Together We Stand.
  Commissioner and provider checklists of performance on Child and Adolescent Mental Health.
  Devised by: Health Advisory Service
  (0181 642 6421)

- Suicide Prevention—The Challenge Confronted.
  Commissioner checklist of performance on preventing suicide.
  Devised by: Health Advisory Service
  (0181 642 6421)

- Clinical Standards Advisory Group Report on Schizophrenia and Severe Mental Illness
  Commissioner and Provider Checklists, including scoring mechanism to assess performance on schizophrenia and other forms of severe mental illness.
  Devised by: Clinical Standards Advisory Group
  (0171 972 4926)

- Good Practice and Minimum Standards Working Document
  Aimed primarily at alcohol and drug services but with a useful format for assessing general mental health services provided by the non statutory sector.
  Devised by: Alcohol Concern

References

1   Williams, H. (1992) *Innovation and the Quality Movement..Beneath the Rhetoric.* Innovating. Rensselaerville Institute. New York.

2   Maxwell, R. (1984) *Perspectives in NHS Management.* BMJ, **288**, 1470 - 1472.

3   Donabedian, A. (1988) *The quality of care. How can it be assessed?* JAMA, **260**, 1743 - 1748.

4   Cumella, S. (1994) *Purchasing Mental Health Services in the United Kingdom.* Birmingham University/Health Advisory Service. Birmingham.

5   Mawhinney, B. and Nichol, D. (1993) *Purchasing for Health: A framework for action.* Health Publications Unit.

6   NHS Executive (1994) EL (94) 79 *Towards a primary care led NHS.* Department of Health.

7   Health Advisory Service (1995) *Together We Stand,* HMSO. London.

8   Health Advisory Service (1994) *Suicide the Challenge Confronted.* HMSO. London.

9   NHS Executive (1994) EL (94) 27 *Discharge from hospital of mentally disordered people.* Department of Health.

10 NETRHA/SETRHA (1994) *Report of the Inquiry into the Care and Treatment of Christopher Clunis.* London. HMSO.

11 Department of Health (1995) *Inter-Agency guide on working with sever mental illness.* London. HMSO.

12 Greenfield, S., Kaplan, S., Ware, J. E. (1985) *Expanding patient involvement in care.* Annals of Internal Medicine **102**, 520 - 28.

13 Hardy, G. and West, M. (1994) *Happy Talk.* Health Services Journal **104**; 24–25.

14 Peters, T. and Waterman, R. (1982) *In Search of Excellence.* Harpers and Row.

6 Conclusions: From Purchasing to Commissioning

GRAHAM THORNICROFT & GERALDINE STRATHDEE

This book describes a pyramid of commissioning. At the apex, the Department of Health and the National Health Service Executive have produced a policy framework, based upon commonly accepted principles. Effectively the policy framework is now one that is enabling, and which allows staff at the local level to use statutory and guidance instruments as tools to construct meaningful applications on the ground in each area. Its enabling role is quite deliberate and reflects a form of subsidiarity in devolved local decisions to the local level. It does however leave those local practitioners, managers and purchasers who wish to have much greater clarity from the centre with considerable flexibility. The intention of policy is that this will be a creative uncertainty from which specific local pragmatic solutions can be created. Indeed it is almost axiomatic in policy terms that the variability of local requirements for services, the local blends of agencies which are historically developed over long time periods, the complexities of funding packages, the varying topography of urban and rural areas, and the blend of local working relationships cannot be prescribed or proscribed from Whitehall.

The injection of some market principles into the National Health Service has produced a culture shift that was unimaginable only 5 years ago. These processes and pressures have been especially intense within psychiatry where simultaneously a second historic transformation has taken place: the rapid move from long institutional services towards small local teams as the defining element of mental health services. Historically marginalised within the larger health service, mental health services managers have often a limited set of knowledge and experience upon which to base decisions in the new purchasing and commissioning roles. They may also feel ill equipped to support change management in terms of physical relocation of fabric, personnel, service functions, and negotiating the waves and undercurrents of the stream of policy guidance.

Already a number of themes are emerging from this stream. First, the new arrangements explicitly favour co-operation between agencies, between service sectors, and between providers from different institutional sectors. Secondly, it is likely that a new breed of service entrepreneur will rapidly develop among those who can seize the opportunities available from effective de-regulation of mental health service provisions. Thirdly the range of groups who are able to exercise an interest in service development and service provision will widen considerably, and hitherto unanticipated alliances of stakeholders may well emerge. Fourth, such an increasingly mobile market will, as any other market, be increasingly dependent upon the supply of accurate, rapid and useful information. Fifth, it is likely that the initiative historically held be service providers will re-equilibrate towards those making and guiding purchasing decisions. Finally, as those making assessments of service needs become more practised, more competent, and more certain about the growth of consensus which their views can command, contracts for services can be expected to occur within a framework that progressively moves from purchasing towards commissioning. We trust that this book can support these processes in the implementation of care, treatment and support that most effectively helps those who require such help.

Appendix
Health Service Indicators for Mental Health

GYLES R. GLOVER

Introduction

This paper is a glossary which gives details of the Indicators within the current Health Services Indicator (HSI) set which relate to the mental health area, and highlights any that are published via the Public Health Common Data Set (PHCDS) or Health of the Nation (HoN). Basic information is presented here in an abbreviated format as a point of reference for commissioners.

Summary

- There are 9 indicators in the HSI set dealing specifically with mental health: 2 for the Mental Illness Group Specialty (SO 71), 5 for the Adult Mental Illness Group Specialty (SO72), 1 is a Community Indicator for mentally ill people, and 1 for patients admitted under the Mental Health Act, 1983. None of these indicators overlaps with the PHCDS/HoN.

- There are a further 13 Indicators in the set that, whilst not specifically for mental health, include the Adult Mental Illness Group Specialty (SO72) as a variant. None of these indicators overlaps with the PHCDS/HoN.

- The HoN Mortality Indicator for Suicide rates (HoN-C2) under Section C Mental Illness is duplicated in the HSI set. Variants are 'Suicide and self-inflicted injury, and injury undetermined whether accidentally or purposely inflicted'

- The PHCDS Indicator of Standard Mortality Rates (SMRs) for selected causes of death in the period 1988 to 1992 (CDS–C3A) is republished in the HSI set and includes the variants 'Suicide and self-inflicted injury' and 'Suicide and self-inflicted injury, and injury undetermined whether accidentally or purposely inflicted'.

Definitions of HSI indicators

(i) *Indicators for the mental illness group specialty (SO71) including adult MI group (SO72) child and adolescent psychiatry (S711) and covering hospital activity and hosptialisation rates.*

- **HA78.% MI Episodes where residents not treated within District**
  The percentage of all consultant episodes in the Mental Illness specialty group that started in the year, if District residents where treatment was not in that District
  Level: DHA

- **HA73.% of Residents who are Statutorily Detained**
  The percentage of all unfinished consultant episodes of District residents in the Audit MI specialty group where the patient was detained under any section of the Mental Health Act 1983 or related Acts
  Level: DHA

(ii) *Indicators for the adult mental illness group specialty (SO72) including mental illness (S710) forensic psychiatry (S712) psychotherapy (S713) old age psychiatry (715) and covering hospital activity and hospitalisation rates*

- **HA56. First Admissions (EMI) 75+: Resident Population**
  The number of first psychiatric admissions of District residents aged 75+ treated anywhere in England per 1,000 District resident population aged 75+
  Level: DHA

- **HA72.% of patients who are statutorily admitted**
  The percentage of all consultant episodes in the Adult MI specialty group that started in the year, where the patient was detained under any section of the Mental Health Act 1983 or related Acts.
  Level: Unit

- **HA73.% of Patients who are Statutorily Detained**
  The percentage of all unfinished consultant episodes in the Audit MI specialty group where the patient was detained under any section of the Mental Health Act 1983 or related Acts [see HR73 for District of residence version of this indicator]
  Level: Unit

- **HR46. Admission Rate of Residents—Elderly & Mental Health**
  The number of admissions of District residents treated per 100,000 District resident population, by specialty and age
  Variant by Age:
  16–64
  65+
  Level: DHA

- **HR75.% of 1st Admissions of Residents in Mental Illness Group**
  The percentage of all completed episodes of District residents that were first ever psychiatric admissions in the specialty, by specialty
  Age Variant
  16–64
  Level: DHA

(iii) *Community indicator and patients statutorily detained*

- **CP41. CPN Contact Rule**
  First contacts by community psychiatric nurses per 1,000 District resident population, by age
  Level: DHA
  Variants by Age:
  0–15
  16–64
  65+
  Level: DHA

- **HA57. Patients Statutorily Detained: Resident Population**
  The number of admissions of patients formally admitted under any section of the Mental Health Act 1983 or related Acts per 10,000 District resident population
  Level: DHA

(iv) *Indicators which, although not specifically for mental health, include the adult mental illness group specialty (SO72) as a variant and cover outpatient clinics, day care, hospital beds, hospitalisation rate and length of stay*

- **CL01. Expenditure OP: Referral Attendances**
  Expenditure on out-patient attendances divided by the number of referral attendances seen at consultant out-patient clinics, by specialty
  Level: Unit

- **CL51. OP % Non-Attendance Rate**
  The percentage of appointments at consultant out-patient clinics where the patient failed to attend, by specialty
  Level: Unit

- **DC01. Expenditure Day Care Patients: 1st attendances**
  Expenditure on day care patients divided by first attendances at day care facilities
  Level: Unit

- **HB01. Expenditure Patients Occ Beds: Consultant Episodes**
  Expenditure on patients using a hospital bed divided by the number of consultants episodes, by specialty
  Comment: This uses only patient treatment costs. It excludes elements reflected in contract prices such as hotel costs and capital charges. Because lengths of stay are more variable in chronic specialities, their costs are compared on a daily basis in HB02.
  Level: Unit

- **HB02. Expenditure Patients Occ Beds: Patients Days**
  Expenditure on patients using a hospital bed divided by the number of patients days, by specialty
  Level: Unit

- **HR51. Standardised Hospitalisation Rate of Residents—All Admissions**
  The hospitalisation rate for all admissions per 1,000 District residents treated anywhere, in [specialty], standardised by reference to the 1992 England age and sex profiles
  Source: HES/Mersey
  Variants by Age
  16–64
  65+
  All ages
  Level: DHA

- **LS41. Average Length of Consultant Episodes (Including Day Cases)**
  Average length of consultant episodes, by specialty (all ages).
  Level: Unit

- **LS82–83. Patients in Hospital and Over Time: Resident Population**
  The number of finished consultant episodes of District residents treated anywhere by length of episode per 100,000 District resident population, by specialty (All ages)
  LS82—28 days or more but less than one year
  LS83—1 year or more
  Level: DHA

- **LS96. Standardised Average Length on Non-day Case Episodes**
  The average length of consultant episodes in [specialty] other than those where admission was as day cases, standardised by reference to the 1992 England age, sex and casemix profiles
  Level: Unit

- **LS97. Standardised Average Length of Consultant Episodes**
  The average length of episodes in [specialty] standardised by reference to the 1992 England age, sex and casemix profiles
  Level: Unit

- **LS98. Standardised Average Length of Residents' Non-day Case Episodes**
  The average length of consultant episodes, in [specialty], other than those where admission was a day case, of District residents, treated anywhere, Standardised by reference to the 1992 England age, sex and casemix profiles
  Level: DHA

- **LS99. Standardised Average Length of Consultant Episodes for Residents**
  The average length of consultant episodes, in [specialty], of District residents, treated anywhere, standardised by reference to the 1992 England age, sex and casemix profiles
  Level: DHA

Definitions of other indicators duplicated in HSI set

4.1 *Health of the Nation indicators duplicated in HSI set*

- **YC20. All persons**
- **YC21. Male**
- **YC22. Females**

Indicator title:	**Suicide rate (DHA)**
Target C2:	To reduce the overall suicide rate (including undetermined deaths) by at least 15% by the year 2000 (from 11.0 per 100,000.
Definition:	The directly age-standardised mortality rates for the following definitions of suicide: **X82** Suicide and self inflicted injury (ICD E950–E959), and injury undetermined whether accidentally of purposely inflicted (ICD E980–E989) **X88** Suicide and self-inflicted injury (ICD E950–E959). Rates are calculated for persons of all ages resident in each area
Period covered:	Deaths registered in 1990–92
Areas covered:	District health authorities
Source:	OPCS

4.2   Public health common data set indicators duplicated in HSI set

- **ML66–ML68. Five Year SMRs**

  The five year standardised mortality ratio of District residents, by cause of death

Males	**ML66**
Females	**ML67**
*All	**ML68**

  Variants by Underlying Cause of Death

Code		ICD Code
X82	Suicide and self-inflicted injury, and injury undetermined whether accidentally or purposely inflicted	E950–E959 E980–E989
X88	Suicide and self-inflicted injury	E950–E959

Printed in the United Kingdom for HMSO
Dd 302128 C15 8/96 9385 3814